il grido
l'avventura
la notte
l'eclisse

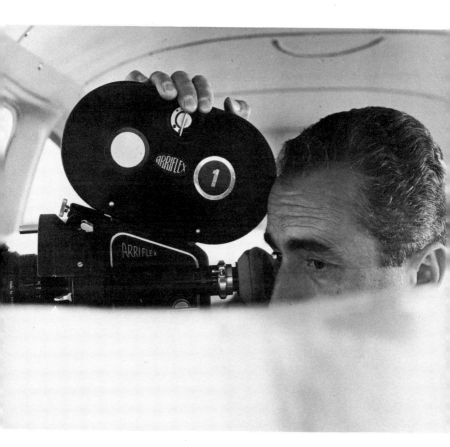

the orion press • new york

Third Printing
Translation © 1963 by The Orion Press, Inc.
Published by Grossman Publishers
44 West 56th St., New York, N.Y., 10019
Library of Congress Catalog Card Number: 62-15018
Designed by Wladislaw Finne
Manufactured in the United States of America

Contents

Introduction by Michelangelo Antonioni   VII
Il grido   1
L'avventura   93
La notte   209
L'eclisse   277

Introduction

In my country, anything can be easy and anything can be hard. The movies were hard for me. It was hard to get into the field, hard not to make certain pictures in order to make others, hard to develop an audience. It took me ten years.

It's a pity to have ideas and not know what to do with them. For ten years, the movies forced me not to use ideas but empty words, cleverness, business sense, patience, stratagems. I am so scantily blessed with such gifts that I recall that period as being the most painful one in my life. I was compelled to lead a life which wasn't mine, talk to stupid and presumptuous people, spend hours in waiting rooms, tell stories to unfamiliar faces, write pages and pages uselessly, from 1940 until 1950. I must really love the movies if I forgave them all this.

In 1950, a friend of mine introduced me to someone who knew an individual with money to invest and who had the movies in mind. I had him read the plot of *Cronaca di un amore*. He didn't like it. He was a likeable fellow with a carefree disposition. His name was Franco Villani. He told me that if I were able to convince him that the plot was good, he would finance the film. We went to his hotel, and I started talking about this story, which was set among the upper middle class of Milan. I could tell that he liked that background and was trying hard to develop interest in the plot but wasn't able to. I kept talking for three hours—that's a lot for a reserved fellow like me. Villani kept looking at me half amazed and half amused. I almost had the impression that he was watching my mannerisms.

Those three hours were unnerving, absurd. He finally told me that the subject still didn't appeal to him, but since I liked it so much he was willing to go along with me. On one condition: that I find him a co-producer.

It would be too long and complicated to relate how we closed the deal with fifty million non-existent lire. One fine day I began shooting; it still doesn't seem possible.

I have always had to contend with the suspicions of producers. I have never been lucky enough to find one with whom I could work continuously in a calm and secure atmosphere. My relations with producers can be explained by these episodes. Turin, 1955. I have been shooting Le amiche for two weeks. I try to move ahead quickly, faster than my usual pace. But the producer isn't used to certain films or to working in an earnest and diligent manner; he is alarmed and confesses to my assistant, "I wanted to do artistic work, but not that artistic!"

The producer of L'avventura, instead, having come down to Sicily to see me during shooting, takes me aside and tells me, in an absolutely serious tone, "Now listen, Antonioni, have it prohibited to children under sixteen!"

Strange characters, who think they know and understand everything about our audience and ourselves, life and art. Until a couple of years ago I was considered a cold person, perhaps even intelligent, but stubborn as a mule, sad and taciturn. It's true I was taciturn, that I'll admit, but not sad. I wonder what producers can understand about a man they see only sporadically, with whom they only talk business, what they can know about his character, his sensitiveness, his life. And yet all of them have their own categorical opinion. That one's an idiot. That other one's an intellectual gone sour. I'm sad. I can allow them only one excuse: When I'm with others, I get worse. I'm better by myself. I can't help it. However, only I know it.

A director is naturally a man like everyone else. Yet his life isn't normal. For us, seeing is a necessity. For a painter too, the problem is to see. But while the painter has to discover a static reality, or even a rhythm perhaps, but a rhythm stopped in mid-air, the problem for a director is to catch reality an instant before it manifests itself and to propound that movement, that appearance, that action as a new perception. It isn't sound: words, noise, music. It isn't an image: scenery, an expression, a motion. But an indecomposable whole.

When we say that the persons we approach are all potential characters, over whose faces pass expressions, from whose mouths come lines; that places are not just images but rhythms, vibrations; that everyday events very often take on symbolic meanings; we must add that it is the relationships of all those things among each other in time and space which make sense to us. It is the tension that forms among them.

This is, I think, a very special way of being in contact with reality. To lose this contact, or rather to lose this "way," can mean sterility.

That's why, for a director even more than for other artists, it's important to work, directly or indirectly, on an ethical plane, exactly because of the particular material he deals with.

People often ask us, "How is a picture born?"

A picture probably has its birth in the disorder within us, and that's the difficulty: putting things in order. Knowing how to pick out the right thread from the skein.

I remember Rimini one spring a few years ago. Under the rotunda of the Grand Hotel, still closed off with the barbed wire which they put around it every winter, two girls about nine years old are playing. One of them is going around the rotunda on a bicycle. The other one goes nimbly into a handstand, stiffening up in vertical position, her skirts falling over her face, her skinny legs straight up in the air. Then she lets herself fall over and starts again. They are poor girls. The one going around the rotunda on her bicycle yells, in sing-song manner,

"Oh such love, oh such suffering! . . ."
She disappears. Then comes back.
"Oh such love, oh such suffering!"

It's early morning, there's no one on the beach except me and those two girls. No sound other than that of the sea and that frail voice crying love and suffering.

For me, that was a film the rest of that day.

I know that this episode, when so simply narrated, is not at all suggestive, and it isn't easy to understand how it could have suggested a story. You would have had to hear the tone of those two voices to understand. It was a very peculiar tone, I can still hear it, it was fresh and heart-rending at the same time, and gave to those words a dimension which was surely unwitting but penetrating, all the love, all the suffering in the world. The words were absurd at such a time, in the mouths of those characters, but the tone was not. I must say it had a kind of mystery.

And that's a limit when staging scenes: forcing words into events which reject them.

Then another time, in Rome, on the fourth day of a garbage men's strike. Rome flooded with rubbish, piles of colored filth on the street corners, an orgy of abstract images, extraordinary pictorial fury. And in contrast, a garbage men's meeting under the ruins of the Baths of Caracalla, two thousand garbage men dressed in their bluish shirts, silent, waiting for Heaven knows what. An unusual situation in which to insert a plot. But that was the time Italian censorship was campaigning against even slightly raw films, so you can imagine using this.

Before shooting L'eclisse I went to Florence to see—and shoot—an eclipse of the sun. In that darkness, in that icy cold, in that silence so different from all other silences, in that almost complete motionlessness, those pale, earth-colored faces, I speculated whether even sentiments are arrested during an eclipse. It was an idea that was only vaguely connected with the picture I was making, which is why I didn't retain it. But it could have been the nucleus of another film.

The most difficult thing is to recognize an idea out of the chaos of feelings, reflexions, observations, impulses which the surrounding world stirs up in us. Among thousands of possibilities, why do we isolate one idea, that one and not another? There are a thousand ways to answer this, none of which is satisfactory. All I can say is that, having singled out a theme, I generally let it ripen for quite a while. I think it helps not to make it mature right away, never to chase after a film, let the film come along very gently by itself. It almost always comes to me at night. I get very little sleep.

I am convinced that good ideas for films are not the same as those used in real life. If that were so, the way a film is created by a director would coincide with his way of life. On the contrary, no matter how autobiographical we are, something always intervenes in our fantasy to interpret and alter what we see into what we

want to see; what we have into what—for the moment—
we would like to have; what we are into what—for the
moment—we would like to be. We are our own characters to the extent to which we believe in the picture we
are making. But between us and them there is always
the picture, there is that concrete, definite, crystal-clear
fact, that mental and physical act which unequivocally
qualifies us, which frees us from abstractedness and
leaves our feet firmly planted on the ground. Thus the
proletariat—for instance—becomes bourgeois again, a
pessimist changes back into an optimist, the lonely and
estranged is once more someone anxious to start a conversation and communicate.

Lopert Pictures Corp.

After *L'eclisse* many people asked me, "What will you do now?" Meaning: Now that you have said what you wanted to say.

It would be very immodest of me to believe that I had conducted with my pictures a conclusive study of sentiments. I believe on the contrary that there is still a great deal to say and show. It's a task that I may not do myself, but I think it would be worth-while. It's important to try to understand the man of today under this aspect too. What have we done up to now? We have scrutinized, vivisected, analyzed thoroughly his feelings. This we have been able to do. But not to discover new ones. I am positive that the world today is filled more with dead feelings than with live ones. I would like to know more about these residues. Perhaps we have to go back to the beginning and ask what is a feeling. And to identify it almost as an effect—according to the scientific meaning of the word—in relation to not only its protagonist but also its observer.

For example. A man is in love with a woman who does not reciprocate. The woman doesn't even know it. Nobody knows it. The man suffers in silence, without mentioning it to anyone, without letting out a single hint of what is happening inside him. His life goes along as though that feeling did not exist. I wonder whether it isn't true that that feeling doesn't exist until the time someone discovers it.

Take another case. A husband and wife think they love each other, but it isn't true. They act with one another and with others as though they did love each other; no one seeing them doubts that they are in love. But it's not true. Yet for whom is it not true?

Perhaps it's nature itself. There are times when we have the feeling that nature is an intelligent being watching us. I don't know. I would have to put us on film to understand. Both of the above-mentioned cases are taken right from real life. There is no doubt that this is new, stimulating material. Except that, having stated my doubts about the certitude of sentiments today, perhaps it's time for me to deal with a different subject. It's true that never have we been dubious about everything the way we are today. That everything has

become uncertain, oscillating between two extremes: the principles of knowledge and those of morality, the basis of authority and the basis of philosophy, the premises of law and those of politics. We are surrounded by a reality which is not defined or corporeal. Inside of us, things appear like dots of light on backgrounds of fog and shadow. Our concrete reality has a ghostly, abstract quality.

But at least one thing remains positive: a sincere effort, even if by a few, to understand and find a solution. If ever my pictures have a purpose, I believe it is to contribute in a humble way to this effort.

Rereading these scenes, what I feel most is the memory of the moments which inspired me to conceive and write those things. Visits to certain places, conversations with people, time spent at the very spots where the story is said to take place, the gradual unfolding of the picture in its fundamental images, in its tone, in its pace: This is very important to me. Perhaps the most important time. The arrangement of scenes is an intermediate phase, a necessary but transitory one. To shoot the film right, in my opinion, I have to reconnect it with that moment, I need to recall that emotion, those feelings, those figurative intuitions, that confidence.

The discussions during the arrangement of scenes, the often cold and systematic search for a construction, for a solution suggested by technical experience, contribute of course to the best articulation of the story. But they are liable to cool the original enthusiasm. That is why there is always a critical moment during the arrangement of scenes when it seems as though the story won't hold up and everything has to be done over. The only thing to do then is to stop work. Left to myself, I start reconsidering the film, thinking about its features and the way I came to discover them during the preparatory phase on location.

I say this not to slight the work of my collaborators, but because at those difficult times it was always I who had to revive a film which was fading away in the labyrinths of a discussion or in the desert of an hour of fatigue. It's hard to keep on believing in what you're doing if you have a tired face in front of you, friendly though it may be.

For these four films, the faces that I most often had before me were those of Tonino Guerra and Elio Bartolini. The former, who is closer to me, is a poet who writes in dialect; the latter is a writer. They are very different one from the other and from me. When speaking of Guerra we start with his qualities, for Bartolini we begin with his defects. With Tonino we have long and violent arguments; he's helpful to me that way. But with him I can keep quiet as long as I wish without feeling embarrassed. And for this he's even more helpful to me.

I have had another feeling when reading these screenplays, a rather strange one. A kind of stupor mixed with mild irritation. I think I understand why. Arranging scenes is a truly wearisome job. You have to describe images with provisional words which later will no longer have any use, and this in itself is unnatural. What is more, the description can only be general or even false because the images are in the mind without any concrete point of reference. You sometimes end up describing weather conditions. "The sky is clear, but

large clouds block the horizon. As though coming out of these clouds, X's car appears on the horizon." Isn't it absurd? Another example. Take this scene from *L'eclisse:*

Piero's house. A typical house of the Roman bourgeoisie. The entrance hall is dark, large and cool. Vittoria, coming in from the brilliant light outside, hesitates as though the inside of the house, a presentiment of it—those high ceilings, rooms leading to other rooms, the black, heavy furniture, the profusion of knick-knacks on it—repelled her. She even sits down on a chest next to a vase with two umbrellas, her hands between her knees. Piero, standing next to her, feels embarrassed.

Now let's look at the film. Vittoria goes in, pauses to look at an old painting on the wall, continues toward the inner rooms, stops before a window to look at the wall beyond the courtyard, where a woman appeared in the black frame of another window. The woman disappears almost immediately as though swallowed by the shadows. Vittoria turns back toward the chest. Piero is standing next to the door leading into the living room.

Why did I change it? Why, because when the scene was composed we had no idea what Piero's house would have been like, so that the screenplay was of value to me only as a psychological note. And even then, only to a certain point. In the film, then, Vittoria, upon entering, walks immediately toward the interior of the house, and Piero is not embarrassed—this behavior corresponds better to the personality of the two characters. The changes were suggested to me by the actual circumstances at time of shooting. It can be seen that I also cut out three lines of dialogue, which are superfluous in the new arrangement of the scene.

As far as I'm concerned, it's only when I press my eye against the camera and begin to move the actors

Lopert Pictures Corp.

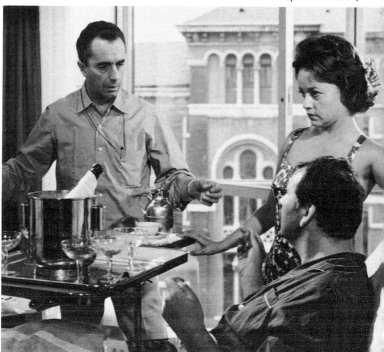

michelangelo antonioni

that I get an exact idea of the scene; it's only when I hear dialogue from the actor's mouth itself that I realize whether the lines are correct or not.

Besides, if it were not so, pictures would be clumsy illustrations of a script. It often happens, but I disapprove of making movies that way.

Writing the words, "making movies that way," it occurs to me that there were other ways, in screenplays of ten years ago, which were full of technical specifications such as P.P., F.I., C.L., dolly, pan, etc. Today all that has disappeared, but in my opinion this isn't enough. Screenplays are on the way to becoming actually sheets of notes for those who, at the camera, will write the film themselves. The turn being taken by other arts as well, such as music and painting, inexorably headed toward freer forms, authorizes us to think so. The world is changing. Why not alter the movie industry? It's been such a long time since they showed *The Kid,* described as "a great story with a new and delicate touch, simple and moving, interpreted by Jackie Coogan and Charlie Chaplin."

Today the movies have a different function, different rules. The Hollywood myth has fallen. The movie myth has fallen. Right in Hollywood, Marilyn Monroe commits suicide.

It is almost with a feeling of emotion, as though I were thinking of a departed friend, that I recall my professor of History of Economics at the university, who used to say, "For us old people, the movies are as the grapes were to Phaedrus' fox: *Nondum matura est, nolo acerbam sumere.* Except that I have the courage to say so and to leaf through one of your magazines once in a while. So many beautiful photographs, so many beautiful photographs!"

Michelangelo Antonioni
(Translated by Roger J. Moore)

Screenplays
of
Michelangelo
Antonioni

il grido (the outcry)
1956-1957

translated by louis brigante

Credits

Director:	Michelangelo Antonioni
Cast:	Steve Cochran
	Alida Valli
	Dorian Gray
	Lyn Shaw
	Gabriella Pallotti
	Mirna Girardi
	Betsy Blair
Original story	Michelangelo Antonioni
Scenario:	Michelangelo Antonioni
	Elio Bartolini
	Ennio De Concini
Director of Photography:	Cianni Di Venanzo
Cameraman:	Erico Menczer
Assistant cameraman:	Dario Di Palma
Assistant Directors:	Luigi Vanzi and Sergio Zavoli
Director of Production:	Danilo Marciani
Script Girl:	Elvira D'Amico
Sound Engineer:	Vittorio Trentino
Costume Designer:	Pia Marchesi
Dressmaker:	Elena Cricchi
Scene Designer:	Franco Fontana
Assistant Scene Designer:	Mario Armanni
Make-up:	Otello Fava and Libero Politi
Hairdresser:	Vasco Reggiani
Editing:	Eraldo da Roma
Music:	Giovanni Fusco
Producer:	SPA Cinematografica in collaboration with Robert Alexander Productions of New York and Franco Cancillieri of C.E.I. Incom.

The time is early autumn and the place is a small industrial town on the banks of the Po.

Aldo, a mechanic employed at a sugar refinery plant, has been living for the past eight years with Irma, a married woman whose husband emigrated to Australia before she had met Aldo and has not been heard from since. They have a child, Rosina, a sensitive little girl of about seven. Aldo's main ambition is to marry Irma and thereby justify their relationship in the eyes of the community. However, because of Irma's marital status he has not been able to do so.

Their home is a drab and simple structure surrounded by many trees. It is located on the outskirts of town, just a stone's throw away from the river.

Irma comes out of the house. She is carrying a large canvas handbag, and as she closes the door, she casts a reassuring glance inside—a typical gesture of a housewife who wants to be certain that she has left everything in order. Then, with an urgency characteristic of someone anxious to attend to an important matter, she hurries off.

Walking along the river bank, she turns into a pathway that leads her into town. Crossing the square, she enters the city hall to the accompaniment of curious glances and comments from a group of women standing near the doorway.

Inside, seated in front of the Mayor's desk, Irma is listening attentively to what the Mayor is telling her.

Mayor: Personally, Madame, I don't know if you'll find the news I'm about to tell you good or bad. However, that's beside the point.
Irma (apprehensive): What news?
Mayor: About your husband...He died in Sydney, twenty days ago.

The Mayor falls silent. He searches Irma's face in an effort to determine the effect of the news, but she is impassive. Her only reaction is a slight relaxation from her tense and rigid posture. She shuts her eyes for a second, then quickly opens them again as the Mayor hands her a letter.

Mayor: Here's the letter I received from the consulate... I don't know if you were aware of it, but your husband had been working in a factory ...

Irma suddenly springs to her feet as though nothing else the Mayor might have to say to her could be of any interest. She goes to the window and looks out. In the distance, she sees the sugar refinery plant with its aluminum shafts gleaming in the sun.

The Mayor rises from his desk and comes forward to comfort her, but Irma quickly draws away from him and abruptly goes to the door.

Irma: I'm sorry, but you'll have to excuse me. I'll come back tomorrow.

She turns and immediately goes out of the office, leaving the Mayor standing with a startled expression on his face. In the distance the wail of the factory siren announcing the noonday break.

The sound of the siren increases as the plant itself comes into view. It is a beautiful day and the aluminum tank, the shafts, and even the building itself shine brightly in the sun. Work has temporarily halted and the laborers are scattered all over the area. Some of them are already eating while others mill around, waiting for their wives to bring them their lunch.

The siren finally stops and an absolute stillness pervades the air. No sound, not even a voice, is heard. Then faintly, almost imperceptibly, music comes drifting down somewhere from the top of the blast furnace. It is one of the laborers seated on the gangway of the smokestack playing his harmonica. Aldo is beside him listening to the music and gazing out over the surrounding landscape: a vast expanse of open country; running through it like a roadway is the Po.

Another worker from below shouts up to Aldo.

Worker: Aldo!... Irma's here.

Aldo rises to his feet, leans over the railing and looks down His face brightens. Irma enters through the gate and into the courtyard of the plant.

Aldo (shouting): Irma!

She looks up and waves hello, then calls out to him.

Irma: I'll leave it here!
Aldo: No, wait; I'll come down.

Irma shakes her head, then sets Aldo's lunch bag down on the ground. She looks up again, then waves good-bye.

Aldo: Wait! Irma, wait till I come down!

Jumping over to the head of the stairway, Aldo starts running hurriedly down the iron steps. Instead of waiting for him, Irma immediately walks away and leaves the plant. By the time Aldo reaches the ground, Irma is gone. He sees the lunch bag lying nearby, but he ignores it. Perplexed by Irma's strange behavior, he turns to one of the workers standing nearby and asks:

Aldo: Where did she go?
Worker (pointing toward the gate): What's wrong with her?
Aldo: Why?
Worker: Well, she was crying...
Aldo: Crying?

For a moment Aldo remains motionless, deeply engrossed in his thoughts. Then, as one of the factory foremen passes by, he goes up to him.

Aldo: Sir, if it's okay with you, I'd like to take a run over to my house... for about ten minutes.

The foreman gives his assent and Aldo leaves on the run.

A few minutes later, Aldo reaches the house, opens

the door with his key and enters, leaving the door slightly ajar. As he walks through the hallway, he calls out:

Aldo: Irma!

There is no response. He enters the kitchen and looks around, puzzled. The room is empty. On the table is Rosina's school bag. He goes over to the screen door, looks outside and sees Rosina playing in the backyard. As soon as she sees her father, she comes forward to greet him.

Aldo: Isn't your mother home?

Rosina shakes her head, then turns and Aldo goes back into the kitchen. Rosina follows behind him.

Rosina: Papa, I got an "A" on my report card!

Aldo gives her a casual hug, then he sits down on a chair and decides to wait for Irma. Rosina runs back into the yard. Hearing the sound of the door being opened, Aldo turns around. A moment later, a middle-aged woman enters. It is Lina, Irma's sister. She appears somewhat surprised to see Aldo.

Aldo: Have you seen Irma?
Lina: No, I haven't ... I thought she was here. How come you're home at this hour?
Aldo (ignoring her question): Your sister was in a bad mood this morning.
Lina: For what reason?
Aldo: Who knows!
Lina: Well ... I'm going back home. If Irma wants to stop by later, I'll be at my place.

Aldo bids her good-bye with a slight nod of his head, and Lina leaves in haste. A few yards away from the house, she encounters Irma and they stop for a moment to talk to each other.

Lina: Is it true...I mean the news about the tragedy?

Irma nods her head, but otherwise remains silent.

Lina: What are you going to do about Aldo? I think you should tell him everything...He's waiting for you inside, you know.
Irma (alarmed): No!

Irma turns and walks toward the house. Lina remains there for a moment, looking after her sister, then turns and continues on her way.
The door opens and Irma appears in the hallway. She goes directly to the bedroom, takes off her coat and throws it on the bed. Then she passes her hands over her face, indicating fatigue. Aldo's voice is heard behind her.

Aldo: Why were you crying?

Irma hesitates for a moment, then without turning around to face him, replies:

Irma: My husband died.
Aldo: But why didn't you wait for me at the plant and tell me then?

Irma: I didn't feel like discussing it then. But we can talk about it now, in quiet.
Aldo: Seems to me there's nothing to talk about. We'll get married now and that's that.

Irma turns around. Her face reveals overwhelming sense of grief, and she begins to cry. Aldo stares at her suspiciously feeling that she is hiding something from him. He draws up close and tries to soothe her as he wipes the tears from her cheeks.

Aldo: Sure, I know it's rotten to feel happy after a tragedy like that, but we've been waiting for eight years. Eight solid years . . .

Irma looks up at him with a deep sense of despair.

Aldo: What is it, Irma?
Irma: Nothing, Aldo. I'll get over it soon.

The gray light of dawn filters through the kitchen door which has been left ajar. The silence is broken by the sound of a tugboat whistle coming from the Po. Aldo, asleep in bed, is just waking up. From outside come the shouts of people calling to one another from a distance. Aldo suddenly sits up in bed, realizing that Irma is not beside him. He looks toward the hallway and calls out:

Aldo: Irma!

There is no response, so he jumps out of bed, puts on his trousers and goes into the kitchen. He finds the door open and steps out into the yard. Irma is seated on the bank of the river with her arms folded over her knees staring out into the water. With a puzzled expression on his face, Aldo comes up to her, but she is so absorbed in her thoughts that she remains completely unaware of his presence.

Aldo: Irma! . . .

Finally she turns around but shows not even the slightest surprise in seeing him standing there. In fact, it seems as though she had been waiting for him to arrive just now.

Irma: Aldo, last night there were other things that you and I should have talked about.
Aldo: What other things?
Irma (somewhat annoyed): Oh! . . . Come over here and sit beside me.

No sooner is Aldo seated than Irma starts speaking again. Her tone of voice is affirmative and determined.

Irma: We should have talked about them even before last night. When it reaches a point where we can't speak up and be honest with each other, it means . . . Well, it means that one of us no longer cares, that's all.
Aldo (amazed): Irma, have you gone mad?
Irma: No. I'm not mad. But if things go on like this . . . Aldo, I've changed. Of course, I still love you, but it's just not the same anymore . . . It's probably my own fault, but I'm sure that I'm not making a mistake . . . that

what I'm doing is the right thing, because I'm being honest about it.

Aldo: But what is this, all of a sudden?

Irma: It's not so sudden.

Aldo: Then why didn't you tell me about this before?

Irma: Because only now is it possible to make a decision.

Aldo (angrily): What kind of a decision?

Irma: Please, Aldo, don't force me to explain. It would make it worse for both of us. Just let me go away.

Aldo: Go where? What are you talking about?

Irma (firmly): I'm leaving you for somebody else.

Aldo is stunned. For a moment he remains absolutely still, then he starts to raise his hand as though to strike her, but he hesitates and merely grabs hold of Irma by the collar of her jacket.

Aldo: What did you say?

Irma: You understood very well what I said.

Aldo: Irma!

Irma remains firm and steadfast. She is cool and collected, and the more anger and violence Aldo displays the more certain she becomes of her own conviction. Aldo manages to control himself by adopting a sarcastic tone.

Aldo: And who would this somebody else be?

Irma is silent. Receiving no response to his question, Aldo raises his voice again.

Aldo: Did you hear me? Answer!

Irma: Please, don't ask me that, Aldo. Please, not that! Even if I do tell you, what good will it do? What does he have to do with it?

Aldo: Sure, what does *he* have to do with it! First your husband ... then me ... and now him! That's too many men for an *honest* woman.

Aldo's remark comes like a slap in the face. It is too

much for Irma to take, and she breaks out into tears. Her head is bowed low and her body trembles.

Aldo turns away from her as if she were something too painful for him to look at. He stands up, takes a few steps towards the river, then turns around and looks at her again, throwing out his arms in an awkward gesture of despair.

Aldo: Then all these years together meant nothing to you at all!
Irma: They meant everything to me ... until four months ago.

There is a moment of silence. Then, in a sudden burst of fury, Aldo rushes over to Irma, pulls her up from the ground and forcibly leads her back into the house.

As soon as they enter the kitchen, a knock is heard at the door. Irma frees herself from Aldo's grasp and goes over to open the door, while Aldo watches her. It is the milkman. After a brief exchange at the door, Irma comes back into the kitchen carrying a bottle of milk. The sound of the siren from the sugar factory is heard, but Aldo completely ignores it. Instead, he continues to stare at Irma as she prepares to warm up a saucepan of milk. She goes about her business as though Aldo were not there. But he comes up next to her, grabs her by the arm and forces her to turn around. As Irma is twisted around, she accidentally knocks over the pan and the milk spills over the floor.

Irma: Now what am I going to give Rosina?
Aldo: And what will you give her if you leave? Did you forget you have a child?
Irma: I've thought about that, too.

Aldo moves away from her and starts pacing nervously across the room.

Aldo (angrily exclaiming to himself): I should have known it would come to this! ... A woman who runs around while her husband is breaking his back for her working in Australia ...

Irma: Yes, my marriage was a failure. But you certainly didn't hesitate to take advantage of it!

Aldo: Look at the results! ... And to think I had somebody else ... somebody I could have married with full ceremonies and all!

Irma: You still have time! ... Elvia is a nice clean girl ... As for me, what am I to you anyway? Go on, say it, what am I!

Aldo: The only thing I have to say to you is this: that I won't let you go even if you drop dead. You're staying right here, for better or worse!

Irma turns away from him and looks out of the window. Aldo stomps out into the backyard. He goes over to a cage where there are some rabbits, grabs one of them, looks at it, puts it back into the cage, then returns to the kitchen. But he hesitates at the doorstep as he sees another woman in the kitchen giving Irma some eggs.

Woman (counting the eggs): Four, five, six. You gave me six, didn't you, Irma?

Irma: Yes, I think so ...

The woman senses the feeling of hostility between Irma and Aldo, and leaves immediately.

Irma casts a glance at Aldo as he crosses the kitchen and goes out through the hallway.

It is payday at the factory. At the sound of the siren, Aldo stops working and goes over to a small office in front of which other workers are already lined up. A clerk behind a window is handing out the pay envelopes. Although the other workers have apparently washed themselves before collecting their pay, Aldo's hands are still dirty with grease. Even his clothes are soiled with a number of conspicuous stains. As he gets into line, several of the other workers begin talking among themselves. Aldo stands there silently, self-consciously feeling that people are staring at him.

Aldo: What are you looking at?
Worker (surprised): Who, me? The only thing I'm looking at right now are the pay envelopes.
Aldo (menacingly): If there's anything on your mind, you ought to have the courage to come right out and say it!
Worker: Courage? What courage?
Second Worker: Hey, what do you want to do, start an argument?

It is Aldo's turn. He steps up to the pay window, and the clerk hands him his envelope.

Clerk: Here you are, now just sign here.

Aldo signs his name, takes his envelope and leaves the office. Coming out of the plant, he walks into the center of town and comes to the market place where he sees Irma buying some food at an outdoor vegetable stand.

The woman behind the stand weighs the vegetables, then places them into Irma's shopping bag.

Vendor: You know nowadays they go around with a pushcart and sell you vegetables right at your door. But what you gain in convenience, you lose in quality. Remember that! ... Don't you want any lettuce?

The vendor shows Irma the lettuce, but Irma is momentarily distracted as she notices Aldo approaching.

Irma: Yes, let me have some.

Calmly and without any sense of haste, Irma takes some money from her purse and pays the vendor while Aldo stands fuming, waiting impatiently for Irma to join him. As he comes up to her, she gives him a cold, almost severe glance.

Irma: Why did you come here?
Aldo: What do you mean, why did I come here?

They start walking along the street, heading towards the house.

Irma: Are you afraid I'll run away?
Aldo (awkwardly): Irma . . . don't you think that with a little good will we can straighten things out?
Irma: Good will alone is not enough!
Aldo: But why don't we try it!
Irma (aggressively): All right! Let's try it. What do you want me to do?

Aldo stops. He looks at her with such a painfully helpless expression that it makes her even more irritated.

Irma: Go ahead, tell me!

Aldo remains motionless, incapable of giving her an answer. Now Irma starts walking ahead as he sheepishly follows behind. They pass in front of a little gift shop and Aldo stops as though remembering something he had thought of earlier. He takes Irma by the arm and leads her into the shop. He goes up to the counter with Irma and as the salesgirl is about to greet him, he interrupts her.

Aldo: Gianna, there was a little belt in the window last week . . . with a gold buckle . . . It was a black belt.

The salesgirl goes over to a box from which she draws out the belt and holds it up.

Salesgirl: Is this it?
Aldo: Yes . . . that's the one. *(To Irma)* Why don't you try it on?

Irma looks at Aldo without saying a word. Aldo is insistent.

Aldo: Don't you like it anymore? *(To the salesgirl)* Are there any others?
Irma: But why waste your money like that?
Aldo (frustrated): What do you mean, waste it?

The salesgirl is left standing there, holding the belt in her hand. Then, realizing the awkwardness of the situation, Irma decides to cut it short.

Irma (to the salesgirl): In any case, if I want it I'll be back for it later . . . Good-bye, Gianna.
Salesgirl: Bye, Irma; good-bye, Aldo.

Aldo and Irma walk out of the shop in silence.

Walking side by side towards the house, which is now only a short distance away, Aldo suddenly stops, and with an angry, bitter tone of voice, he turns on Irma.

Aldo: How could you? How could you forget everything!
Irma: I haven't forgotten anything, Aldo.

Aldo grabs her by the hand, takes her forcefully into his arms, squeezes her tightly as though it were his one last hope, then kisses her. Irma offers no resistance, but when they emerge from the embrace, her face is drawn with sadness.

Irma: The reason I don't want it to go on this way is because I haven't forgotten. If we were to go on living like this it would become humiliating for both of us . . . And I don't want that to happen . . . Oh, Aldo, I feel so miserable that I don't even want to talk about it . . . But it seems there's nothing much I can do now.

Aldo remains silent. He stares at her with an expression so pitiful to behold that Irma quickly turns away from him and starts running in the opposite direction. Aldo looks mechanically at Irma leaving. He starts walking, slowly at first, then quickening his pace. He too is headed away from the house.

The house of Lina, sister of Irma. Lina is at the type-writer writing a letter. Irma sinks into a chair near the window through which can be seen the house she had originally intended to enter.

Irma (pointing to the house across the way): I wonder if he's at home.
Lina: I saw him go in a little while ago.
Irma: I must see him . . . He's got to help me . . .
Lina: Did you talk to Aldo?
Irma: Yes. But I had to run away from him; otherwise, I would have stayed with him, I would have married him, I would have done everything he wanted . . .
Lina: Now don't worry about him.
Irma: I don't know if I have the right to think only about myself . . . Aldo has always treated me well . . . For eight years! If I start thinking about those eight years . . . And I feel so uncertain about the whole thing . . . maybe I'm making another mistake . . . After all, a man who is younger than I am . . .

She stands up and takes a few steps around the room. She is upset and nervous. Lina looks at her, sharing her sister's anguish.

Lina: That has really nothing to do with it. Age doesn't matter. If one is sure . . .
Irma: Deep down inside I *do* feel sure . . . but is that enough?

Aldo, meanwhile, has gone to his mother's place and has told her about Irma's intention to leave him.

Mother: Let's say, for example, that instead of dying her husband had come back to her. In that case, what would Irma have done? You know, I have never opened my mouth, I have never said anything . . . But what you two were doing wasn't very nice. You can say what you want, but people have been talking about you all along. They don't care whether Irma is a special case, as you say. A good woman is one thing and a whore is something else.

As if struck by a blow, Aldo reacts to his mother's remark by grabbing a bottle and smashing it down on the floor. His mother looks at the broken pieces for a while, then continues in a more restrained manner.

Mother: And gossip, you know, is like hail; it is always falling somewhere. And now that it's falling on your own back you come to your mother. And me, what can I do for you? You'll have to work it out on your own, my son.
Aldo (sullenly): I know.
Mother: There might even be a way that you can make her love you again!

Aldo turns and glares at his mother as she proceeds to gather the broken pieces of glass from the floor. Then, as if seized by some uncontrollable urge, he abruptly goes to the door and leaves.

At Lina's house, the two sisters are still discussing Irma's decision and its consequences.

Irma: He'll want to keep Rosina with him, you'll see. Besides, she's his as much as mine. I'm afraid there will come a day when I'll regret this, too.
Lina: Don't let fear hold you back, Irma. The only reason I didn't get married was because I was afraid. And now look at me!

As she says this, Lina picks up a stack of sheets beside the typewriter. She drops them again with a gesture of self-deprecation.

Irma: At least you didn't make any mistake!
Lina: Maybe I made a bigger mistake than you did. *(Pause)* Do you want me to go and call him?
Irma: No, no . . .
Lina: Then why don't *you* go.

Irma rises to her feet, comes up close to the window, looks out into the street, then quickly withdraws.

Irma: No, it's a bad hour to go now. There's always somebody around . . . and I don't want anyone to see me.
Lina: But by tomorrow everybody will be talking about it anyway!
Irma: First I've got to iron things out with Aldo, once and for all. At least I've got to get that settled.

There is a knock at the door and the two sisters look at each other apprehensively. As Lina goes to open the door, Irma hides herself in the adjoining room. At the doorstep, there is a young girl who is speaking to Lina in whispers. She appears very excited. Finally, Lina closes the door and comes back into the room.

Lina: It's Mariuccia . . . She says that Aldo is looking all over town for you like a madman . . . I'm sure he'll come here, too.
Irma: I'll take care of Aldo . . . All I want you to do is to watch out for him. *(She nods towards the house across the way.)* That nobody tells him about it, and that he doesn't leave the house; otherwise, who knows what'll happen.

She starts for the door, then turns around to look at Lina whose face is filled with apprehension.

Lina: Irma . . .
Irma: I'd be making another mistake if I didn't go.

Irma hurries out, leaving Lina standing there, wringing her hands in fear.

The square is crowded with people, the local tavern filled with the usual Saturday clientele. On the sidewalk girls, arm in arm, pass by. Walking briskly across the square, Aldo appears so visibly shaken with rage that many of the people passing by stop and look up at him. He is about to turn a corner, then changes his mind and heads off into another street instead. Suddenly he stops, for directly up ahead he sees Irma approaching. She comes straight at him and stops abruptly in front of him. She appears unusually calm in the face of Aldo's obvious fury. She is about to speak, but even before she has a chance to open her mouth, Aldo slaps her hard across the face. She staggers backward under the blow, then Aldo comes at her again and starts beating her with both hands.

A crowd begins to form but no one dares to intervene. All remain silent as Aldo keps slapping her back and forth across the face. The only thing Irma can do to defend herself is to cover her face with her hands. But as the blows continue, she slips and falls, and Aldo finally relents.

Aldo: Now get back to the house!

Slowly Irma rises to her feet, then summoning all her strength and courage, she says in a decisive tone of voice:

Irma: That did it, Aldo; now it's definitely all over.

Adjusting her clothes, she casts a defiant glance at the crowd, then leaves in the direction from which she has just come. The onlookers step aside and give her the right of way.

Aldo remains absolutely still, looking at Irma as she walks away. The expression on his face would seem to indicate a masculine sense of satisfaction, but deep inside he is emotionally shattered. He slowly begins moving through the crowd. All eyes are fixed upon him and this awareness makes him feel self-conscious. However, his despair is much too profound for him to be really piqued by their curious stares. He turns around again to look at Irma as she gradually disappears out of sight. Then, as if suddenly taken by a new determination, he quickly leaves the scene.

It is dusk on a barren country road not far from the town of Porto Tolle. Aldo and his little daughter, Rosina, are riding on top of a horse-drawn cart being driven by a man in his sixties. Aldo is silent and sulky.

Rosina is looking around at the landscape and occasionally glancing up at her father. The owner of the cart is speaking, though more to himself than to Aldo.

Man: ... but here we're so far out of touch with the rest of the world. Luckily, there was a flood not too long ago, which washed away some of the old and managed to bring us a little of the new! ... Well, let's hope for the best. If we're going to get anywhere, we've got to look ahead and forget about the past.

The old man turns around to look at the town which is now far off in the distance but still visible. The road on which they are traveling runs along the banks of the Po, and further away, on the opposite side of the river, can be seen the lights of another little town, sparkling in the stillness of the twilight like something out of a fairy tale.
The man pulls the reins and stops the horse with a grunt.

Man: See how lovely the town looks from here! One would think that the people who live there are well off! ...

Aldo also turns around to look at the town but it is obvious from the expression on his face that the confusion stirring within him, aggravated still more by the old man's remarks, is far too great for him to be distracted by the beauty of the scene. With another grunt, the man signals for the horse to start off again, and the cart continues slowly along the muddy road.

Slowly, with the current, a boat whose outboard has stalled in the middle of the river, drifts over the water. The pilot is signaling to a group of young men standing along the shore; he hollers and shouts as the craft draws near. Two of them jump into a rowboat tied to the bank and go out to meet the motorboat.
Aldo and Rosina walk along an embankment. After a casual glance at the goings-on, Aldo leaves the road and climbs down the slope of a ditch leading to a

house overlooking the river. Attracted by the sight of the motorboat on the river, Rosina remains behind and calls out to her father.

Rosina: Papa, I'll stay here...I want to watch the boats.

Without stopping, Aldo gives his assent by nodding his head. A voice is heard coming from behind the embankment. It is one of the young men calling to somebody in the house.

Voice: Edera!...Edera!...

A girl of eighteen comes out. Her clothing is rather gaudy. Aldo stops to look at her with a certain amount of surprise. The young man who was calling to her appears at the top of the embankment.

Young man: Edera, bring me a rag from the house.
Edera: Come and get it yourself!

Young man: Come on, will you . . . The motorboat is stalled.
Edera: What motorboat?

The young man doesn't answer but disappears over the other side of the embankment just as Edera goes back into the house, unaware of Aldo following directly behind her.

Inside, seated in front of a sewing machine at the far end of a large kitchen, is Edera's sister, Elvia. She is a seamstress about twenty-eight years old.

Edera: Elvia, they want a rag.

Elvia looks up at her sister, but suddenly her face registers surprise as she sees Aldo standing in the doorway behind Edera.

Elvia: Aldo! . . .

Aldo enters the room with a self-satisfied smile on his face: he has achieved the intended surprise. In an

effort to hide her emotion, Elvia takes refuge in the banality of platitudes.

Elvia: Well, sooner or later, I knew we'd see each other again ...
Aldo (extending his hand): I'm glad I surprised you ... And how are you?
Elvia: All right ... Good enough, I guess. You know, one manages to keep alive and busy. And you?
Aldo: Not bad. I wanted to see you, so ... Well, I was just passing by ... *(Aldo turns to face Edera and looks at her from head to foot.)* Say, you must be Edera! The last time I saw you, you were so high ...

Aldo indicates with his hand the height of a little child, and Edera follows suit by placing her hand high over her head as she says:

Edera: And I remember when you were this tall!

Both Aldo and Edera break out into a laugh. Meanwhile, Elvia has gone to a chest nearby and taken out a rag which she then hands to Edera, almost as if she were in a hurry to send her off.

Elvia: Here you are.

Edera takes the rag from her sister and as she goes out, she turns to Aldo.

Edera: Are you going to stay awhile or do you plan to leave right away? Will we see you later?
Aldo: I don't know yet.
Edera: Why don't you at least stay for dinner.

Edera goes out and a brief period of embarrassed silence follows between Aldo and Elvia. Then Elvia takes a chair and offers it to Aldo who, in turn, sits down.

Aldo: Everything's the same here, eh?

Elvia smiles feebly, almost apologetically, then with a typical feminine gesture, she pulls her skirt down over her knees. Aldo tries to look at her left hand to see if she is wearing a wedding ring, but Elvia becomes aware of his gaze and she awkwardly tries to conceal her hand.

Elvia: No, I'm not married.
Aldo: I know . . . I know.

There is another embarrassing moment of silence, then Elvia says, almost timidly:

Elvia: Seriously, why don't you stay for dinner? . . . Are you all alone? . . . I mean, I want to know for how many I should set the table.
Aldo: Rosina is with me. You know that I have a child? . . .

Aldo points through the doorway where Rosina is seen on the embankment looking towards the river.

Elvia: She's so big . . . It certainly has been a long time. But tell me, what brings you here to Pontelagoscure?
Aldo: I'm not at Goriano anymore. I'm not anywhere anymore . . . It's much better this way . . . much better than being tied down to one place. Believe me.

The young man who had asked for the rag appears in the doorway.

Young man: Elvia, don't you have a screwdriver somewhere?
Elvia: The tools are over there on the machine.

He goes over to the sewing machine and starts looking around for the screwdriver.

Young man: There's going to be a boat race today with five guys from Ferrara with whom we made a bet.
Elvia: A boat race?
Young man: That's if we can get the motor fixed in time.
Aldo: What's wrong with it?

Young man: Who knows!

Aldo: What do you mean, who knows! What about the man who runs it, what does he say?

Young man: He knows less than I do.

Aldo: I'm almost tempted to come out and have a look myself.

Young man: Are you a mechanic?

Elvia (jokingly, but with a certain amount of satisfaction): He's the best mechanic in the world! *(To Aldo)* Come, let's go ... this way you can introduce me to your child, too.

The young man goes out, breaking into a run. Aldo and Elvia follow after him.

About an hour later, the motorboat is completely repaired and the pilot is ready to start it. He pulls the cord; the motor roars and the boat gets underway. He waves to Aldo who is standing on the shore rubbing the grease from his hands.

Pilot: Thanks, very much!

Aldo makes a gesture in return as if to say it was nothing at all. He washes his hands in the water, then turns and climbs the embankment where Elvia and Rosina wait for him. They are both watching the motorboat as it speeds through the water, sending up a wide track of spray behind it.

Rosina: Why does it make all that foam?

Elvia: The propeller does that.

Rosina: It makes me thirsty.

Elvia (laughing): Now we'll go and have something to drink ... and something to eat, too.

She passes her hand over Rosina's head and the child looks up at her, smiling affectionately.

Aldo comes up to them and turns around to take a look at the motorboat which is now some distance out on the river.

Aldo: I'm really anxious to see how they'll make out today.

They make their way to the house. Elvia looks at Aldo attentively, then says:

Elvia: And what about your job at the refinery?
Aldo: I'll find another one someplace ... Maybe even around here. Pontelagoscuro is full of refineries.

The doubtful expression on Elvia's face slowly disappears and is quickly replaced by a hopeful one. She is about to say something else but stops, almost afraid that the discussion will become too obvious.

A boat race is underway on the Po. Three outboard motorboats, skimming over the water, sweep around the buoy, almost one on top of the other. Several follow close behind, bouncing over the swells cast by the motorboats in the lead. The motors roar full speed ahead as they pass a crowd of spectators lined up along the river bank. In the crowd are Edera and her friends. One of them points to the river, shouting:

Young man: There it is! There it is!

A motorboat marked with a "5" comes into view but loses ground as it makes a turn around the buoy.
Aldo turns to Elvia who is standing directly behind him. She is holding Rosina by the hand. Shaking his head to indicate his doubts about the outcome of the race, Aldo says:

Aldo: Ah! ... It's sixth ...

Edera looks back at him and pointedly remarks:

Edera: But it'll win. You wait and see, it'll win!

As a matter of fact, Number 5 is gaining on the two boats ahead of it. But then, as it makes another turn around the buoy it begins to lose ground again.

Edera (shouting excitedly): Come on!...Come on!...
Elvia (to Aldo): Do you want to bet it'll win?

Aldo shakes his head again, skeptically.

Elvia (insisting): If Number 5 comes in first, you'll have
to take me to the dance tonight.
Aldo: Where to—the Blue Dance Hall?
Elvia: No. It's not there anymore. They built a mill
where it used to be. But now there's a new dance hall
in town.

Aldo reaches out and takes Elvia's hand.

Aldo: All right. It's a bet.

Rosina is tense and excited as she watches the race,
holding on to Elvia's skirt to keep her balance. Number
5 is now grouped together with several other boats as
it prepares to make another turn around the buoy. As
the boats list to one side in making their turns, one of
the pilots loses his balance and falls overboard. To
avoid a collision, Number 5 is forced to turn off its
course. The other boats follow suit to steer clear of the
pilot swimming in the water. Elvia looks up in fright
and Rosina covers her eyes with her skirt. Aldo makes
a move to head towards the water, along with several
of Edera's friends, in case their help is needed. One of
the boats, however, coming back on course manages to
rescue the pilot.

Almost instinctively, Elvia moves up close to Aldo,
holds him tightly by the arm, and without even realizing
it, places her head against his shoulder. Seeing this,
Edera teases her sister by calling out in an ironic and
exaggerated drawl:

Edera: Eeelvia!...

Elvia reacts immediately and becomes extremely
self-conscious of her proximity to Aldo. She withdraws
her hand from his arm and quickly moves away from
him. Her face is flushed, and she smiles at her sister

although it is evident she will not forgive Edera for taunting her in a silly sing-song fashion.

Meanwhile, the boats have crossed the finish line and the race is over. Number 5 is fourth. On the faces of Edera and her friends, as well as on Aldo's, there is obvious disappointment. The crowd begins to disperse. Climbing back up to the embankment, the people begin to move towards an area where a number of refreshment stands have been set up for the occasion.

Aldo, Elvia and Rosina are walking together looking much like a family. Approaching an ice cream stand, Elvia turns to Rosina.

Elvia: Rosina, would you like chocolate or vanilla?
Rosina: Both.
Elvia: And you, Aldo?

Aldo doesn't respond. As he leans up against the stand, he seems deeply absorbed in his thoughts. To attract his attention, Elvia places her hand on his arm. He turns and stares at her with a faraway look in his eyes. Then he lowers his head and moves away into the crowd. Elvia takes Rosina by the hand and follows behind him. He walks on ahead until he comes to an isolated section along the embankment where he sits down and looks out over the water. A short distance away, Elvia and Rosina stare at him sitting there alone on the bank. Then Rosina breaks away from Elvia and runs over to her father's side. Elvia remains standing there by herself, her face reflecting her emotional confusion. She is obviously very anxious to know what Aldo is thinking. At the same time, she is both bitter and angry with herself for feeling so desperately lonely. Yet despite all this, she is still hopeful that the situation will improve. As she stands there alone, looking at Aldo and Rosina at his side, she becomes so emotionally upset that she is no longer able to bear it. She turns around and slowly begins walking home.

Rosina, who is now standing in front of her father on the bank, looks at him inquisitively. Without even so much as a glance, Aldo snaps at her:

Aldo: Stay there and be quiet!

Rosina sits down a few feet from Aldo, as he continues to stare out over the water.

Elvia climbs down the embankment, heading towards the house where she sees a woman standing with a valise beside her. Elvia goes to the door, and as she puts the key into the lock, she stares up at the woman with a quizzical expression on her face. The woman is Irma.

Irma: You're Elvia, aren't you?

Elvia nods but remains absolutely silent. She continues to stare at Irma with an increasing sense of apprehension.

Irma: I'm Irma.

Elvia is taken aback. She opens the door and leaves the way clear for Irma, who picks up the valise and enters. Elvia follows, closing the door behind her.

Irma: I've heard your name mentioned quite often ... But I certainly never thought I'd meet you under these circumstances.
Elvia: Under what circumstances?
Irma: Well, I mean in such an ugly situation as this ... for me ... for Aldo ... You see, we have just separated ... And when Aldo left with the child, he was so angry and in such a hurry ... I thought perhaps he might have come here ...
Elvia: Why should he come here?
Irma: I'm sure he'll be here sooner or later.
Elvia: But why?
Irma: You two have known each other for such a long time. Aldo always spoke well of you ... Really, I don't know why myself but I'm sure he'll be here ... May I leave this valise? There's some of his things in it, his

overalls and his working papers ... And there's also Rosina's things ...

Irma suddenly hesitates as she mentions the name of her daughter, pronouncing it with a great deal of emotion, but she forces herself to continue and to say what is ultimately the most important thing on her mind.

Irma: I know it may seem cruel for me to want to take her back. Certainly, Aldo has the right to keep her ... But she will only be a burden for him. Don't you agree with me?
Elvia: No. If you say it was your fault ...

There is a long, heavy moment of silence. Then, as she prepares to leave, Irma points to the valise and says:

Irma: Then may I leave it here?
Elvia: Yes, do that.

Irma goes to the door and as she is about to open it, Elvia comes up to her and looks directly into Irma's eyes. Then, with a resolute tone of voice she says:

Elvia: I'm sure that Aldo is still very much in love with you. For you to throw away such a love ... Well, I just think you'll regret it.
Irma: Perhaps.

In a crowded dance hall, a contest for the most popular dancing partner is underway. Several girls on the dance floor have won ribbons that are pinned to their bosoms; the one with the most ribbons is the winner. Edera already has acquired four ribbons.

Aldo approaches the ticket-window where the ribbons are sold.

Aldo: Give me five ribbons.

The man behind the booth hands him the ribbons and Aldo goes back to a small table where Elvia is seated. He is about to pin the ribbons on Elvia but she restrains him.

Elvia: No, let's give them to Edera instead.

Elvia rises from the table and, together with Aldo, goes out on the dance floor. They come up to Edera who is dancing. Aldo takes the ribbons and places them in Edera's hand which is resting on the shoulder of her partner. Edera looks at the ribbons with surprise; she is so happily excited with them that she even forgets to say thanks.

Elvia and Aldo start dancing but they have hardly begun when the orchestra stops playing. Slowly, the two of them return to their table. Elvia is gloomy and preoccupied. Before Aldo has a chance to sit down, she turns to him and says:

Elvia: Come, let's go.
Aldo: But why? It's just beginning to get lively now!
Elvia: I have something to tell you.

The expression on Elvia's face convinces Aldo that the matter is something serious; without questioning her further, he follows her out towards the exit. Elvia hesitates for a moment and looks at the dance floor to see if her sister is there. The orchestra has started again and Edera is dancing away in a frenzy. She finally glances up and notices her sister waving good-bye. She responds with a slight nod, somewhat surprised to see them leaving so soon.

Side by side, Elvia and Aldo exit from the dance hall. As they gradually move away, the music of the orchestra becomes fainter and fainter. They come to a low wall on which they both sit down. Aldo waits for Elvia to speak.

Elvia: Aldo ... In all these years, did you ever once think about me?

Aldo is astounded. He looks upon her with uncertainty; he does not know how he should answer.

Aldo: But, of course . . .

Elvia: And was it perhaps because you had wondered whether or not I had gotten married, that is, whether I was able to get along without you . . . Is that it?

Aldo: Is this what you have to tell me?

Elvia: First of all, I want you to know that it wasn't very easy for me to resign myself.

Aldo (slightly embarrassed): I'm sorry about that . . .

Elvia: Then why did you come back? Why? . . . If Irma hadn't left you, the thought of coming back to me wouldn't even have entered your mind.

Aldo: Yes, that's true, but . . .

Elvia: Go ahead, tell me, tell me what I can do for you, then go . . . Please, go away from me . . . and the sooner the better!

Aldo is completely taken aback by these words. He grabs Elvia in his arms.

Aldo: I don't even know myself what you can do, Elvia . . . For some reason, I just felt I had to come back . . . I want so much to be left alone, to have some peace and quiet . . . And you seem to be the only person who can put up with me.

Elvia draws away. She looks at him, then after letting a few moments go by, she says drily and decisively:

Elvia: Irma sent you a valise with your clothes and Rosina's.

Aldo (startled): What? And you didn't throw the valise into the river? . . . Were you worried about the clothes?

Aldo pauses, then continues with a false sense of disinterest.

Aldo: Did she bring it herself, by any chance?

Elvia: No.

There is a moment of silence. Aldo leans up against the wall. The music from the dance hall is heard in the distance, and the lights are seen flickering in the dark.

Elvia (bitterly): I think we had better go home.
Aldo: Yes, I think so too.

The silence of the night is suddenly interrupted by the sound of voices and laughter coming from a group of boys and girls who have stopped in front of Elvia's house. It is Edera and her friends. She bids them all good night, unlocks the door, then enters. Groping her way through the dark, she searches around unsuccessfully for the light-switch.

Edera: Where is that damn thing?

Finally she finds the switch and puts on the lights. As she turns around and sees someone in the room, she lets out a tiny shriek.

Edera: Oh, it's you . . .

Lying on a bed at the far end of the room is Aldo. He is awake and fully clothed. Beside him, on the floor, is the opened valise containing both his and Rosina's clothes. His appearance is that of a person who has been unable to sleep and who has gone through hours of mental agony.

Edera: Did you hear I won the contest?

She pulls out a handful of ribbons from her purse and scatters them over the table.

Edera: And you're the one who gave me the most!

Edera giggles. It is obvious that she has had just a little too much to drink.

Edera: How silly it all is, huh?

A sudden dizziness comes over her and she reels for a second, then sinks down on a cot nearby.

Edera: Oh, my God, I'm getting dizzy . . . They made me drink too much.

She stretches herself out on the cot with a deep sigh of relief. Then she starts to giggle again.

Edera: First there was that silly fool who kept telling me I smelled so sweet and fresh . . . Is it true that I smell sweet and fresh?

Aldo remains silent. Edera rises to her feet and comes up close to him, putting her face almost on top of his.

Edera: Is it true?

Aldo continues to look at her without saying a word. He appears thoroughly disinterested. Then suddenly, as though releasing himself from under a heavy weight, he takes her in his arms and kisses her. Then he immediately lets her go and stares at her with an expression that reveals both anger and despair. He is about to tell her something, but seeing her so drunk, he decides not to open his mouth. Instead, he gets up, helps her off the bed and leads her to the door of her room which is at the head of a little wooden staircase. He opens the door, pushes her into the room, then returns to his bed where he throws himself face down. He buries his head in his pillow, squeezing it between his fists.

Slowly, the door at the head of the stairs begins to open. It is Edera pushing it with her feet. She is seated on one of the steps, looking at Aldo stretched out on the bed.

It is early morning inside Elvia's house and the usual pile of work is on the sewing machine. In the center of the room, a middle-aged woman is twisting herself around to see her reflection in the window in order to check the cut of a jersey she is having fitted.

Client: I can hold myself in a little.
Elvia: No, we'll widen it.

Client: Not too much, though.

With needle and thread, Elvia sews a series of marks on the jersey to indicate where it will have to be widened. Edera appears coming downstairs, wearing a tight-fitting sweater. She casts a quick glance at the spot where Aldo's cot had been the night before. Elvia follows her sister's glance, and their eyes meet. Elvia immediately turns away and attends to her client who is still looking at herself in the window.

Edera goes into the adjoining room, which is filled with chests and sacks of cloth, and where there is also a bicycle leaning up against the wall. A moment later, Elvia enters and comes up directly behind her.

Elvia: He left this morning ... I hardly had a chance to speak with him.

Edera turns around and scrutinizes her sister's face with a sense of alarm.

Edera: And what did he tell you?
Elvia: Nothing. Only that he was going away.
Edera: But why?
Elvia: I didn't ask him.

Elvia goes back into the kitchen where the client has removed the jersey and is preparing to leave.

Client: Can I be sure that it'll be ready by Thursday?
Elvia: Absolutely.
Client: Good-bye, then.

The client goes out. Elvia picks up the jersey from the table and starts working on it. At the same time, Edera enters with the bicycle and comes over to her sister.

Edera: Are you very sorry he left?
Elvia: Yes.

Edera bites her lip. She is obviously quite nervous and wants to say something but decides against it. She casts a furtive glance at Elvia, then picks up the air pump and starts filling the bicycle tires with air.

Aldo and Rosina are standing at the open doorway of a workers' barrack that overlooks a stone quarry. The room inside is large but dingy and only has a few small windows. In the center is a big table and along the walls is a line of bunks where the laborers sleep at night. The walls themselves are covered with photographs of pinup girls accompanied by obscene drawings. Odds and ends and battered suitcases are scattered everywhere. Over to one side, a laborer in his underwear is busy tending to an injured foot.

Aldo talks to a man while Rosina peeks inside. She makes a move to go into the room but Aldo grabs her by the arm and pulls her back.

Aldo: Wait here outside!

Rosina steps outside and the man continues with the conversation.

Man: As far as I'm concerned, I'll let you have the job, and you can even stay here with the child. But that's up to you.

Aldo peers into the dingy room. The laborer in his underwear looks up and sneers at him. Aldo moves away and steps outside, followed by the man.

Aldo: It's impossible. Two thousand five hundred lire a day, plus overtime, would satisfy anybody. But for her, this place is impossible.

He indicates Rosina, who joins them as they come out.

Man: Well I don't know what to tell you.
Aldo: Thanks, anyway.

There is a bitter expression on Aldo's face as he shakes hands with the man and says good-bye. Then he walks out to the road, and Rosina follows after him. She is almost forced to run in order to keep up with her father. A truck passes by, raising a cloud of dust that covers them both. When the dust settles, Aldo turns around and sees Rosina standing in the middle of the road removing a pebble from her shoe. Then he turns and continues onward, walking ahead at a fast pace. Rosina again starts running to catch up with him.

Overlooking an asphalt street flanked by trees and a cluster of buildings, Aldo is seated on the parapet of a small bridge eating a sandwich. As Rosina approaches him, he points to a packet of sandwich meats beside him. He asks her:

Aldo: Do you want some more?
Rosina: No, no . . .

Suddenly, the sound of children's voices is heard. Over to one side is a schoolhouse and the children have been let out in the yard for their recreation period. Rosina rushes over to watch a group of children playing ball. The ball bounces here and there and then all of a sudden it rolls out into the middle of the street. Rosina looks up and runs out to retrieve it, totally unaware of a car coming directly at her. The car swerves sharply to one side of the road, barely missing her. The driver sticks his arm out of the window, shakes his fist protestingly, and then drives off. Aldo jumps up and runs out into the street. After cursing at the man in the car, he turns to Rosina, grabs her by the arm and slaps her across the face.

Aldo: I told you so many times to be careful when you cross the street... You've got to be careful, understand?

From behind the schoolyard fence, the children are watching the scene, dumfounded. With a gesture revealing both anger and shame, Aldo gathers up his belongings, pushes Rosina aside and walks hurriedly down the road. Rosina follows behind with quick, short steps. Tears stream down her cheeks, and as she comes

to a dirt path that runs off from the road, she turns into it and starts running up ahead.

Aldo looks after her to see that she doesn't get too far away. Rosina continues running along the path; then suddenly she comes to a halt. Directly up ahead of her she sees a group of about twenty men. Some of them are peacefully walking back and forth; others are milling around in small circles, chattering amongst themselves. Aldo approaches without paying them much heed. He is sullen and irritated with himself. Some of the men pass directly in front of him and as he looks at them Aldo gradually becomes aware that all of them have that unmistakable look of the mentally ill. Encircling Rosina, they stare at her in their typically deranged manner of imbecilic gentility. One of them caresses her, then runs off giggling. Unaware of what it is all about, Rosina becomes terrorized and begins to cry. Up from behind a nearby mound, two male nurses appear. With calm assurance, as if rounding up a flock of stray chickens, they walk among the group of lunatics calling:

Nurse: Mario, Osvaldo, Ercolino...Come on, let's go... Giancarlo, Gianni...Time to go home, let's go!

And they are obediently led away along the path that runs under the trees.

Aldo comes up to Rosina, takes her in his arms and walks on ahead, pressing her affectionately close to him.

Aldo: All right, you're all right now ... let's go. They're harmless, don't you see?

Aldo and Rosina remain alone in the open field. The child is still upset and continues to cling tightly to her father. Aldo's angry attitude has changed to one of tenderness. He caresses Rosina's little head but all he can say is:

Aldo: All right now, Rosina ... all right!

Gradually Rosina calms down. She looks around to

see if the lunatics are still there, but they are all gone. Her gaze then falls upon the town up ahead beyond the fields.

Rosina: Papa, are we going there?

Aldo answers as though he were speaking to a grown-up.

Aldo: Life in town is too expensive for us. But we'll stop somewhere. You have to go back to school . . .

He sets her down, then noticing the dress she is wearing, says:

Aldo: Look at that dress! Don't you have any others? There should be one in the valise.

Rosina looks at her dress as if she only now realizes that it is so dirty and torn.

Rosina: Yes, I forgot about that one.
Aldo: Well, be sure to wear it tomorrow morning.
Rosina: But it's my best dress . . . When Momma comes back, I'll ask her to make me an apron.

Aldo looks at her with a stupefied expression on his face, then presses her close to him endearingly. But he immediately checks himself, grabs the valise in hand and abruptly departs.

Rosina is seated on the side of the asphalt road. She is wearing her best dress and playing with a collection of small stones which she has laid out on the road in the shape of an oval. The humming sound of a motor is heard coming from a short distance away. It comes from a road-machine used for melting tar. Around the machine a group of laborers, one of whom is Aldo, is repairing a section of the road that runs across the open fields. The road runs all the way to a distant town where the steeple of a church stands out on the horizon.

Il grido

The sound of a horn is heard coming from a public bus signaling for right of way. The laborers stop working and clear the road. As Aldo looks at the vehicle, his eyes fall upon the list of towns indicated on the front of the bus. Among them is Goriano, Aldo's home town.

The bus starts moving slowly along the side of the road. Aldo is unable to turn his eyes away from the list of towns. He appears completely absorbed in his thoughts, and they are thoughts that disturb him profoundly, so much so that his face becomes twisted with an expression of profound anxiety and an uncontrollable sense of restlessness.

Gradually the bus gets underway. It is forced to drive up close to the shoulder and, as a result, it passes directly over Rosina's oval design. She watches disconsolately as the enormous wheels of the bus scatter the stones in every direction. Turning to one of the laborers standing next to her, she says:

Rosina: It spoiled my circle.
Laborer: Then do it over again.

Early the next morning, a gasoline truck comes into view on the asphalt highway, traveling at moderate speed. Directly up ahead is a little roadside gas station in back of which is a small, newly constructed house. Parked alongside the pump are two motorcycles belonging to the Highway Patrol. The truck slows down and comes to a stop. One of the two drivers leans out of the cab and, turning towards the rear of the truck, says:

Driver: You'll have to get off. There's a Highway Patrol up ahead.

Sitting on top of the truck are Aldo and Rosina. They both climb down. Then Aldo reaches over the side of the truck and pulls out his baggage which consists of a valise and a small bundle.

Driver: Sorry, but I'm not allowed to carry anybody . . . Maybe I'll be able to pick you up later.

Aldo nods to the driver, then both he and Rosina take off on foot while the truck drives on ahead. A few seconds later, it pulls up in front of the gasoline pump and comes to a halt. Both drivers get out and look around. There is no one in sight, so one of them goes up to the door of the house, which is open, and calls out:

Driver: Virginia!

There is no response. The driver turns and looks at his assistant, perplexed.

Driver: Seems like everybody's dead around here.

Sounds of agitated voices coming from the fields break the silence.

Assistant: I'll bet the old man has tried to run away again!

Coming out from behind a path in the rear of the house are the two highway patrolmen and Virginia. They are supporting an old man by the armpits as he staggers along between them. The two patrolmen greet the two drivers with a nod, while Virginia keeps talking to the old man. Virginia is an attractive brunette in her late twenties.

Virginia (angered): I'm fed up with you, understand? Completely fed up!

Assisted by the patrolmen, she sits the old man down on a chair in front of the house.

Virginia: What's the matter, aren't you happy here? You've got everything you need: your own bed, your own radio . . . Is there anything you lack?

The old man remains stubbornly silent.

Virginia: You can't sleep out in the open every night, Papa! . . .

il grido

Aldo and Rosina have appeared and are watching the scene from the road. The drivers of the gasoline truck, having gotten the key to the pump from Virginia, are now refilling the tank with gas. Virginia looks down at her skirt, her shoes and stockings all wet from the dew, then turns to the patrolmen.

Virginia: Look at me, I'm all wet! And it's beginning to get cold, too!

Turning upon her father, she breaks out into a fit of anger again.

Virginia: Why don't you go inside, at least!

But the old man doesn't move. He continues to remain silent and unperturbed. As Virginia goes to the door of the house, she turns and says to the drivers:

Virginia: I'll be right back.

Then she disappears behind the door. The two patrolmen go over to the gasoline pump and one of them says to the drivers:

First Patrolman: Late last night I gave a ticket to a woman who was driving without her lights on ... And she wasn't wearing anything but her nightgown. She had a coat thrown over her shoulders, but you could see everything!
Second Patrolman: And you gave her a ticket!

Aldo approaches the scene, followed by Rosina. The two patrolmen turn around and look at him. Rosina walks over to the gas pump and stares at it curiously, then presses her nose up against the glass covering the meter. Aldo sits down on one of the wayside stones that enclose the area. Directly in his line of vision is a window where Virginia's figure is silhouetted as she proceeds to change her wet clothes. Aldo cannot help but see her since the window is directly in front of him and he would have to purposely turn around to avoid her. Having finished dressing, Virginia takes a quick peek out through the window, and sees Aldo staring at her. Their eyes meet momentarily, then Virginia quickly withdraws. A few seconds later, she appears in the doorway. She has a bottle of wine and an empty glass in her hand. She places the bottle and the glass alongside the old man and stands there for a while, looking at him reproachfully. But she doesn't say a word; instead, she merely turns away from him and comes forward to where the patrolmen and the drivers are gathered.

Virginia: I know it's not good for him, but what can I do . . . I can't let him go crazy!

She adjusts her skirt, buttons up her blouse, then runs her fingers through her hair. Her gestures are extremely feminine, and the kind of looks she receives from the four men leave no doubt as to their meaning. Aldo is also staring at her. Then one of the drivers asks:

Driver: Do you want only regular or some of the high octane, too?
Virginia: There's already enough high-powered merchandise around here, and that's me!

The four men break out into a laugh, and Virginia laughs along with them.

Aldo is also amused by her remark and he continues to look at her with increasing interest.

Rosina goes over to the old man who has just polished off a glass of wine in one quick gulp. He is about to fill up another glass when she looks up at him in amazement. She asks:

Rosina: Are you going to drink some more?
Old man: Yup, right down to the bottom.
Rosina: But when it's finished, then what?
Old man: Well, when there's no more left, then glory be!

Rosina continues to stare at him with her eyes wide open.

The drivers have finished fueling the tank. One of them disconnects the hose while the other presents the bill to Virginia who, in turn, signs it and hands it back to him. They climb back into the truck and the driver starts the motor. Aldo rises to his feet and calls out to Rosina. As she comes running up to him he turns to one of the drivers and tries to indicate that he would like to get back on again. But the driver raises his eyes towards the patrolmen and, shrugging his shoulders, whispers to Aldo:

Driver: Maybe we'll be able to pick you up when we pass by again.

As the two patrolmen prepare to leave, Virginia turns to them and says:

Virginia: Going off to bed?
First patrolman: No, but I'd sure love to!

The patrolmen wait around for the truck to pull out. Aldo follows their movements, then glances at the truck once more. He is obviously annoyed and irritated.

Finally, the truck drives off and the patrolmen mount their motorcycles. They race their engines, then speed away in the same direction.

Virginia turns around, uncertain as to her next move. She glances over at Aldo and their eyes momentarily meet. Then she quickly heads towards the house and goes inside. Aldo is likewise uncertain. He is about to follow Virginia into the house but stops at the doorway and says to the old man:

Aldo: Is the town far away?
Old man: What town?
Aldo: I don't know. There must be some town nearby...

Aldo looks up and sees the steeple of a church far off in the distance. Then he turns to the old man again.

Aldo: Could we stop off here for a while?
Old man: Here? I don't know. I'm not the boss here.

A car pulls up in front of the pump and its driver blows the horn. Virginia appears in the doorway. She is about to attend to the customer, but the old man stops her and says:

Old man: Virginia, this fellow wants to stop off here.

Virginia looks at Aldo as he comes up to her and says:

Aldo: Naturally, I'll pay. You see, it would be easier for me to get a lift from here.

She looks right into his eyes, then with a slightly teasing attitude, says:

Virginia: Now what is it that you really want? Do you want to go into town or do you want to stay here?

Aldo doesn't quite know what to say. Virginia leaves him with his uncertainty and goes over to the gas pump where the customer is looking at a road map he has spread out over the hood of his car.
As Virginia starts to fill up the tank, she casts a glance at the map.

Virginia: So, where are we?
Man (pointing to a spot on the map): We're here.
Virginia: And where do you have to go?
Man: To Bologna. See, here's the road ... And here's Bologna.
Virginia: And where's Rome?
Man: It's further down.
Virginia: Oh, here it is. It's off the map ... And what are all these marks?
Man: They're mountains.
Virginia: Just think, I've never even seen the mountains!

Virginia is so absorbed in the conversation that she doesn't realize the tank is already full. Consequently, the gasoline starts flowing over and begins to spill on the ground. Suddenly the meter's click is heard and the gas flow is cut off. Virginia turns around and sees that it was Aldo who turned off the lever on the pump. With a nod of his head he indicates the gas that has spilled on the ground and Virginia breaks out laughing.

Virginia: How stupid of me!

The driver pays for the gas, climbs back into his car and drives off. Virginia turns to Aldo.

Virginia: You know, you weren't very smart. If you had wanted a lift you should have told me about it before . . . I could have spoken with the patrolmen.
Aldo: I guess I should have known better.
Virginia: Well, don't let it bother you. You're bound to get a lift sooner or later. You've got a long day ahead of you.
Aldo: What do you mean, sooner or later . . . I can't be getting into town too late at night. I've got to get something to eat, then I need to find a place to sleep. I've got a child with me!
Virginia: Is it yours?
Aldo: Yes.
Virginia: And why do you drag her around with you like this? Well, anyway, as far as finding a place to sleep for the night, it all depends on what you're accustomed to!
Aldo: Eh, what kind of a place I'm accustomed to! Why, I've been roaming around like this for three months.
Virginia: Then why don't you go and take a look at that tool shed over there. If it suits you, it's okay with me.

She points to a small shed next to the house. The shed's roof is constructed with strips of metal from old gasoline cans. Aldo turns around and heads toward the shed.

Late at night Aldo and Rosina are asleep inside the shed. The mattress is resting on top of a low spring that barely fits into the space left: the shed is crowded with oil barrels, tin cans and other similar objects. There are no covers on the bed. The sound of a horn is heard outside, followed by the noise of a window being opened, then by Virginia's voice.

Virginia: Just a minute!

Aldo turns around on the bed and looks at the door. A ray of light shines through the door from the illuminated gas pump outside. The door of the house is heard opening, then Virginia's voice again.

Virginia: Here I am.

A few footsteps are heard, followed by the sound of the pump dispensing gasoline and a brief muffled conversation. Then everything seems quiet once again. Aldo turns over on his side and is about to go back to sleep, but his attention is drawn once again by the sound of footsteps approaching the shed. A few soft raps are heard on the door. Aldo gets up. He has his shoes off but otherwise he is fully dressed. He goes to the door and opens it. Virginia appears in the doorway. Her hair is dishevelled and she is dressed in an overcoat under which she wears nothing but a nightgown.

Virginia (under her breath): I'm sorry, but they want Number 5.
Aldo: Number 5?
Virginia: Yes, Number 5 oil. It should be in here.

Saying this, she enters, turns on the light and starts searching around on the dingy shelves nailed up against the wall. As she bumps up against the oil barrels, Aldo casts a glance at Rosina. She is sound asleep. Virginia finally locates the right oil and takes two cans from the shelf.

Virginia (leaving): See what kind of life this is? Even in the middle of the night ...

Then she goes out and closes the door behind her. Her footsteps are heard as she moves off. Aldo stares at the door for a moment. Then he turns to look at Rosina again. Outside, other voices and other sounds are heard, followed by Virginia laughing. Aldo draws up close to the door and places his ear against it in an attempt to hear what is being said. Then he picks up his shoes and puts them on. A moment later the sound of the car taking off is heard. Aldo opens the door and goes out, closing it silently behind him.

Outside there is a fine mist. Virginia is heading back to the house but upon seeing Aldo approaching, she stops.

Virginia: How is it in there? Cold, eh?
Aldo: Not very.
Virginia: It certainly would have been better in the house. Now that I think of it, I could have put you up with my father . . .
Aldo: Really? With your father?

Virginia giggles as she wraps the overcoat tightly around her to ward off the cold. Aldo is also chilly; he has his hands in his pockets and the collar of his jacket is turned up.

Virginia: Oh, oh . . . What were you thinking . . . in the same room with me, perhaps? You're pretty smart, aren't you?
Aldo: Just a while ago you said I was stupid . . .
Virginia: When was that? Oh, yes, I remember . . .

They stare at one another for a moment, as if measuring each other's strength.

Virginia: And what have you decided? Are you leaving tomorrow morning or not?
Aldo: It depends on so many things: money, willingness, a job . . .
Virginia: Which one do you lack the most?
Aldo (smiling): Willingness.

There is a moment of silence. Virginia shivers slightly, then laughingly says "Goodnight" as she heads toward the house.

She comes up to the door and enters but leaves it slightly ajar. Aldo is about to return to the shed, but suddenly realizes that the door of the house is still open, so he stops. A moment goes by, then the door closes. Aldo goes back to the shed.

It is early morning. Virginia is opening the gas station, placing the oil barrels out front, straightening out the advertising displays, etc. The door of the shed opens and Aldo appears carrying his valise and bundle, which he rests on the ground. Rosina follows after him and sits down on the valise.

Virginia looks at Aldo with a certain amount of surprise, but continues on with her business. Aldo comes up to her and stands around as though he were waiting for her to open up the conversation.

Virginia: So, we've finally decided? Anyway, you could have come into the kitchen. You wouldn't have been in my way.
Aldo: I'm waiting for the gasoline truck . . .
Virginia: Are you in such a hurry?
Aldo: No, it's not a matter of hurry . . . What am I going to do here?
Virginia: Where do you want to go?
Aldo: To Levenola. I heard they're looking for workers there. But anywhere else is just as good. As long as I can find a job . . .
Virginia: Uh huh, I understand.

The sound of a motorcycle pulling up in front of the pump makes her turn around. It is a small one driven by a young man who has all the airs of a country bumpkin who has studied in the city. He unscrews the cap on his tank, then turns to Virginia and says:

Young man: Five litres.

Virginia turns on the pump and as she fills the tank she glances over at Aldo. As soon as she finishes, she replaces the hose on the hook. The young man screws the cap back on his tank.

Young man: How much?
Virginia: Six hundred and eighty lire.

Meanwhile, the young man has started the engine. He turns and looks at Virginia with a grave and sorrowful expression on his face.

Young man: No, M'am, it's this much!

In an obscene gesture, he slams the palm of his hand on the hollow of his elbow, then steps on the accelerator and speeds away.

Virginia is momentarily stunned. But only for a second. She quickly runs out into the middle of the road, shouting:

Virginia: Hey, you son-of-a-bitch! Thief! Thief! ...

Aldo comes up to her. Virginia is furious and looks at him with an absurd expression on her face.

Virginia: Who does he think he is? ... Did you see what he did to me? ... But I know who he is ... I know him.
Aldo: What did he do?

Virginia is much too enraged to answer him. Instead she turns around and looks down the road.

Virginia: Where are the police? Aren't they around anywhere? ... They're always here when you don't need them!

At that moment a small truck is seen approaching. Virginia stands out in the middle of the road, waving her arms and motioning for the vehicle to stop. The driver slows down and comes to a halt. Without bothering to ask him for a lift, Virginia jumps on the running board and climbs into the cab, shouting:

Virginia: Now I know who he is! ... *(To the driver)* Come on, hurry up! ... Follow that motorcycle ...

The truck drives off. Aldo watches it speeding away, then turns around and sees Rosina running up to him. Aldo places his hand on her head and they walk back to where he left his valise.

Rosina: Papa, how old is Momma?

Aldo stops and looks at Rosina in amazement.

Rosina: And you, Papa, how old are you?
Aldo: Come, come now, Rosina ... What's going on in that tiny little head of yours?

A small car pulls up in front of the pump. Aldo turns around. The driver looks up and down, and seeing nobody else in the area, he turns to Aldo.

Driver: What do you say, Chief?

Aldo is perplexed. He goes over to the pump and then, with a certain amount of hesitancy, takes the hose off the hook.

Aldo: How many litres?

A short while later, Virginia returns, riding on the back seat of a motor scooter that pulls up in front of the gas station. As she gets off the scooter, she turn to the driver.

Virginia: Thanks, Carlo, thanks very much!

Then coming up to Aldo, waving the money in her hand, she joyfully exclaims:

Virginia: I even made him say thanks! . . . But I'm much too kindhearted.

Aldo also has some money in his hand. He comes up to Virginia and gives it to her.

Aldo: Somebody bought some gas while you were away. Ten litres: one thousand two hundred and eighty lire.

Virginia takes the money. She looks at it as though it were something even more important than money. Without saying a word, she goes over to the little cabin next to the pump. She enters, pulls out a key from her pocket, opens the cash box and puts the money inside. With a smug expression on her face, she comes out of the cabin, walk up to Aldo and ironically says to him:

Virginia: This time you found yourself a job pretty fast.

Virginia hesitates a moment, then in a rather different tone of voice, as if she were trying to force him into making a choice, she adds:

Virginia: What do you say?

Suddenly the gasoline truck that had given Aldo a lift the day before pulls up. The driver leans out of the cab's window and signals to Aldo.

Driver: Are you ready?

Virginia looks at Aldo. Aldo looks at the truck, then back at Virginia. Then he looks at the truck again. He raises his arm and makes a gesture indicating they should leave without him. Then he calls:

Aldo: Good luck!

The driver responds with an understanding gesture and takes off.

It is late in the evening and the area around the road-side station is fully illuminated. Virginia is in the little cabin drawing out an imitation leather pouch from the cash box. She closes the cash box as Aldo enters. He is carrying several oil cans which he places on the floor. At the same time, Virginia accidentally hits up against the main light switch and all the lights, except the small night bulb, suddenly go out.

Aldo stares at Virginia who is standing up close to him. For a moment they both remain still, looking at each other in the darkness. Then a sudden flood of light from a passing car startles Virginia. She abruptly comes out of the cabin and heads towards the house with Aldo following close behind.

He stares at the movement of her body as she walks ahead. Virginia's stride is slow and sensual, like that of a woman who knows she is being observed. When she reaches the doorstep, she stops, turns around and looks at Aldo as he comes up close to her. She doesn't say a word but merely fixes him with an ambiguous look. Then Aldo pushes the door open and lets Virginia precede him inside.

The interior of the house is divided into three rooms. The entrance leads into the kitchen which is in the center; over to one side is Virginia's bedroom; on the other is a small room where the old man sleeps.

Rosina is seated on a stool beside the old man. In the background, Virginia enters the kitchen and passes directly into her bedroom. Aldo comes in and stops in front of the window. After following Virginia with his gaze, he turns around, leans against the wall and proceeds to look out through the kitchen window.

Rosina (to the old man): Now I'll tell you another one. A man with a collar and no head, with two arms and no legs. What is it?
Old man: What did you say?

Rosina looks up at him with a tolerant glance, as if it were she who was dealing with a child.

Rosina: A man with a collar and no head, with two arms and no legs. You have to guess what it is.
Old man: Without legs?
Rosina: It's a shirt!

And Rosina laughs with satisfaction.

In her room, Virginia places the money pouch into a drawer, then comes out and re-enters the kitchen. As she moves about the kitchen, removing the dishes from the table and placing them inside the cupboard, Rosina's voice is heard, explaining to the old man.

Rosina: Don't you see . . . Your shirt has a collar but it doesn't have a head. It's your head . . .

Aldo turns and looks at Virginia who has finished with the dishes. Almost instinctively she smoothes out her dress, running her hand down over her body as she does so. Aldo has noticed the gesture. He abruptly moves away from the window and takes a few steps towards Virginia as though he were about to say something to her. But instead he turns to Rosina and says:

Aldo: Rosina, it's late. Let's go to bed.

Rosina immediately responds. She gets up from the stool, says goodnight to the old man, then goes to the door. As Aldo follows her out, he turns around and looks at Virginia once again. Virginia exchanges his look with an anxious and passionate glance. Aldo stares back at her for a moment, then finally goes out, closing the door behind him.

Virginia starts heading towards her room. The old man rises wearily and goes over to the cupboard where he takes down a bottle of wine and an empty glass. He does this gingerly and with the thought that no one is around, but a second later Virginia comes up behind him and grabs the bottle out of his hand.

Virginia: No, tonight you'll do without it. Now go to bed.

She nudges the old man into his room and closes the

door, then goes back into the bedroom and slowly begins to undress.

Early the following morning, Virginia is out in front filling a customer's gas tank. As the driver pays her, Virginia asks him:

Virginia: What time is it?
Driver: It's seven-thirty, M'am.
Virginia: My, it's late.

The car drives off and Virginia hurries back to the house. But upon seeing the door of the shed ajar, she stops and goes over to look inside. The shed is empty. Virginia then enters the house and checks to see if the old man is still asleep. But he is not in his room, so she closes the door and returns to her room. Aldo is there, sitting on the bed, and as soon as Virginia enters, he says to her:

Aldo: I've really got to get back. If the child awakens...
Virginia (interrupting): But I just saw her; she's sound asleep . . . Aldo, why don't you just relax, and be a gentleman for a change . . .

She sits down beside him on the bed, cuddles up close and gives him an affectionate kiss.

The old man and Rosina are out in the fields watching a group of farmers who are clearing away a row of poplar trees. One of the trees already has been felled and lies on the ground. Two men are sawing another tree while two others hold the end of a rope which is tied around the tree, waiting to pull it down. The old man appears sad and resentful as he watches the men at work. The two farmers who are sawing the tree stop for a moment and check to see if they have gone deep enough. The old man takes a few steps forward and angrily shouts at them:

Old man: Delinquents! . . . Hooligans! . . . You just can't cut down a tree that's live and healthy! . . . You idiots! . . . Bandits!

First Farmer: (placatingly): We'll plant some others. Okay?

Old man: No; it's not okay. One tree is not the same as another!

One of the other farmers, the oldest, comes up to the old man. He has a determined look on his face.

Second farmer: Look, we paid you for this land, didn't we? We paid you for the house, the stalls, the trees, the animals and everything. We paid you a stack of money this high.

He makes a gesture to indicate a large pile of thousand lire notes.

In the meantime, the other farmers are pulling down the tree with a series of grunts and shouts. The tree begins to give way. The old man watches the scene with clenched teeth. Rosina is staring at the swaying tree with her eyes wide open. Then she turns to the old man and whispers:

Rosina: Was it yours?
Old man: They were all mine!

With a loud crash, the tree comes falling down, raising a cloud of dust and stirring up a flurry of dry twigs that settle all over Rosina and the old man. They both remain motionless for a while, looking incredulously at what for them is an act of vandalism. Then the old man bends over, picks up a stone from the ground and flings it at the farmers. The stone barely misses one of them, who turns around and glares at the old man. Then he exchanges glances with the other farmers who immediately move across the field and start sizing up another tree further away.

Rosina: And why aren't they yours anymore?
Old man: Because my daughter didn't want to be a farmer.

Back in Virginia's bedroom, she and Aldo are seated close to each other on the bed. Virginia is in her nightgown; Aldo is fully dressed. Virginia is speaking.

Virginia: . . . and ever since my husband died I have felt a need for somebody. What could a woman do with a farm all by herself? So when they offered us the gas station, we took it. The land was ours . . . But I would like to do some traveling, too . . . like you. At least you get to see places and people . . .

Aldo (interrupting): There are ways and ways of traveling around, Virginia. And the way I've been doing it doesn't make sense . . . it's not worth a damn.

Virginia: Yes, but still . . . look at me, I haven't seen anything.

Aldo (smiling): I know . . . You haven't even seen the mountains!

Virginia: How do you know that?

Aldo (still smiling): Well!

Through the window, Virginia sees one of the farmers coming to the door. She is somewhat surprised and at the same time extremely annoyed. She jumps up and says to Aldo:

Virginia: You stay here.

Then she quickly puts on her overcoat and hurries into the kitchen. As she opens the door, the farmer comes up to her. He is furious.

Farmer: For two lire I'd . . . I'd . . .

Virginia: What happened?

Farmer: He came around with a little child, and he called us bandits . . . He even threw stones at us . . . He'd better stop it, do you understand?

Virginia: Don't get so excited.

Farmer (furiously): I will get excited . . .

Virginia: All right, then don't bother me about it.

She is about to go back into the house but the door opens and Aldo appears.

Aldo (to the farmer): Did you say he was with a child? Where is she?

Aldo's excitement alarms the farmer who looks at Virginia in amazement.

Aldo (insisting): Where is she? I'll go and get her myself. *(To Virginia)* I thought you said she was asleep!

The farmer looks at Virginia again, then finally decides to go along with Aldo.

Virginia is left standing at the door, worried and concerned over Aldo's reaction. Then she decides to follow them, but as soon as she gets underway, a car pulls up for gas. Irritated and very much against her will, she stops in her tracks, looks at Aldo and the farmer as they disappear behind the house, then turns around and goes over to serve the customer.

It is early afternoon now. Rosina and the old man are seated in the kitchen. The table is still filled with the leftovers of the noonday meal. The old man, who is quite drunk, is teaching Rosina an old anarchist song.

Old man (singing): "Down! Come down off your throne, you cowards, and lay aside your crowns ..."

Rosina is repeating the lines after him, but as soon as Aldo enters, both of them immediately stop singing.

Aldo grabs a rag and starts wiping the grease from his hands. He looks at Rosina and the old man without saying a word. Then he tosses the rag aside and goes into Virginia's bedroom.

The old man nods to Rosina understandingly and they both sneak out of the house.

A short distance away, a fruit and vegetable truck has swerved off the road into a ditch. Scattered over the ground are numerous crates of persimmons which have fallen from the truck. Some have been smashed open and the juice from the squashed fruit has formed a thick slime in the middle of which both the old man and Rosina are happily playing. The driver of the truck is arguing with a hunter whose dog is licking its wounded paw.

Driver: But you'll have to pay for the damages! After all, I did it to avoid hitting your dog. Why do you think I swerved off the road ...
Hunter: It's not my fault if you don't know how to drive.
Driver: But it's the dog's fault!
Hunter: Then let the dog pay for the damages.
Driver: What kind of logic is that! And who does the dog belong to!

The driver and the hunter continue arguing. Meanwhile, the old man bends over and starts gathering some of the fruit that is still intact. Then, in a childish spirit of joyous abandon, he squeezes a persimmon between his fingers, letting the juice squirt all over his clothes. Rosina, who is on her knees in the slime, laughs. She picks up the fruit, tastes it, then throws it down again. Her clothes are also smeared with juice.

Aldo comes running out of the house and rushes to the scene, followed by Virginia. They stop for a moment and stare at the spectacle, not knowing exactly what to make of it. Then Rosina turns to her father and asks him:

Rosina: Papa, do you want one?
Aldo (brusquely): Come on, now; get up out of there and go home!

Virginia, meanwhile, goes over to her father and tries to prevent him slipping. Aldo comes to her aid and they both take the old man by the arms as he continues laughing joyously.

Several hours later, Aldo is seated at the kitchen window, looking out at the road. Virginia is busy at the sink.

Virginia: We just can't go on like this! He runs away in the middle of the night, gets into fights with the farmers—he pesters everybody! The only time he behaves is when I give him enough wine until he gets drunk ... and that's bad for his health! And now he doesn't even behave when he's drunk.

Aldo: Yes, but when you get right down to it, what harm has he really done!

Virginia: Oh, one day he hurts his foot, the next day his spine ... Before you know it, I'll have a cripple on my hands. He needs a nursemaid to take care of him. No, I can't go on like this. I know it's a shame, but I really don't know what else I can do but put him away.

Aldo: Well, that's something you've got to decide for yourself.

Virginia: I've decided already. As soon as he's able to walk ...

Aldo (angrily): Oh, damn this rotten life!

Aldo jumps to his feet and angrily stomps out of the house. Virginia goes to the window and looks after him. She appears anxious and worried. She turns around and, seeing Rosina in her nightgown standing in the doorway of the bedroom, her anxiety boils over into a wild fit of anger:

Virginia (shouting): Get to bed, you too!

Rosina quickly disappears into her room and Virginia follows after her.

Aldo and Rosina are waiting impatiently on the porch of a rest home for the aged, somewhere in Ravenna. The door opens and Virginia comes out, holding several sheets of paper in her hand. She walks up to Aldo.

Virginia: Well, that's it. All we have to do now is fill out these forms and pay them. Come, let's go. If I stay here another minute, I'll get sick.

Aldo and Virginia, with Rosina trailing along behind them, stroll along a street in Ravenna. Walking slightly up ahead, Virginia suddenly finds herself surrounded by a group of tough young men. As they draw closer, she angrily turns around and glares at them. Aldo runs to her aid and a fist-fight ensues, which is quickly dispersed by the arrival of a policeman. Aldo breaks away from the crowd and, not seeing Virginia or Rosina anywhere in sight, runs off.

Turning into a side street, he spots Virginia up ahead, and comes to a stop. She sees him approaching, waits there for him to join her. Aldo is angry and upset.

Aldo: Where's Rosina? She was with you. Why didn't you look after her?
Virginia: I don't even want to take care of my own father; why should I look after your daughter!... Oh, all right, I'll go and see if I can find her.

She turns around the corner and starts heading down another street. Aldo passes his hand over his face in a gesture which clearly indicates that he has had enough of the whole situation. The wailing sound of a clarinet is heard, coming from a nearby luncheonette—a sad and melancholy tune.

Later that afternoon, Aldo and Virginia are lying on the grass in a public park somewhere on the outskirts of Ravenna. Aldo has his hands folded under his head and Virginia is close beside him, gently caressing his face. A short distance away, Rosina is lying on her side, asleep. Aldo and Virginia kiss. Then Virginia suddenly sits up and glances over toward Rosina. She rises to her feet and nervously starts walking away. Aldo also rises and follows her.

Virginia: It would have been better if we had left her at home. We paid that woman to look after my father; she could have looked after her, too.
Aldo: No, it's not the same thing. *(Alluding to her obvious urge)* Then you think this is the right time for it?

They go down along the side of a small embankment where they are entirely hidden from view. Aldo seats himself on the ground but Virginia remains standing. She has a sullen look on her face. Aldo reaches up and takes her hand, then pulls her down next to him. Virginia is still sulky, but Aldo presses her close, then rolls her over on the grass, and proceeds to smother her with kisses.

Rosina starts in her sleep, then awakens. Seeing no one around, she rises to her feet. She spots a large white pebble in the grass and picks it up, then hunts around in search of others. She finds about four or five, but continues to look for more. Suddenly she stops. Her eyes are fixed on the area below the embankment. She takes a few slow steps forward, her eyes open wide. She is transfixed by what she sees. Then, suddenly, she turns and starts running. She runs through the park as fast as her feet can carry her and stops only when she reaches a wall that stands in her way.

Down along the embankment, Virginia looks at Aldo. He is standing with his back to her, wrapped in his own sense of guilt and shame.

Virginia (sweet and gentle): Aldo, don't let it bother you; the child couldn't have understood what it was all about. I remember when I was her age I didn't under-

stand anything. And I even slept in the same room with my mother and father.

There is a moment of silence. Aldo remains motionless, showing no sign of having heard what Virginia has said.

Virginia: Aldo, please, tell me, are you angry with me? But it's really not my fault. I told you this morning it would have been better if we had left her at home... And even now I didn't want to. I knew something like this would happen.

Aldo is still cloaked in a mantle of shame. He leans back on the ground in despair and looks up at the sky, murmuring to himself.

Aldo: If Irma only knew about this ...

Upon hearing the name of Irma, Virginia is suddenly taken aback, realizing that it belongs to a part of Aldo's past of which she is totally ignorant. Slowly, she turns her gaze from Aldo. Her lips begin trembling, and, to avoid being seen in tears, she rises to her feet and gradually starts climbing the embankment.

Aldo has just finished filling up a customer's car and, as he walks slowly back to the house, Virginia appears in the doorway.

Virginia: Aldo, dinner's ready; the food's on the table. Go and call Rosina.

Aldo is thoughtful for a moment. Then, almost imploringly, he says:

Aldo: Why don't you go?
Virginia: Are you trying to say that when she's hungry, she'll come on her own . . . Aldo, we can't go on like this. You know, we'll have to do something about the child, too.
Aldo: I know, Virginia. I know I'll have to do something about her.

Aldo leaves to find Rosina, and Virginia goes back into the house.
Walking along the path leading out to the open farmland, Aldo stops and sees Rosina playing with the farmer's children. She is dirty and disheveled. Aldo stands there for a moment, looking at her without saying a word. Rosina sees him and immediately stops playing; as if he were a complete stranger, she heads directly toward the house without once looking at him.

The following afternoon, on the town square, Aldo is standing beside a crowded bus which is preparing to depart. Inside the bus, Rosina is looking out at her father. She is visibly shaken and nervous.

Rosina: And when are you coming home, papa?
Aldo: I don't know, Rosina.

The last few passengers have boarded the bus and are taking their seats. The windows are shut and the bus gets underway. As though something had suddenly snapped inside him, Aldo desperately reaches up and grabs hold of Rosina's hand through the window, running alongside the bus as it starts to pull away. His voice is shattered with emotion as he tries to say a few last words to his daughter.

Aldo: Rosina, don't say anything, don't say that your father is unhappy because he is no longer with both of you. Because my thoughts are never far away.

Rosina is leaning out of the window, but she is unable to comprehend exactly what her father is trying to say.

Aldo: Rosina, I don't know how to explain to you why your father no longer has any desire to work ... But let's hope things will change ...

The bus finally pulls out. Aldo releases Rosina's hand and is left standing there alone, shouting:

Aldo: Good-bye, Rosina ... Good-bye ... and good luck!

It is a cold winter morning along a barren stretch of countryside overlooking the mouth of the Po. The river's banks are lined with trees and the water is full of whirlpools. Tied up alongside one of the banks is a barge equipped with a dredging machine. On the shore, close to the waterfront, is a tin-roofed barrack. Its stove-pipe chimney gives off a trail of smoke. The· dredging machine lies idle, but two workers are working on another part of the barge nearest to the bank.

A man smoking a fat Havana cigar comes out of the barrack. He is dressed in a rather bizarre manner, wearing a plaid vest, a Gaucho-type hat and a large kerchief tied around his collar. He is Gualtiero, owner of the barge. Aldo approaches the barrack and comes up to Gualtiero.

Aldo: Excuse me . . .
Gualtiero: Yes, what can I do for you?
Aldo: Maybe you can give me some information . . .

In an open, warm-hearted manner, Gualtiero takes hold of Aldo's arm and invites him into the barrack.

Inside, seated around a large make-shift table, are three workers who have just finished a meal consisting mainly of porcupine meat. Gualtiero seats himself at the table and, after introducing Aldo to the other men, asks him to do likewise. Then Gualtiero pours him a glass of wine.

First worker: It doesn't taste bad but I never thought a porcupine had such tough meat.
Gualtiero: It should have been put away in a cold place for at least four days. That way the meat would have had a chance to get tender, like a woodcock.
Second worker: It must have been a month since I ate with such appetite!
Gualtiero: It seems almost impossible that a small animal like this would have such meat. Take a hippopotamus. Now there's an animal that weighs over three tons, and yet a hippopotamus steak is as soft as butter.
First worker: Did you ever eat one?
Gualtiero: Sure, in Kenya, before the war. And do you know who's crazy about hippopotamus steaks?

Gualtiero looks at each of the workers around the table to be certain he has their full attention, then he continues.

Gualtiero: The crocodile.
First worker: The crocodile?
Gualtiero: That's right. And when the crocodile is finished polishing off a hippopotamus, he stretches his mouth wide open and lets the birds fly in to clean his teeth with their beaks.
Second worker: But how come he doesn't eat the birds, too?
Gualtiero: Then who would clean his teeth?
First worker: Are there crocodiles in Venezuela too?

Aldo, who has been listening to the conversation, puts his glass on the table and turns to Gualtiero.

Aldo: Have you been in Venezuela? How is it over there?

Gualtiero: In Venezuela there's the iguana which is something like a crocodile but not exactly ... When I first landed there it was at night, and they put me in a truck and took me to some out-of-the-way place in the middle of the jungle, and they said to me: "This is where you sleep tonight." So I turned to the Negro guide and said to him, "Excuse me, but can you tell me where I can pass some water?" And he answered, "Go over to the bank and do it in the river."

Second worker: But why couldn't you do it right there?

Gualtiero: Nope, because with me, if I don't have something in front of me I just can't do it. So, when I went to the river, coming right at me I saw what looked like six motorcycle headlights. And do you know what they were?

He pauses for a moment to heighten the curiosity of his listeners who all look at him as if they were hypnotized.

Gualtiero: They were three iguanas. And as soon as I saw them, I said to myself "Oh no, they're not going to keep Gualtiero in Venezuela!" So then I went to Chile. And those Chileans! They sure are beautiful. You see, they're a mixture of two races: German and their own native stock.

With his eyes sparkling brightly, he picks up the flask of wine and pours a drink for everybody.

Gualtiero: Drink up, boys, for tomorrow you may be dead ...

Aldo: But is it true that you can earn a lot of money in Venezuela? I mean, if a worker goes there ... say, a mechanic ... You, for example, how did you make all your money?

Gualtiero: You've got to bow your head, my friend.

You've got to bow your head at all times! You've got to keep saying "Señor" or "Mister" or "Monsieur." Yes, be sure to bow your head! That barge outside cost me seven years of bowing!

Suddenly a female voice is heard calling from outside.

First worker (anxiously): Here she is!
Gualtiero: Now, don't you start acting like a wolf.

Gualtiero rises to his feet, then puts on his Gaucho-type hat and goes to the door. They all look at him. He opens the door and a young girl steps in. She wears a threadbare coat but flaunts it in such a manner that she would have one believe it is an elegant garment. Her face is heavily made up; however, beneath all the make-up her girlish features are still quite evident.

Gualtiero: Well, how did you manage to come all the way out here?
Andreina: A car passed by and gave me a lift.
Gualtiero: Good for you. Do you want to have a drink?
Andreina: What is it, red? No, I don't like red wine.
Gualtiero: Then how about a smoke. Boys, anybody got a cigarette for Andreina?

One of the workers comes forward with a package of cigarettes and is about to offer one to Andreina, but Gualtiero intervenes, then pulls one out and offers it to her himself. He flicks the ash from his cigar, and, holding it up to her, attempts to light her cigarette but she refuses.

Andreina: No, thanks. It makes the cigarette taste bad.

She moves further into the room and looks around for someone to give her a light. Aldo pulls out a box of matches from his pocket and strikes one. But before he lights her cigarette, he holds the match in his hand for a moment to let the sulphur burn. As he does this, Andreina stares at him with a sense of curiosity, wondering whether he is serious or merely trying to tease her. Finally, Aldo comes up to her and lights the cigarette.

Then Gualtiero ceremoniously takes her by the arm and together they leave the barrack, closing the door behind them.

Aldo and another man are walking along the banks of the Po. They are both leafing through some pamphlets.

Aldo: It says that everything is written down here: the documents you need to have and all the necessary information.

Man: Hey, there's even a map; did you see it? My God, look how big Venezuela is!

Aldo (reading): And listen to this: machine mechanic in Spanish is *mecánico de motores;* a welder is *soldador;* metal construction worker is *obrero de construcciones metálicas!*

The other man starts laughing. Aldo shakes his head and smiles. Then the man turns off into another direction and they bid each other good-bye. Aldo continues

to walk along the bank of the river. Suddenly he stops and looks down at the water as it swirls around in little whirlpools and splashes up against the embankment. He becomes filled with a sense of doom. His eyes are fixed on the river; then he slowly looks up and gazes at the familiar landscape, breathing a deep, sorrowful sigh that seems to leave him broken and spiritless. He remains standing there with his shoulders hunched, sad and helplessly alone.

Almost automatically, he extends an arm over the side of the bank and drops the pamphlets into the water. They fall directly into a whirlpool that quickly sucks them under. Only one of them escapes. It drifts on for a while, then is taken up by the current and carried downstream—a white spot on the muddy, gray water.

Aldo stands there for a while, watching it disappear; then he turns and heads towards the road. The area is completely deserted. He walks on, almost aimlessly, utterly alone. Suddenly he sees a white flag attached to the end of a pole rising up from the embankment along the side of the road ahead. Then it disappears. But a few seconds later it is raised again, and starts to gyrate as if signaling a message of some kind. Then once more it disappears.

Aldo walks over to the edge of the embankment and looks over it. A young girl is standing on a chair in front of the doorway of a clapboard shack. She is shabbily dressed and in her hand she holds a long flag-pole which she is trying to raise as high as possible above the roof level. She makes another attempt but is apparently much too fatigued to get anywhere. She totters slightly and almost falls off the chair. Finally she gives up and drops the flagpole to the ground. She is about to go back inside the shack when she notices that Aldo is watching her. She waves to him and tries to shout out something but her voice, though sweet and delicate, is hardly audible.

Aldo goes down the embankment and stops a few feet from her. The girl points to the flagpole and says:

Andreina: Help me. It has to be raised way up, otherwise it won't be seen.
Aldo: Here, let me have it.

But the girl is suddenly overcome by a dizzy spell. She immediately turns and enters the shack. Aldo follows her inside.

The interior is damp and squalid. As soon as Andreina enters, she reaches for the table to support herself. Aldo rushes up to her and leads her over to the bed. She collapses on it immediately.

Andreina: Oh, I'm dying. I feel like I'm dying!

Aldo is standing next to the bed, trying to calm the girl's apparent hysteria. She looks up at him.

Andreina: Haven't I seen you somewhere before?

Aldo searches his memory and tries to place her but Andreina's appearance is quite different from the time he saw her that time at Gualtiero's. She has no make-up on and her face is deathly pale and wan.

Andreina: Oh, yes, now I remember. It was with those fellows down at the barge. It must have been about a week ago.

Aldo: Oh, are you that same girl? . . . Say, you'd better get under the covers. You're trembling.

He picks up a bedsheet that has fallen to the floor and is about to place it over her. But she sits up in bed and pushes the sheet aside.

Andreina: Leave me alone! What do you think you are, a nun?
Aldo (smiling): Instead of talking so foolishly, you ought to think about getting well.
Andreina: I don't want to think about anything. I'm thirsty.

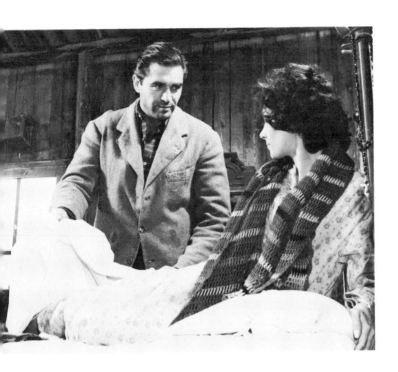

She jumps out of bed, pushes Aldo aside, and goes over to the cupboard to fetch a glass. She dips it into a bucket of water and fills it. As she is drinking, she looks stealthily at Aldo who starts for the door.

Andreina: Where are you going?
Aldo: Don't be frightened, I'm not running away. I'm just going outside to call for the doctor.

As soon as Aldo leaves, Andreina walks over to the bed. As she passes a mirror hanging on the wall, she stops to look at herself.

Andreina: My God, Andreina, what a mess you've become. Look at those eyes! And that complexion: it's as yellow as a lemon.

She turns around and looks disgustedly at the miserable condition of the room.

Andreina: To think that I've sunk so low! And with nobody to take care of me ... My mother was right after all ...

Aldo reappears in the doorway and, having heard her last few words, looks at Andreina and says:

Aldo: Leave your mother out of this and get back into bed. Don't stand there in your bare feet.
Andreina (defiantly): Feet are made to stand on. Why don't you stop being so stupid!
Aldo: I may not be so smart, but when I'm sick I know how to take care of myself.

The sound of a horn is heard outside, and Aldo goes to the door. A car has pulled up alongside the embankment, bearing a Red Cross emblem. It is the Public Health Service, and as the doctor climbs out of the car, he says to Aldo:

Doctor: Are you the one who's sick?
Aldo (indicating Andreina inside): No, she's the one.

Andreina appears in the doorway and, upon seeing the doctor, makes a slight bow. The doctor remains on top of the embankment and looks down at Andreina.

Andreina: Hello, Doctor.
Doctor: How do you feel?
Andreina: I've got a fever.
Doctor: Do you have diarrhea?
Andreina: No, sir.
Doctor: Do you have a sore throat? A headache? ... Did you vomit?
Aldo (impatiently): Excuse me, Doctor, but wouldn't it be better if you came down here, so that you can examine her?
Doctor: She'll get over it by tomorrow. It's probably

nothing more than a touch of the flu. Give her some quinine.

The doctor is about to climb back into his car but Aldo suddenly dashes up the embankment and grabs him by the collar.

Aldo: Oh, no you don't. Now come down and examine her.
Doctor: But I have other calls to make!

Aldo drags him down the muddy embankment as the doctor continues to protest. But he finally desists as they reach the doorway. Then he turns to Aldo and looks at him with fire in his eyes.

Doctor: Okay, but you'll hear from me! I'll teach you to play the bully with me!

Aldo: So what are you going to do?
Doctor: What am I going to do? That's simple: I'll report you.

Then he enters, leaving Aldo standing there with a worried expression on his face.

Later that evening, Andreina is resting in bed. Her condition is somewhat better. Aldo is standing close by, leaning on the table.

Andreina: Come over here. Let's think about something cheerful.
Aldo: And do you ever manage to feel cheerful yourself?
Andreina: Sometimes. When I drink white wine.
Aldo: Wait, first I'll go out and take the flag down.
Andreina: Oh, why don't you leave it there.
Aldo: Nope. When I was in the army, I learned one thing: that when the sun goes down the flag is lowered. They called it "taps."

He goes outside and climbs on top of the chair to take down the rag from the pole. While he is doing this, he casts a glance over the embankment and sees two *carabinieri* approaching on bicycles. He jumps down off the chair and shouts into the doorway:

Aldo: Andreina, that son-of-a-bitch . . .
Andreina: What is it?
Aldo: That doctor! . . .

Without completing his sentence, Aldo starts running beneath the embankment and disappears in the distance.

At the mouth of the Po, a motorboat wends its way through the quiet waters of a canal flanked by a wide stretch of marshland. The boat touches the bank and Andreina steps out, assisted by one of the seamen.

She looks around and, seeing a group of small straw shacks up ahead, she walks towards them. Several men are gathered outside one of the shacks. Andreina stops to ask them something. The men consult each other; then one of them points to a shack further down and Andreina heads in that direction.

Aldo is seated on a stool in front of the shack, repairing a hole in one of his rubber boots. Inside, a fisherman is squatted over a makeshift stove, frying some fish. Aldo looks up as he hears Andreina's voice calling him. She approaches with a smile on her face, then bends over and gives him a quick kiss on the cheek.

Aldo: My God, what kind of a greeting is that! I expected something better. What brought you all the way out here?
Andreina: I just felt like coming.
Aldo: And who told you I was here?
Andreina: The country isn't as big as Texas, you know.
Aldo: Did you have any trouble with those *carabinieri*?
Andreina: What *carabinieri*? . . . Oh, you mean those . . . They just happened to be passing by . . . There's no need for you to worry; nobody's chasing you.

Aldo has finished fixing his boot, and as he stands up Andreina looks at him with a satisfied expression on her face.

Andreina: We're going back by boat, you know.
Aldo: Where to?
Andreina: To my place. You don't want to stay here, do you?
Aldo: But this place suits me fine.
Andreina: Here! In this place! . . .

She peeks into the shack and the fisherman inside returns her glance with a friendly smile.

Andreina: My God!

She looks around and sees the dilapidated shacks almost sinking in the mud, then the tattered rags hanging on the clotheslines and dirty children sloshing around in the filth.

Andreina: I can't understand why things are so bad around these parts.
Aldo: It seems you've recovered.
Andreina: I'm feeling better, thanks. *(She turns to the fisherman inside the shack.)* Say, what kind of fish is that?
Fisherman: It's dory. Would you like to try some?
Andreina: I don't like it, but I'm starved . . . Come, Aldo, let's eat.

She enters the shack which is furnished with two cots, a table, and a piece of canvas stretched across the room to catch the rain seeping through the roof. Some fish nets and various other pieces of fishing equipment hang on the walls.

Aldo: You'd better get a move on right after you finish eating.
Andreina: Who me? I'm staying here with you.
Aldo: And where are you going to sleep?

Andreina: Don't think for a moment that I won't be able to find a bed!

Aldo: But do you always carry on like this?

Andreina: No ... During the summer months there's even work for women, in the threshing mill or in the hemp fields ...

The fisherman has placed some of the cooked fish on the table on a piece of wrapping paper. Andreina begins to eat as Aldo looks at her in amazement.

Aldo: But what do you do with the money you earn?

Andreina: I spend it. That's the safest place for it.

She bites into her piece of fish with evident appetite, then turns to the fisherman and asks:

Andreina: Tell me, what do you think the weather will be like tomorrow?

Fisherman: Oh, it's guaranteed to be sunny.

On a small strip of beach along the mouth of the Po, Aldo and Andreina are seated on a sandy spot that overlooks the sea. There is a weak sun above and the landscape seems bathed in a soft, melancholy light. Andreina is looking out at the seascape: the waves of the sea collide with those of the river, causing the reeds along the banks to sway. She points to this spectacle, and with a sense of childish wonder exclaims:

Andreina: Aldo, look, how beautiful!

Aldo looks up disinterestedly and merely nods his head. Andreina gazes at him for a while, then says:

Andreina: Say, I've come across a lot of types, but I've never seen anybody who gets so little enjoyment out of life as you do.

Aldo (smiling): But I wasn't always like that, you know. I remember once we were climbing up a little hill in Ferrara ... Have you ever been to Ferrara?

Andreina: No, but I should have.
Aldo: Well, anyway, it was a Sunday and some friends had come to visit me . . .
Andreina: Were they all men?
Aldo: What a question! Yes, there were also some women. But to make a long story short, the others all decided to go dancing. But the girl I had—her name was Irma—said to me: "Who wants to go dancing! It's the same old thing. Let's go inside this place, instead." And we went there. It was a museum . . .

Aldo stops. Andreina turns and looks at him, then seeing that he is making no effort to continue with his story, she says:

Andreina: So, what happened then?
Aldo: Nothing. We just saw the museum.
Andreina (somewhat angrily): What kind of a story is that! It has no ending!

Aldo doesn't respond. He gathers up a handful of sand in his fist and gradually lets it run through his fingers.

Andreina: Now, that's what drives me crazy! First you start yapping away, then all of a sudden you stop and you don't say a word . . . You do everything your own way! If that's the way you behave when you work . . . When you're working on a job, my dear, you can't have your own way, you know!

Aldo: Oh, please! I'm not like that at all. As a matter of fact, when I was working at the sugar refinery, don't think that I was just sitting around watching the sugar beets . . . I was one of the few people who worked there steady; I was in charge of the blast furnace. From up there I could see my house . . . and even my little daughter playing in the backyard . . .

Andreina: Do you have a daughter?

Aldo: Yes, Rosina.

Andreina: As soon as I have some free time, I'd like to try and have a daughter too.

There is a moment of silence, then Andreina continues in a sad tone of voice.

Andreina: I was pregnant once, but it didn't work out. It would have been too good if it did. At that time I was married . . . Now, who knows where he is . . .

They both look out to sea in silence.

Inside the shack, smoke billows out of the beat-up stove. Aldo is poking around in the ashes trying to get the fire started again. Andreina is standing on one of the cots, trying to tie down the canvas sheet, sagging from the heavy accumulation of rainwater coming through the roof. She lifts the canvas and some of the rainwater spills out over the floor. Then she sits down on the cot and looks at Aldo.

Andreina: If it isn't one thing, it's another; now that I've found a place to sleep, we don't have anything to eat . . .

Aldo stops poking the stove. He goes over to the door

and opens it to let out some smoke. He takes a few steps outside. It is pitch black; then he returns. His hair and his face are slightly wet from the rain.

Andreina: I wonder what you would do if I wasn't around.

Aldo dries his face with a handkerchief.

Aldo: I'd wait for some good weather.
Andreina: And when it comes, what would you do?
Aldo: So, now you're giving *me* advice. How old are you?
Andreina: Eighty!
Aldo: Then I'm ninety.
Andreina: Okay. Then we'll do something about it . . .
Aldo (interrupting angrily): No, we won't! We won't do anything!

He paces back and forth for a moment, then sits down on his cot. Andreina looks at him as though expecting him to say something else. But Aldo remains silent, wrapped up in himself as though she weren't there at all.

Andreina (bitterly): I see; if I don't make a move around here then nobody will . . .
Aldo: Where do you think you're going in this rain?
Andreina: Oh, just for a little walk.

She runs a comb through her hair, then slips into her overcoat and heads toward the door.

Andreina: I'll see you later.

She opens the door and vanishes into the night. Aldo throws himself upon the cot and stares up at the ceiling. A puddle forms on the floor from a leak in the canvas.

Aldo remains there for a while, disturbed and restless. Then suddenly he jumps to his feet, tips the canvas to one side spilling the accumulated rainwater over the hot stove. There is a loud hissing sound and the room becomes enveloped in an even greater shroud of smoke. Aldo opens the door and runs out over the marshland toward the village.

Entering the main street, Aldo looks around at the houses and shops. They are all dark and apparently closed for the night. The area appears completely deserted, illuminated only by a single lamp post. Aldo turns and calls out Andreina's name. Then he notices that the door of a small restaurant across the street is slightly ajar and a night light is still on in the rear. He walks over to the door, opens it and again calls out Andreina's name. As he slowly enters the restaurant, Andreina suddenly appears from the back. She gradually comes toward him.

Andreina: What are you shouting about?
Aldo: Get home!
Andreina: Will you stop shouting. And then will you please explain to me why I should go back. Don't you know why I came here? . . . Because I'm hungry, that's why! And so are you. And if you tell me you aren't, then you're a liar!

Aldo looks at her, dumfounded. He turns around slowly and starts walking towards the doorway. Andreina follows him for a few steps, shouting after him.

Andreina: I'm just a poor, unfortunate thing. But you, who do you think you are? I don't say you haven't any troubles of your own, but it would take me months to tell you about mine!

Aldo quickens his pace and is out on the street. Andreina follows behind, crying and calling out to him.

Andreina: Where are you going? . . . Wait . . . Let's talk. Where are you going?

Aldo keeps walking straight ahead without bothering once to turn around. Andreina stops; then she bursts into tears. She continues to look at Aldo as his shadowed figure disappears into the night. Then she turns and goes back to the restaurant.

At daybreak, a small truck comes traveling at high speed down the asphalt highway. In back of the open truck, huddled in one corner and partly covered by a heavy piece of canvas, Aldo sleeps.

The truck slows down and makes a turn at a cross-road. Aldo wakes and looks around. He sees a roadside gas station up ahead illuminated by a neon light. The truck pulls up in front of the pump and the driver sounds his horn.

Aldo is about to cover himself with the canvas and go back to sleep again. But suddenly he recognizes the gas station. In fact, a moment later, the door of the house opens and Virginia steps out. Her eyes are still drowsy with sleep and her hair is disheveled. Aldo sits up and looks at her. Virginia goes over to the pump as the driver unscrews the top of his tank.

Driver: Fifty litres.

Virginia inserts the hose into the tank and grumbles to herself.

Virginia: I swear this is the last winter I'll stay open at night.

She turns to look at the road and sees Aldo in back of the truck. She is slightly startled but doesn't say a word. Aldo is also silent. Their eyes meet for a moment but neither of them says anything. Their actions and reactions resemble a mute skirmish, typical of the previous rapport that existed between them when they lived together. Finally, Virginia moves up to him and says:

Virginia: Still roaming around in search of a job? Or are you looking for something else? Aren't you tired yet?
Aldo (indifferently): Tired is not the word for it, Virginia.

Virginia: Look, I don't know if you remember it, but you left your valise here.
Aldo: Where is it?
Virginia: In my father's room.

Aldo jumps down from the truck and casually strolls over to the door of the house. He enters, and passes through the kitchen into the old man's room. As soon as he turns on the light, the old man awakens and looks up at him.

Old Man: So, you've come back?
Aldo: No, just passing through. But weren't you ...

The old man winks and then with a quick gesture of his hand indicates that he ran away from the rest home. Aldo goes over to the corner and picks up his valise.

Aldo: Good for you, Grandpa! You're back in circulation again, eh?

The old man now winks again, then Aldo turns off the light and goes out.

The driver is paying Virginia for the gas. As soon as she sees Aldo coming out of the house, she turns and looks at him. His clothes are soiled and muddy and his face is unshaven. His appearance is that of a man whose spirit is completely broken. He tosses his valise into the truck, as Virginia comes up to him.

Virginia: There was also a postcard that came for you . . .
Aldo (startled): A postcard?
Virginia: Yes, and for a while I kept it aside for you . . . It was from Irma.
Aldo: And where is it?
Virginia: It didn't seem to say anything important. I think I must have lost it somewhere.
Aldo: You lost it!
Virginia: All it said was that Rosina was well, that she had grown up . . . and she sent her regards. The usual stuff . . .
Aldo: What else did she say?
Virginia: There were a few other things, but I don't remember anymore.

Aldo grabs her by the arm and shakes her.

Aldo: You don't remember! I've got to know what she said!

Virginia looks at him in amazement, discovering, for the first time, by the expression on his face, tone of voice and his sudden outburst, the depths of his innermost feelings. She continues to stare at him with increasing bitterness. Aldo gives her a dirty look, then releases her arm and abruptly climbs back onto the truck. The driver starts the motor and the vehicle gets underway. Virginia remains standing there near the pump. As the truck drives off, she makes an attempt to run after it, but stops. Aldo doesn't bother to look back. The wind ruffles his hair and the expression on his face reveals a growing sense of anger.

Aldo is seated up in front of a large carrier truck trans-
porting new automobiles. It is traveling at high speed.
Aldo has changed his clothes, but he is still unshaven.
As the truck speeds along, he begins to recognize the
familiar landscape. Directly up ahead he sees the church
steeple and the outline of the houses. It is his own home
town. As they come to a lane that turns off from the
road, Aldo tells the driver to stop. The truck comes to
a halt and Aldo climbs down. Then, as the truck drives
away, he heads for the lane and starts walking towards
town. Anxious to get there as soon as possible, he
quickens his pace, but as he comes to a path that cuts
across the lane, he is forced to stop. A patrol of several
uniformed soldiers is blocking the way and the soldiers
prevent him from entering the path.

Soldier: You're not allowed to pass through here.
Aldo: But why?
Soldier: Orders.
Aldo: But I have to go to Goriano . . . I live over there.

The soldier shrugs his shoulders. Aldo is irritated and
insists. Then he points to another path that also leads
into town.

Aldo: Can I use that one over there?
Soldier: Well, I don't have any orders on that one. So
go ahead.

The soldier steps aside and Aldo hurries on down
the path, grumbling to himself in protest. After passing
through a clump of thickets, he comes to a small
country house on which a manifesto is pasted up
against the wall. But he ignores the poster and walks
around it without bothering to stop and read the bold
lettered print which says: TO ALL CITIZENS AND
PROPERTY OWNERS THREATENED BY THE EX-
PROPRIATION DECREE—A PROTEST RALLY WILL
BE HELD TODAY AT 3 O'CLOCK IN FRONT OF
THE TOWN HALL.
As Aldo passes by the front of the house a watchdog,
tied to a chain starts barking. A well-dressed farmer

appears and his face lights up with surprise as he recognizes Aldo.

Farmer: Hello, Aldo. You'll have to excuse me if I don't ask you how you are or why in the world you've come back to this place, but I really don't have much time. I've got to get over to the rally. You know, they want to take everything away from us! And I'm supposed to be one of the fortunate ones; they're only taking three acres from me! They certainly have some nerve! Even the parish. You know the parish vineyard, a gem of a vineyard . . . Well, they're even taking that!
Aldo (absent-mindedly): That too!
Farmer: They're going to build an airstrip. A runway for airplanes, for those jet planes. I don't know what good it would do to have airplanes in a place like this, but they're going to do it. So, after the rally we're going right up to the Mayor's office . . .

Aldo, who had been listening to the farmer without saying a word, is absorbed in his own thoughts. Annoyed with the farmer's endless chatter, he hurriedly says good-bye, then turns off the path and heads into the fields.

Aldo: I'm taking a short cut . . . Bye.

He approaches a vast open area, bordered on the one side by the Po and on the other by a long line of poplar trees. In the center of the area a large crowd of people, mostly women, is being held back by a cordon of *carabinieri.* In the middle of the crowd, several men are raising their shovels high in the air, following the instructions a man further away is giving. Standing next to him is a man with a large map on which he is putting down certain figures.

Aldo comes up from under the poplar trees and starts walking a little way towards the men with the shovels. Then he stops and looks at the group of people being held back by the *carabinieri,* wondering which direction he should take to reach the embankment. Suddenly, he makes a dash across the open field. One of the *carabinieri* breaks loose from the cordon and yells "Halt!" But seeing that Aldo is too far away, he decides to give up and let him go.

Aldo has reached the clearing and hurriedly walks along the embankment leading into town.

Approaching the center of town, he sees four huge tractors crowded into the square. They are driven by four soldiers in uniform. They are busy rounding up the factory workers and a crowd of other men who emerge now from the Town Hall where the rally has just ended.

All the shops are closed. Only one cafe is open, which is overflowing with people. Aldo walks hurriedly across the square. Many of the townspeople recognize him but, seeing him so agitated, none have the courage to stop him.

Suddenly there is a stir among the crowd as a young boy emerges shouting:

Young boy: They're starting to burn up the fields!

There is general excitement among the people, then all at once they start heading for the fields. Aldo, who

is almost swept up in the crowd, grabs hold of a woman by the arm and stops her. The woman recognizes him immediately.

Woman: Aldo!
Aldo: Have you seen Irma anywhere?
Woman: She was just here a moment ago. I think she was going home.

Aldo releases his hold. The woman joins the crowd and Aldo starts walking back in the direction from which he came.

A short distance away is the sugar factory. A group of workers come pouring out of the factory gates heading towards the center of town. A foreman is following them.

Foreman: I'd like to know one thing: why are you all so interested in the farmers. They're better off than you are . . . Big or small, they're all property owners . . . And after all, even if they do take away a little piece of land from them, it's for the defense of the nation, no?
First Worker: You, sir, are absolutely correct . . . but between us and the farmers, there's such a thing a solidarity, you know!

The foreman stops in his tracks and makes a gesture of resignation, as the workers continue on their way.

Aldo enters a small side street at the end of which can be seen the river. He passes about fifty feet away from the workers but he completely ignores them and goes on his way. But one of the workers spots him and, turning to his companions, says:

Second Worker: Hey, did you see who that was?

The other workers stop and look at Aldo. They are about to go over and join him but Aldo quickly turns off into another street, the one on which Irma's sister lives. He heads towards her house but before he is half way there, he stops short. Rosina is crossing the street up ahead and enters the house directly opposite the one of Irma's sister.

After a moment of hesitation, Aldo starts walking slowly up the street. He is so overwhelmed with emotion that he seems to move like an automaton. He comes up to the house which Rosina had entered and cautiously peeks in through the window. He sees a small dining room with an open doorway in the rear that overlooks a little flower garden. Over to one side of the room is Irma. She is holding a newborn infant in her arms, bathing him in a basin of water.

Unable to withstand the sight of that peaceful, intimate scene, Aldo tears himself away from the window and walks out into the middle of the street. Then he stops and looks back at the house which has for him an aura of tranquility and well-being about it.

Inside, Irma is still bathing the newborn child with gestures of love and tenderness: all her anxieties seem assuaged. Suddenly she lifts her eyes towards the window and sees Aldo standing in the middle of the street. For a moment she remains almost petrified; then she turns towards a door in back of the room and calls out:

Irma: Anna! ... Anna!

Outside, Aldo takes a few steps towards the window again, but suddenly he changes his mind. He stops and turns around, then slowly and wearily starts walking down the street towards the factory.

A thick cloud of smoke rises up from the fields and darkens the sky. The fields are in flames and crowds come rushing out from another street, heading towards the burning fields.

Aldo continues to walk towards the factory. He stops in front of the gates to look up at the smokestack. Finding the gates open, he enters. There is no one in sight, not even the guard. Aldo walks across the courtyard and stops at the foot of the stairway leading up to the tower. Then he starts to climb the iron steps.

Out on the street, Irma appears. She is following Aldo and having seen him enter the gates of the factory, she crosses the road and goes in.

Aldo continues to climb up the steps. He has almost reached the top.

Irma enters the courtyard and looks around in search of Aldo.

Aldo is now at the top of the tower. He looks out over the countryside and sees the Po and the outline of his house. Beyond a small canal, slightly to the left of his view, a patch of land is burning and a crowd of people is rushing towards it. But Aldo is totally unaware of the scene. He is in a state of complete exhaustion.

From the courtyard below, Irma looks up and sees him standing there behind the railing.

Irma: Aldo! . . .

Aldo hears her voice and he looks down. Irma calls again.

Irma: Aldo! . . .

That call is the only thing in the world that could pull him out of his depression. He leans over the railing and reels for a moment as though overcome by a sudden vertigo.

Irma looks up from below. Her eyes are wide open. Her face becomes twisted with a sudden, tremendous fright. She emits a blood-curdling scream.

In the silence, her loud, long outcry accompanies Aldo's fall, covering the sound that his body makes as it strikes the ground.

There is a moment of absolute stillness. Slowly, Irma moves toward Aldo's corpse. She stops for a moment and stares at it. Then, with the same petrified look on her face that preceded her cry, she falls to her knees.

From the office of the factory building, three employees and a foreman come out. They go to the gates where they join the crowd still running towards the fields.

No one is aware of Aldo and Irma.

In the twilight, dark with shadows and smoke, Irma is alone in the courtyard beside the body of her Aldo.

l'avventura

1959

translated by louis brigante

Credits

Director:	Michelangelo Antonioni
Cast:	Monica Vitti
	Gabriele Ferzetti
	Lea Massari
	Dominique Blanchar
	Renzo Ricci
	James Addams
	Dorothy De Poliolo
	Lelio Luttazzi
	Giovanni Petrucci
	Esmeralda Ruspoli
	Enrico Bologna
	Franco Cimino
	Giovanni Danesi
	Rita Molé
	Renato Pincicoli
	Angela Tommasi
	di Lampedusa
	Vincenzo Tranchina
Original story	Michelangelo Antonioni
Scenario:	Michelangelo Antonioni
	Elio Bartolini
	Tonino Guerra
Director of Photography:	Aldo Scavarda
Scene Designer:	Piero Polletto, C.S.C.
Assistants to the Director:	Franco Indovina and
	Gianni Arduini
Special Assistant	
to the Director:	Jack O'Connell
Costume Designer:	Adriana Berselli
Script Girl:	Elvira D'Amico
Sound Technician:	Claudio Maielli
Cameraman:	Luigi Kuveiller
Make-up:	Ultimo Peruzzi
Hairdresser:	Mario Mandini
Production Supervisors:	Enrico Bologna and
	Fernando Cinquini
Music:	Giovanni Fusco
Editing:	Eraldo da Roma

l avventura

Production Manager:	Luciano Perugia
General Manager:	Angelo Corso
Producer:	Cino Del Duca

A French-Italian Co-production of Produzioni Cinematografiche Europee (Rome) and Société Cinématographique (Paris)

It is the afternoon of a summer's day. Anna, a twenty-five-year-old brunette, comes out from the entrance of a stately building and walks along a pathway that leads up to a dirt road. She is in a great hurry and becomes a little annoyed and surprised at seeing her father, a meticulously dressed and elderly gentleman, standing near the curb busily talking to his chauffeur in front of a black British car.

Anna: So, there you are . . . I've been upstairs looking all over for you . . .

There is a moment of silence during which Anna's father deliberately ignores her presence. She stares at him intently, trying to determine his mood and wondering how she is going to tell him what she has to say before she leaves. Finally, he turns around and faces her.

Father: Oh, I thought you were already on the high seas.

Anna is barely able to control her temper, but realizing that the discussion is about to take the usual sarcastic turn, she immediately checks herself.

Anna: No, not yet, Dad.

Her father fixes her with a long ironic look. Conscious of his daughter's haste, he is apparently trying his best to detain her.

Father: Isn't it fashionable any more to put on a sailor's cap with the name of the yacht?
Anna: No, Dad, it isn't.

There is another moment of silence. Meanwhile, a car has pulled up on the other side of the road. It is Claudia, a twenty-four-year-old blonde and a friend of Anna's. Both she and the driver get out of the car and remain discreetly in the background, waiting for the conversation to end. Anna's father resumes speaking, after a cursory nod to Claudia who, in turn, responds with a polite but half-hearted smile.

Father: And how long will you be away?
Anna: Four or five days.
Father (resignedly): Oh, very well. I'll just spend the weekend alone by myself and take a little rest. I should be used to it by now.

Anna glares at him furiously but still manages to restrain herself.

Anna: Used to what?
Father: To the fact of my retirement, not only as a diplomat but also as a father.
Anna (protestingly and with a deep sense of compassion): But how could you say such a thing?
Father: Because it's true. After thirty years—not having ever spoken the truth to anyone, I should at least allow myself to do so with my own daughter.
Anna: And have you any other truths to tell me?
Father: You already know what they are.
Anna: You mean Sandro, don't you? Well, I beg of you, please, spare me that. Goodbye, Dad.

She kisses him on the cheek but the father remains unmoved. It is obvious that he still has something else he wants to say to her. In fact, after gazing upon his daughter with a certain amount of pity, he finally does say it.

Father: That type will never marry you, my child.

Anna has a difficult time restraining herself but manages somehow to keep calm as she answers.

Anna: Up until now, Dad, *I*'ve been the one who hasn't wanted to marry *him*.
Father: It's the same thing. Goodbye, dear.

He now returns the kiss his daughter had given him a short while ago. Then, without once turning around, he heads slowly towards the entrance of the house, as Claudia comes into the foreground.

Anna, still very tense and upset over the scene with her father, gets into the car. Claudia follows after her, as the driver puts her suitcase into the trunk.

Claudia: Have you been waiting long? You'll have to excuse me.

Anna doesn't answer. She merely pats Claudia's hand. The car takes off, as Anna's maid, standing to one side of the road, waves a warm goodbye. Claudia responds by waving back, but Anna doesn't even look around. Instead, she turns to the driver and says:

Anna: Please hurry, Alvaro. We're late.

The car speeds ahead along the dusty road, across a verdant strip of land, until it reaches the archway of a stone-wall fence around which it turns and disappears.

It is seen again emerging from behind a cement wall and continues racing swiftly onward over a road that runs between two high walls. There is no sign of traffic. Only silence. It is an ancient road, and a very elegant one. Claudia looks at it admiringly. Anna continues to remain wrapped up within herself. The car now makes another turn, heading into a small, narrow road flanked on each side by gardens of patrician villas. Suddenly, it emerges on a drab, modern street amid the kind of traffic typical of any modern town.

Finally the car enters the street where Sandro lives and pulls up in front of a small but very fashionable palazzo. Anna and Claudia get out. And as the driver starts to remove the suitcases from the trunk, Claudia turns to Anna and says:

Claudia: I'll wait for you here.

Anna starts to walk across the street and is about to enter a building. Surprised, Claudia calls out to her:

Claudia: But where are you going?
Anna: I'm thirsty.
Claudia: If I had a man waiting for me for half an hour and whom I hadn't seen for a month . . .

All of a sudden, Anna stops. She is pensive, almost sullen.

Anna: You know, I could just as well go without seeing him today.
Claudia: What! After giving us such a run around . . . *(Claudia stops, smiles, and jokingly tries to laugh it off)* I see . . . so it's farewell to the yacht . . . and farewell to the cruise . . .

Anna pays no heed to Claudia's teasing comments but follows her own original line of thought.

Anna: You know, it's terrible to be far away from one another. Really, it's difficult to keep an affair going when one is here and the other is somewhere else. But, at the same time . . . it's comforting. Because it gives you a chance to consider what you want and how you want it . . . but when he's right there before you all the time . . . well, he's right there . . . *(Then, with a sense of exasperation)* Oh, let's go back . . . .

Claudia notices Sandro leaning out of the window from his apartment on the first floor of the building. He is looking at them attentively. He is a young man of thirty-five. His shirt is unbuttoned and the tie around his neck is unknotted. Realizing that he has been spotted, he smiles and waves a cheerful hello.

Sandro: I'll be right down.

As if seized by a sudden powerful impulse, Anna heads straight towards the entrance of the building. Claudia looks at her with astonishment, and watches her disappear into the doorway. Then she looks up again at the window. But Sandro is no longer there.

Sandro's apartment is extremely small. Although it contains many books, it has the atmosphere of a place that is very seldom lived in. Sandro has just finished knotting his tie. He closes his suitcase and heads towards the door. He turns back, however, to pick up a towel fallen from the bed. He takes the towel into the bathroom. Then he goes to the door again, opens it, and sees Anna. She appears a little anxious. Without giving Sandro a chance to say a word, she enters the apartment, closing the door behind her. Sandro puts down his suitcase and is about to embrace her, but Anna steps aside and begins staring at him with an intense look upon her face. Taking him all in with her eyes, she examines his suit, his hands, his legs, his shoes. Then her gaze moves back up to his face which she proceeds to scrutinize. Sandro is unable to understand her behavior, so he shrugs and jokingly exclaims:

Sandro: Would you like to see my profile?

He snaps himself into profile, then turns, slowly, in the manner of a store window mannequin. Anna continues to stare at him. This time she peers directly into his eyes. Sandro is no longer amused.

Sandro: Well, what is it?

Finally, Anna puts an end to her staring, and taking Sandro by the hand she leads him around the room. She stops in front of a mirror and looks at herself. The expression on her face becomes taut, determined. She starts unbuttoning her dress as she continues looking at herself in the mirror. Sandro comes up close to her shoulders, caresses her hair, and whispers softly into her ear.

Sandro: But your friend is waiting downstairs.
Anna: She'll wait.

Anna turns around and presses herself up against him with such a violent passion that Sandro is somewhat dismayed. But only for an instant. Soon they are feverishly kissing each other, and it is almost with a sense of sheer animal pleasure that Sandro abandons himself.

Meanwhile, left alone, Claudia is pacing back and forth outside in front of the building. She is bored and obviously tired of waiting. Then, as she is about to cross over to the other side of the street, she sees Sandro and Anna coming out of the doorway. The expression on Anna's face hasn't changed—she appears sad and gloomy. But Claudia doesn't take note of it; she is too busy fuming over Anna's lack of consideration, eager to let them both understand that she is sick and tired of waiting around.

As Sandro opens the window of the car, which is pointed towards Milan, he says to Claudia:

Sandro: I have a feeling that you're not used to being alone.
Claudia (glancing first at Sandro and then at Anna): That seems to apply to you also . . .

Meanwhile, the driver has taken Anna's suitcase out of the black car and puts it into Sandro's. Claudia picks up her own suitcase and is about to do the same but Sandro intervenes and takes it from her.

Sandro: Don't be so humble.
Claudia: How should I be . . . arrogant?
Sandro: But of course . . . arrogant, haughty . . . Hasn't Anna ever told you?

While this exchange was going on, Anna has already climbed into Sandro's car. Sandro follows and takes his place at the wheel; Claudia gets in alongside him. The car takes off at high speed.

Heading south along a state highway, Sandro's car is traveling at high speed over a straight open road. It is twilight and as the evening shadows begin to fall, the surrounding countryside is bathed in an aura of mystery.

Inside the car Anna, Claudia and Sandro sit in complete silence. Anna is deeply absorbed in her own thoughts. Claudia is looking out of the window, enthralled by the dark beauty of the landscape. Another car draws up alongside of Sandro's and is about to pass him. But Sandro steps on the accelerator and pulls ahead with a tremendous burst of speed. The other car lags behind and then turns off at a crossroad. However, Sandro makes no attempt to slow down. In fact, spurred

on by what has now become a definitely hostile atmosphere, he drives even faster.

As Sandro suddenly switches on the headlights, the
violent glare that polarizes the roadside cuts off Claudia's view. She turns to Sandro with a look of disappointment.

Claudia: It was lovelier before.

To please her, Sandro turns the headlights off and
once again the countryside is covered by a veil of thick
but romantic shadows.

Sandro: Like this?

Now Claudia again peers out at the landscape—but
only for an instant. Sandro abruptly turns the headlights
on again, revealing a sharp curve in the road up ahead,
only about a hundred yards away. He quickly shifts
into lower gear, and the car swerves slightly. The sudden shift from fourth to third gear causes the motor
to emit a sound that resembles a cry. The car races
swiftly towards the curve, getting closer and closer. But
at such high speed it appears impossible the car will
be able to make the turn. Further up ahead, where the
curve fades, there is a stone wall that runs along the
side of the road. At this point, even Anna is attentive,
her eyes wide open. Both she and Claudia are petrified
and terror-stricken as the curve and the wall loom
closer and closer. Fifty yards, forty, ten. All of a sudden,
the headlights illuminate a large gap in the wall about
three or four yards away, just on the other side of a
small ditch that separates the road from the wall itself.
There seems to be no other choice. With a frightening
leap—and going well over fifty miles an hour—the car
barely makes it over the ditch and right through the
opening in the wall. The car comes to a sudden halt, but
skids along on the muddy ground of an empty lot until
it finally stops near the door of a small farmhouse in
front of an old man. He is seated on a bench and has
been observing the entire scene without budging an inch.

There is a brief pause—silence. Then Sandro comes

out of the car followed by Claudia and Anna. Claudia is visibly shaken. She leans up against the building for support, as though in search of something solid and dependable. She is also unnerved by the feeling that she is responsible for what has just happened.

Claudia: It's all my fault!

But instead of reproaching her, Sandro turns to the old man and excuses himself for having broken into his property. Imperturbably, the old man looks up at him and says:

Old Man: And who do you think made that hole over there?

Even before he has a chance to be surprised at the old man's remark, Sandro becomes aware that Anna is laughing. It is not the hysterical laugh that normally might be expected after such a close call. It is, instead, a pure and simple laugh, almost a happy one, and it leaves both Sandro and Claudia plainly baffled.

Claudia: There's nothing much to laugh at.
Sandro: And that's what I say, too. We could have all been killed.

Anna looks at them as she continues to laugh.

Anna: I'm sorry . . . but I can't help laughing . . .

On a calm sea, amid the Aeolian Isles, just off the coast of Sicily, a motor yacht is moving quietly and smoothly over the water. It is heading directly towards a small island that appears like a huge rock jutting up from the sea, sharply silhouetted against the sky, about a hundred yards away. A few sea gulls are lazily wheeling around up above.

Aboard the yacht, a sailor is at the helm, peacefully smoking his pipe, while another peers out over the water as he munches on a sandwich. It is almost noon.

Raimondo, a deeply bronzed young man in his thirties, is lying outstretched in the sun on top of the cabin. Towards the prow, lying flat on her stomach upon a small rubber mat, is Claudia. Her arms are dangling over the side of the boat, catching the cool, fine spray of water splashing gently against the prow. Corrado comes out of the cabin. He sits down on a bench near the stern after placing a cushion under himself so as not to soil his suit, which is white and of an elegance that is slightly out of style. Corrado has a sensitive face, with a look that is both sharp and intelligent. In age, he is closer to his fifties than his forties. Following directly behind him is Giulia, one of those impossible women who are so terribly sweet and coy and yet so demanding of attention. The pose she strikes as she looks out over the water, and the saccharine tone of voice in which she speaks, are precisely characteristic of her nature.

Giulia: It's as smooth and slick as oil.
Corrado: I detest comparisons made with oil.

Anna also appears on deck, looks around and, noticing Claudia, goes over and lies down beside her. Claudia rolls over on her back to embrace all that wonderful sun but her outstretched arm comes in contact with Anna, who smiles and joins her in a friendly embrace.

Claudia: Did you sleep well?
Anna: Yes, fairly well. But I went to bed last night planning to do some thinking about a number of things . . . instead, I fell asleep.
Claudia: I didn't know one could sleep so well on a yacht. It lulls you . . .

Their conversation is suddenly interrupted by Sandro's voice shouting "Hello." He comes up to them and gives Anna a warm hug, then nods hello to Claudia. He is in a jaunty mood. Stretching himself out on the deck, he opens a picture magazine he had brought with him and starts to read. But Anna places her hand over the page he is looking at and says to him:

Anna: It would be better for you to get some sun.

Sandro closes the magazine and throws it overboard. The pages come apart in the water. Some of them are quickly swept under by the waves, while others float and slowly drift away: white specks upon which a few sea gulls converge emitting their guttural cries.

As Sandro stretches himself out in the sun, Anna looks upon him with tenderness. She is about to embrace him but stops midway, and then finally changes her mind. Instead, she proceeds to stare at him with a profoundly troubled expression. Then, momentarily dismissing her anxiety, she cuddles up close to him in an effort to provoke his affection. Sandro responds, but only with a fleeting kiss. Seeing them together like this, Claudia gets up and moves away to the far side of the prow. Sandro and Anna remain as they are until they are suddenly enveloped by a dark shadow. Sandro opens his eyes and sits up. Anna does the same.

The rocky island is now quite close, almost directly upon them. It is larger than it previously appeared and casts a long, dark shadow over the yacht. The water beneath the overhanging cliffs is extremely clear and almost motionless. Sandro rises to his feet and shouts out to everybody aboard.

Sandro: Shall we go for a swim?
Claudia: Oh, no ... please ... not here. It looks too dangerous.

The yacht proceeds to encircle the island. Up ahead, another island comes into view. It is smaller, brighter, and less foreboding. Corrado gets up and comes over to the prow to join Sandro, Anna and Claudia. He is immediately followed by Giulia, who peers intently at the landscape.

Giulia: At one time the Aeolian isles were all volcanoes.
Corrado: You must know your third grade geography book inside out.

Giulia looks at him resentfully and abashed. Claudia

points to an island which they have just passed.

Claudia: What is that one over there called?
Corrado: That must be Basiluzzo.
Claudia: Sounds like the name of a fish—merluzzo, basiluzzo . . .

Corrado then points to an even smaller island which they are now approaching.

Corrado: Now that one is Lisca Bianca.

Anna, who had been absorbed all the while in contemplating the landscape, though still preoccupied with certain personal thoughts of her own, suddenly unfastens her thin dress. Stripping down to her bathing suit, she turns to the group and exclaims with a note of exasperation:

Anna: Oh, my goodness . . . All that yapping just for a little swim.

She then goes to the edge of the boat, which has slowed down somewhat, and before Sandro has a chance to call out to her, she dives into the water.

Sandro: Anna!

Once in the water, Anna starts swimming towards the island. The sailor at the helm slows the boat even more so as to keep it within Anna's range. Raimondo, meanwhile, has gotten his skin-diving equipment ready; around his waist he is tightening a belt to which a long knife is attached. The yacht continues to slow down. Sandro now dives into the water and starts swimming towards Anna. Claudia and Giulia are removing their clothes and they too get ready to go into the water. But Claudia is afraid to dive in while the boat is still in motion, so she turns to the sailor and shouts:

Claudia: Stop . . . stop the boat!

The motor is turned off and the yacht soon comes to

a halt. A sailor places a ladder over the side of the boat. Claudia goes down the ladder, easing herself into the water. She moves away from the side of the yacht by swimming backwards. Giulia follows her down the ladder but stops on the last rung.

Giulia: How's the water?

Sandro looks up and, pointing to the rocks at the highest part of the island, answers her.

Sandro: Let's see you dive from the top of those rocks, Giulia. That would be really sensational. Come on, Giulia ... your life is much too circumscribed.
Giulia: What has everybody got against me this morning?

From inside the cabin, a feminine voice is heard shouting:

Patrizia: Raimondo!

Solicitously, Raimondo goes over to the door of the cabin, from which Patrizia emerges wrapped in a filmy nightgown. She is a woman of great elegance, somewhere in her thirties.

Patrizia: Why have we stopped?
Raimondo (kissing her hand): Lady Patrizia! ...

Then, holding her by the hand, Raimondo leads her towards the prow, where Corrado greets her and likewise kisses her hand.

Corrado: Aren't you going in for a swim, Patrizia?
Patrizia: What makes you think I would even dream of such a thing? Raimondo, why don't you go in for a dip?

She turns around to look at Raimondo and becomes somewhat startled to see him all rigged out in his diving equipment, complete with mask, spear-gun, etc.

Patrizia: Raimondo ... Do you enjoy fishing underwater?

Raimondo: I detest it. But, after all, what can you do ... It's the latest ... and I try my best to adapt myself.

He dives in. As soon as he hits the water, he starts shivering and exclaims:

Raimondo: Who ever said that man was originally a creature of the sea!

Then, lowering the mask over his face, he begins to submerge. On deck, Patrizia peers out over the sea and covering her eyes to shade them from the sun, remarks:

Patrizia: I have never understood the islands. With all that water around them, poor things ...

Out on the water, Sandro and Anna are almost at a standstill, keeping themselves afloat with only the slightest movement of their arms. Sandro is laughing and joking as though all this purely physical enjoyment of sun and water has freed him of all other cares. Anna tries to emulate him but is not entirely successful. Every now and then, her face becomes clouded with that same worried expression.

Anna: When do you have to go back?
Sandro: I don't know ... It depends on Ettore ... He's now in the process of negotiating for a contract here in Sicily ...
Anna: Then how come you're not with him?
Sandro: What a question ... Because I want to be with you, naturally. I hope he doesn't close the deal so he'll leave me alone at least for a few days ... Isn't this water wonderful!

He is lying on his back in the water, with his eyes closed, his face to the sun, cradled in the gentle movement of the waves. Anna looks at him, then after a moment of silence, she says:

Anna: I'd like to find a place where I can get some

peace and rest, maybe around here somewhere. I'd like to try . . .

Sandro: What could be more restful than this? . . . *(He opens his eyes and is upright in the water)* Excuse me, what is it that you want to try?

Instead of answering him, Anna starts swimming rapidly out to sea. Sandro tries to hold her back but because she swims much faster, he gives up and finds himself alongside of Giulia.

Giulia (referring to Anna): Where is she going?
Sandro: Ask her.

Giulia is not much of a swimmer; she bobs up and down in the water, doing a crawl, and it seems she is always on the verge of going under. Still, she manages to stay afloat, enjoying herself like a little child.

Slightly off to one side, Raimondo is exploring the depths, with his spear-gun in hand, ready to shoot. He seems to be chasing a fish that is apparently trying to elude him. But the water is so clear that it would be difficult even for a fish to hide. In fact, only a moment later, Raimondo takes aim with his spear-gun, pulls the trigger and the little harpoon shoots out. Then, with a great splash, he swims off in hasty pursuit of the fish.

A rubber raft, piloted by one of the crew and bearing Corrado ashore, comes passing through the swimming area. The sailor is carrying on a conversation with Corrado.

Sailor: I've always worked on pleasure boats . . . even though it's more tiring.
Corrado: Why?
Sailor: Because the owners never seem to have any fixed hours. For example, last night we kept right on sailing . . . We didn't even have a chance to get some sleep. Still, I like it better.

The raft passes alongside of Sandro, and Corrado calls out to him:

Corrado: I'm going ashore to take a look around the island. There are some ruins up there . . .
Sandro: There too . . .
Corrado: Well, we're still in Italy, you know!

The raft continues on its way towards shore. A little distance away, Claudia is floating on her back, basking in the sun, with her eyes closed—almost motionless. Her arms are outstretched and only the very slightest movement of her fingers in the water is sufficient to keep her afloat. Suddenly, her hand comes in contact with something viscous . . . which seems to be a fish that has shot up to the surface of the water. At first, Claudia merely withdraws her hand without bothering to see what it is, but since it persists in following her, she opens her eyes and notices something moving right next to her. Frightened, she lets out a tiny yelp. At that very moment, directly behind the fish, Raimondo's rubber fins appear above the water, and she realizes that it is Raimondo himself. He removes his mask and breaks out into a hearty laugh as Claudia playfully splashes some water into his face.

Observing them from a few yards away is Anna. Having returned from her swim out in the open sea, she was about to join Claudia. But Claudia, involved now in chasing after Raimondo, doesn't notice her.

Meanwhile, Raimondo, outdistancing Claudia, finds himself alongside of Sandro.

Sandro: What kind of a fish is that?
Raimondo: It's a cernia.
Sandro: My God, it's enormous.

Claudia, having given up trying to catch Raimondo, swims up alongside of Giulia, who is busy observing Corrado disembark on a little strip of beach that stands out distinctly white against the dark rocks. Claudia is in a playful mood. She dives underwater, grabs hold of Giulia's leg, comes up, and then dives under once again. Giulia, caught up in the spirit of all this playfulness, drops her concern with Corrado and joins in with the fun and merriment.

Suddenly there is a loud shriek, then Anna's voice is heard screaming:

Anna: A shark! . . . A shark!

They all turn around to look at her. Anna is swimming furiously towards the boat. Then, immediately, the booming voice of the sailor aboard the yacht sounds out:

Sailor: Don't move, lady . . . Stay where you are . . . Stop! Everybody keep still.

But Sandro ignores the warning and starts swimming out towards Anna like a demon. Raimondo, who was about to climb aboard the yacht, grasps his spear-gun firmly in his hand, hurls himself back into the water, and also starts to swim in Anna's direction. Claudia is stricken with fear, and holds on tight to Giulia.

Anna has stopped swimming and is cautiously looking around to see if anything comes up out of the water. Then, she looks up and seeing Sandro and Raimondo approaching, she shouts:

Anna: Stay away!

They both stop. Then, Raimondo hurriedly dons his mask and disappears under water while Sandro again starts swimming out towards Anna. Sandro comes up alongside her.

Sandro: Anna . . .

But Anna doesn't say a word. Instead, they both swim silently back to the yacht, where Claudia and Giulia are already climbing aboard. Patrizia comes out of the cabin to see what is happening.

They all lean over the side of the boat, looking down into the water, expecting the shark at any moment to come into view. But the water remains unruffled, the seaweed below is clearly visible, waving like so many fans. Even the rocks at the bottom can be seen with all sorts of small-gilled fish darting about. A mysterious, fascinating world and yet, because of what happened, one that arouses fear. Everyone aboard is silent. Until Anna and Sandro, followed by Raimondo, finally arrive and climb aboard. Sandro immediately takes Anna to her cabin, and the others follow, making various comments.

Claudia (to Anna): But how did you become aware of it? Did it touch you?

Anna doesn't answer but continues on ahead amid the overlapping remarks.

Giulia: I would have died.
Patrizia: . . . and how ugly they are . . . with all those teeth . . .
Corrado (shouting from the shore): What happened?
Giulia (shouting from the prow): There's a shark in the area. Don't move from where you are!
Corrado: Who's moving?

Inside the cabin, which is partitioned into separate rooms, the general layout is neat and orderly, with a number of prints decorating the walls. Sandro and Anna, followed by Claudia, enter from the outside deck and cross over into Anna's room. It is extremely small, with two cots on one side and a long curtain that partially conceals a bureau from which several dresses are seen hanging.

Anna is soaking wet in her bathing suit and her hair is all knotted into clusters that hang down over her face. Without bothering to dry herself, she crouches down on the cot and, assisted by Claudia, wraps a blanket around her body. Sandro and Claudia look at her with great concern. A member of the crew enters carrying a tray on which there is a half-filled glass of liquor, which Sandro takes and offers to Anna.

Sandro: Here, drink some cognac.

Anna positively refuses it, and the sailor leaves as

Sandro sets the glass down on a shelf. Looking up at both Sandro and Claudia, Anna appears pleased with their solicitude.

Anna: It's nothing... really. Let's go back... It's all over now. *(A pause and then an instant later, she begins shivering under the blanket)* Only, I'd like to change. I'm a little cold.

Leaving Anna and Claudia alone on their own, Sandro turns and goes outside the cabin where the others are still congregated, busy chattering. Among the remarks exchanged, one that is distinctly heard is Patrizia's.

Patrizia: But where did the shark go to?

As soon as Sandro closes the door to the cabin, Anna is suddenly and completely changed. She gets up from the cot, goes over to the curtain and draws it aside, revealing an array of feminine attire. Wondering which dress to choose, she finally selects two and tosses them on the cot.

Anna: Which one shall I wear?
Claudia (picking up one of the two dresses): This one is gorgeous.
Anna: Then why don't you try it on?

As Anna begins to dry herself with a large bath towel, Claudia slips on the dress and looks at herself in the mirror with a coquettish expression on her face.

Anna: It looks better on you than it does on me ... You keep it.

Anna is removing her bathing suit as she continues talking to Claudia with a tone and manner that reveal a sense of excitement mixed with one of amusement.

Anna: You know, that thing about the shark was all a joke.

Claudia looks at her as though dumbfounded, as though she had never known her before. She is obviously piqued and angry, but more with herself than with Anna.

Claudia: There's the difference between you and me: you know how to put over certain things, and I don't. Sometimes I envy you.

Anna is all dressed and ready. She opens the door and steps outside, as Claudia follows behind.

Out on the deck, Sandro, Patrizia, Raimondo and Giulia are looking over the side of the boat, watching the sailor as he approaches the yacht with a rubberized raft. Giulia, with her usual air of affectation, looks down at the water splashing up against the raft and asks the sailor:

Giulia: But aren't you afraid?
Sailor: Madam, sharks never attack anybody. Anyway, the raft is dark, and they wouldn't be able to see it.
Patrizia: So, it is true that they're blind ...

Anna appears at the door of the cabin and Sandro rushes over to meet her, a little surprised to find her looking so cheerful, as though the incident that had just taken place were completely forgotten.

Sandro: How are you?
Anna: Fine. Can't you see so yourself?

Anna goes over to the edge of the boat and stands at the head of the little stairway leading down to the water.

Anna: I have an urge to put my feet on some land. Aren't you coming?

As she starts to go down the steps, Sandro quickly comes over to her.

Sandro: Anna ... Maybe it would be better to wait a while.
Anna: Wait for what?
Patrizia: Well, with a shark running loose around the place, I for one won't get aboard that raft! They'll have to catch it first. I want to see it right here before my feet, dead or alive.
Claudia: Better dead.

But Anna has already stepped aboard the raft, and Sandro follows her. Giulia has her eyes fixed on the beach where Corrado in his white suit is waiting for them. Her desire to join him is greater than her fear of the shark, so she looks down at the sailor and asks:

Giulia: Will the three of us fit?
Sailor: Sure, sure. There's plenty of room.

Patrizia, instead, turns around and heads back to the cabin. And Raimondo follows her shortly after. Giulia descends into the raft and, as it moves away from the boat with a slight pitch, she lets out a few hysterical shrieks. Anna laughs and then shouts out to Claudia:

Anna: Claudia, aren't you coming?
Claudia: I'm certainly not going to swim across.
Anna: We'll send the raft back to you.
Giulia: And bring some cushions when you come, and a towel ...

Claudia nods assent, and remains there looking over the side and watching the water splash against the boat. Suddenly, she looks up at the sky and realizes that the sun has disappeared. Actually, it is hidden behind a cloud, and over on the horizon a group of other clouds have accumulated.

The sailor left aboard the yacht is now signaling the other sailor on the raft who, having deposited Sandro, Anna and Giulia on the beach, is returning to pick up Claudia. He sounds the depths with his oar and then shouts up:

Sailor: Okay. Come ahead, come ahead.

The sailor aboard the yacht goes over to Claudia and says:

Sailor: I'm taking the boat right up to the shore, and we'll let you get off from the gangplank as soon as we get there.

Then he disappears inside and soon the yacht starts moving towards the shore. Claudia peers out over the landscape; the islands are sharply silhouetted against the sea and sky, the volcano on Stromboli smokes feebly, and in the distance a ship passes by. Claudia is plainly enchanted by the view. Then she collects her thoughts and slowly heads towards the cabin.

Patrizia, seated at a small table inside the cabin, is busy working on a complicated jigsaw puzzle, which, once completed, is supposed to represent a typically classical scene. One by one, she selects the various pieces of cardboard and inserts them in their rightful places. Simultaneously, she is munching on some crackers spread with jam, and a piece of cold fruit. Beside her is Raimondo. He is staring at Patrizia with such an intense expression that she becomes thoroughly annoyed and says to him, as she continues working at her puzzle:

Patrizia: What do you want, Raimondo? Do you want me? A few years ago, maybe . . . but now . . . And, then, at this hour of the day!

Coming down the steps that lead into the cabin, Claudia overhears the end of the conversation, and decides to withdraw. But Patrizia sees her and calls her back.

Patrizia: Come, Claudia, do come in . . . There's no romance going on here.

Claudia enters. Raimondo continues to stare at Patrizia, particularly at her legs. Patrizia becomes aware that Raimondo is staring at her, and with a condescending gesture, she lifts her skirt a little higher to make him see better.

Patrizia: There, have you seen enough now? Are you satisfied?

Raimondo nods yes. Claudia is amused by their behavior but also a little surprised.
Patrizia calmly resumes her game and Raimondo again begins to stare at her. This time, at her breasts. And again Patrizia becomes conscious of the fact that he is staring at her. She assumes a bored attitude and looks up at the ceiling in a gesture of quiet forbearance. Raimondo reaches out with his hand and gently caresses Patrizia's breast. Claudia looks on in amazement. Raimondo withdraws his hand.

Patrizia (regretfully): Now, tell the truth, aren't you a bit disappointed? . . . But I already told you . . .
Raimondo: If women's breasts were colored, yours would be blue . . .

Patrizia laughs at Raimondo's remark and looks at him sympathetically. Then she turns to Claudia.

Patrizia: Tell me, Claudia, what do you think of Raimondo?

Claudia: I would say he's pretty depraved.

Patrizia: Oh no; quite the contrary. He's really just a child.

Raimondo: Patrizia, don't start in again . . . I would rather be called depraved. Unless you happen to love children.

Patrizia: You know, I don't love anybody.

Raimondo (angrily): I know, dammit, I know! *(Turning to Claudia)* And just think—if there ever was a woman so right, so perfectly cut out for all kinds of dissipations, degradations, infidelities . . . of . . . of . . . of debaucheries, it's her. Well, anyway, she's faithful. Faithful out of laziness . . . of unwillingness.

Raimondo has such a disgruntled look on his face that Patrizia laughs.

Patrizia: He amuses me. I don't know of anything more amusing. Outside of this jigsaw puzzle. Don't you find it so, Claudia?

Claudia: One would have to be in love with somebody to know that.

Patrizia: Have you ever been in love?

Claudia: Not really . . . It's suffocating in here . . . Shall we go out?

Claudia leaves the cabin and goes up to the deck. Patrizia returns to her game, and Raimondo continues to stare at her.

Along a narrow strip of beach on the island of Lisca Bianca, Sandro, Anna, Corrado and Giulia are waiting for Claudia to come ashore. There are some patches of vegetation growing here and there, but by and large the island is one huge rock with rugged cliffs which descend perpendicularly to the water. Jutting promontories give the place a sense of raw, primitive beauty.

Seeing Anna and Sandro climbing a short distance up along the rocks to find a comfortable place where they can lie down and stretch themselves, Corrado remarks:

Corrado: If any of you get into your bathing suits again, you can be sure we shan't be seeing one another for the rest of the year. I just can't stand seeing anybody in the city after having seen them naked on the beach.

The yacht finally has arrived and the gangplank is laid out between the boat and the shore. Claudia descends and as she wades ashore she stops, bends over to dip her hand in the water, and with a tone of voice resembling that of a mother speaking to its newborn child, she pretends she is speaking with someone or something in the water.

Claudia: Oh, how sweet ... What a dear little darling!

They all turn around to look at her, wondering to whom or what she is referring.

Giulia: Who are you talking to?
Claudia: To the shark.

They all break out into a laugh, and Claudia continues her comic bit as she playfully pretends to lose her balance on the slippery pebbles along the shore. Corrado looks at her somewhat surprised, as though up until now he had never seen her comport herself with such a lively sense of humor and wit.

Corrado: Say, Claudia, wouldn't you like to climb up with me and take a look over there?
Claudia: At what?
Corrado: At the ruins. They're very ancient, you know.

Out of the entire group, Claudia is perhaps the only one who really has the desire to explore, to see, and to generally take advantage of whatever the cruise has to offer.

Claudia: That sounds like a good idea. But why don't we all go together?

Though Claudia's suggestion is heard by all, none of them make a move. Relaxing so comfortably in the sun as they are, it seems the last thing they would want to do is to climb up the rocky slopes. So Claudia starts to go up on her own, following Corrado who is already under way. But Giulia immediately comes up to him and, squeezing his arm to emphasize her plea, whispers to him:

Giulia: Please, I beg of you, stay here.

Giulia's plea is expressed with such a pitiful sense of humility that Claudia is immediately taken aback, although she does not fully understand its motive.

Corrado (noticing Claudia's hesitancy): Well?
Claudia: Well, what?
Corrado: Have you decided?
Claudia: All I said was that it sounds like a good idea.

Disappointed and rather irritated, Corrado turns back, while Claudia looks around for a place on the rocks where she can comfortably set herself down. Giulia, in turn, approaches Corrado.

Giulia: Why didn't you ask me to go with you?
Corrado: Do you know why? Because if you saw those ruins I'm sure you would have said they were very, very beautiful. You always say "how beautiful" to everything—whether it's the sea, or a baby, or a cat! You have such a sensitive little heart that it throbs for *anything*.
Sandro (ironically): But Corrado ... If something is beautiful why shouldn't one say so?
Giulia (referring to Corrado): He never misses a chance to humiliate me, to let me know that he doesn't care about me any more.
Corrado: Giulia, that remark is not worthy of our twelve years of honest concubinage. I repeat, once and for all, and publicly, that I admire you. Does that please you?

Claudia (under her breath to Anna and Sandro): Twelve years . . . But why haven't they married?
Sandro (with a faint smile): And why haven't they left each other?
Claudia: I'm beginning to have my doubts. It couldn't be that they're in love?
Sandro: Could be. They're the kind of people who are capable of anything.

Sandro suddenly grabs Anna around the waist and pulls her to him. His action is so unexpected that even Anna is astonished. But Giulia's voice is heard again.

Giulia (to Corrado): The trouble with you is that nobody can speak to you, that's all.
Sandro (placatingly): Giulia, don't you understand that the more involved you become with people, the more difficult it is to speak with them?
Giulia: You men are all so dreadful!
Sandro: I know we are. But as the years go by, we become even worse. Isn't that so, Corrado?
Corrado: I hope so.

Breaking the nervous tension that has spread itself throughout the group, a seaman appears with a small basket of frozen peaches brought from the yacht. Claudia runs to the basket, picks up a peach and quickly bites into it.

Claudia: How wonderful!
Corrado: That's Patrizia's way of letting us know she's with us.

Claudia takes another peach from the basket and gives it to Corrado.

Claudia: I think you're very sweet, Corrado.
Corrado: More so than the shark?
Claudia: There's no comparison.
Corrado: Then why don't we go up and see the ruins?

Anna and Sandro have left the group and are ensconced further up among the rocks, on a grassy slope overlooking the beach.

Anna: Sandro ... A month is too long a time. I have become used to being without you.
Sandro: You'll get over it soon. It's the usual anxiety.
Anna: A little more so this time.
Sandro: So, it will just take you a little longer to get over it.
Anna (angrily): But I think we should talk about it. Or are you fully convinced that we too won't understand each other?
Sandro: There will be plenty of time to talk about it later. We'll get married soon. That way we'll have more time ...
Anna: In this case, getting married means nothing. Aren't we already the same as being married? And Corrado and Giulia—aren't they already the same as being married?
Sandro: But why rattle your brains by arguing and talking ... Believe me, Anna, words never help at all. They only serve to confuse. I love you, Anna. Isn't that enough?
Anna: No. It's not enough ... I told you before that I would like to get away for a while and be alone.
Sandro: But you just said that a month was too ...

Anna (interrupting): I mean, to stay away longer—*two* months ... a year ... three years ... Yes, I know, it sounds absurd. And I feel awful. The very idea of losing you makes me want to die ... And yet ... I ... I just don't have the same feeling for you any more.
Sandro: And what about yesterday ... at my house ... didn't you have any feeling for me, even then?
Anna (angrily): There you go ... Must you always spoil everything!

She turns and walks away in a rage. Sandro breathes a deep sigh, as though the scene had exhausted him, then stretches himself on the ground, his face turned skyward, his eyes shut tight.

The sky over the island of Lisca Bianca is completely filled with clouds. It is early afternoon, the atmosphere has darkened, and occasional sounds of thunder are heard in the distance.

Sandro is asleep with his arms folded under his head. Further below, Claudia, Corrado and Giulia are also taking a nap. Gradually, however, with the sound of thunder, they become aroused.

Giulia: Looks like the weather is changing.
Corrado: Please, Giulia; must you always emphasize the obvious? I can see for myself that the weather is changing.

Corrado rises and looks around lazily, listening to what appears to be the sound of a motor boat and which seems to be coming from the other side of the island. Claudia, spotting a sailor approaching, also rises.

Sailor: We'll have to get going.

Claudia turns around, looks up, and see Sandro asleep by himself.

Claudia: And where's Anna? *(Then, turning to the sailor)* Isn't she on the yacht?

Sailor: I don't know . . . you see . . . we were taking a little nap . . .

Out on the yacht, Patrizia is completing her puzzle. Only a few pieces are missing but the area to be filled in is a very difficult one. Raimondo, who has grown impatient over Patrizia's long and tedious concentration, exclaims:

Raimondo: You've made some mistake there with the bushes . . . that's why you can't finish it.
Patrizia: Take it easy, Raimondo. Why are you getting so impatient?

Claudia's voice is heard, calling out from the shore.

Claudia: Patrizia! . . .

Patrizia raises her eyes and gives a quick, casual glance at the porthole. Raimondo immediately takes the hint that she would like him to get up and see what Claudia wants. So he goes out to the deck where he sees Claudia calling from the shore.

Claudia: Is Anna there?
Raimondo: I don't think so.

He goes over to the cabin, and looking through the portholes, calls out Anna's name. But there is no answer, so he returns to the side of the boat and shouts back.

Raimondo: She's not here.

Meanwhile, on the beach, Sandro is also looking for Anna, disturbed and amazed that she is not in sight.

Sandro (angrily, to himself): This is the kind of behavior that drives me crazy!

Down at the shore, Giulia is getting ready to step on the gangplank and go aboard the yacht but, anxious about Anna's whereabouts, she changes her mind and turns back. Claudia, also deeply concerned, decides to remain and look around for herself. She turns and starts climbing up towards the rock in an opposite direction than that taken by Sandro, who has now reached the top.

The search is fruitless; there seems to be no trace of Anna. But Sandro continues to explore the area, stopping every now and then to call out Anna's name. Then, looking down over the slope, he notices Claudia, Giulia and Corrado coming towards him.

Sandro: Did you find her?

None of them answer but it is clear from the worried expressions on their faces that they too have found no trace of Anna. Still they continue the search, each going off in different directions. Claudia, walking over land covered with large white rocks and clumps of dry brush, spots something moving behind one of the bushes. Anxiously, she starts to walk up closer. Suddenly the branches begin to move and a stray lamb emerges. Surprised, but also somewhat relaxed, she turns around and calls out to Corrado, who is following her only a short distance away.

Claudia: It's a lamb!

Corrado looks at her without answering, then stops and notices further up ahead a jumbled pile of rocks which he feels might very well be the ruins he had previously intended to explore. He is about to head towards them but suddenly realizes that Giulia is following directly behind him. He quickly changes his direction in an effort to avoid her.

Sandro comes upon a small stone hut that leans up against a high section of rock. As he starts to approach it, another stray lamb appears, as if from nowhere, and runs off, frightened by Sandro's approach. He tries to open the door to the hut but finds it locked. As he looks around the area, uncertain as to his next move, he sees Claudia and Corrado coming towards him.

Claudia: Find anything?
Sandro: No.
Corrado: Perhaps she's taking a swim somewhere ...

Though no less concerned over Anna's disappearance

than any of the others, Corrado attempts to lighten the tension by feigning a calm and sensible attitude. Taking note of the stone hut before him, he observes it carefully and remarks:

Corrado: It's really a fact—there's nothing new under the sun. Now, look here. Look at this structure . . . a kind of natural shelter. Sandro, that's how you should design your houses.
Sandro: Me? . . . I no longer have any interest in building . . . And, then, where can you find boulders of rock like this in Milan?

Claudia comes up close to the hut and tries to peer through the tiny window but inside it is so dark that nothing can be seen. Suddenly, she finds a small piece of bread on the ledge of the window. She picks it up and starts examining it. Then, realizing the bread is still fairly fresh, exclaims:

Claudia: Somebody must live here!
Corrado (after examining the bread himself): But Anna wouldn't be staying with the kind of people who live here.

The discussion is suddenly interrupted by the arrival of one of the sailors who has come up from the shore.

Sailor: We had better get started. The storm may break any minute now.
Claudia (angrily): What do you mean! What about Anna?
Sandro (to the seaman): Tell Lady Patrizia that we can't leave now. In fact, we'll have to make a tour around the island . . .
Sailor: Wouldn't it be better if you told that to the Lady yourself. I can't assume the responsibility for keeping the boat here. There's no place to tie it up . . . And then, you know, it's got a flat bottom, and if the sea gets a little too rough . . .
Sandro (angrily): That doesn't make any difference! If we have to stay, we'll stay!

Aboard the yacht, which is circling the island, Sandro, Patrizia, Raimondo and one of the sailors are peering out over the side, scrutinizing the banks and rocky slopes in hope of finding some trace of Anna. The jagged cliffs appear enormously tall and ominous, harboring tiny grottoes in which someone could easily hide.

Patrizia: Perhaps she wasn't feeling well ... Maybe a cramp or something ...
Sandro: Anna is an excellent swimmer. Even with a cramp, she would have managed to reach shore somehow.
Patrizia: But you have to consider all possibilities, Sandro.

Incensed by her remark, which he considers to be absurd, Sandro moves away from Patrizia and goes towards the stern of the boat where he notices Corrado signaling to them from a remote section of the beach.

Corrado (calling out): There are some footprints around here ...

But he stops in the middle of the statement, and throws up his arms to indicate that the discovery is really of little significance. So he proceeds to climb back up along the pathway from which he descended, and the yacht continues on its way.

Sandro (calling from the stern, excitedly): Patrizia!

Both Patrizia and Raimondo come rushing over to the stern and look towards where Sandro is pointing at something dark and obscure afloat on the water up ahead.

Raimondo (to the sailor): Mario ... Steer the boat that way.

The yacht heads in the direction of the black object in the water, but as they come up close, they realize it is nothing more than some wooden piece of furniture. The turn has taken the boat slightly away from Lisca Bianca and they now find themselves closer to the little island of Basiluzzo.

Sailor: Shall I turn back?
Sandro: No. Now that we're here, let's have a look around Basiluzzo. *(Then turning to Patrizia)* When we were swimming, she swam out in that direction.
Sailor: It won't be easy to find a place to go ashore.

The first shadows of evening begin to fall over the island of Lisca Bianca. The sky is now even gloomier, streaked with flashes of lightning. Rumbling sounds of thunder are heard in the distance. The entire group is once again reunited on the beach, and the impending storm has heightened their fears and anxiety. They are cold, restless, and exhausted, but profoundly moved and shaken by the reality of Anna's strange disappearance.

Sandro: Let's try to be practical about this. The best thing to do is for all of you to go to the closest island that has a police station, or something, and report the disappearance. I'll remain here ... because ... well, I don't know, but it seems to me that something may turn up. Anyway, I just don't feel like leaving.
Corrado: Then let's get started ... It's senseless to waste any more time.
Patrizia (to the sailor): How long will it take to go there and come back?
Sailor: If there's a police station at Panarea, it should take us a couple of hours. But if we have to go to Lipari, it will take much longer. Then it also depends on how rough the sea is.

Giulia is about to get on her way but she stops and turns around to look for Corrado, who notices her looking at him.

Corrado: I'll stay here also.

Giulia (alarmed): But why? . . . What if it starts to rain?
Corrado: If it rains, I'll buy myself an umbrella.

Claudia, who has remained to one side, wrapped up in her own thoughts, doesn't make a move to leave. Sandro and Corrado look at her in surprise.

Corrado (to Claudia, understandingly): Claudia, I know how you feel, but there are already two of us staying . . .
Sandro: I'll go even further and say that her presence here—I don't want to sound offensive—could be a great hindrance.

Ignoring Sandro's remark, Claudia turns and determinedly heads towards the interior of the island. Meanwhile, Patrizia and Giulia have gone aboard the yacht.

Giulia (calling to Corrado from the boat): Do you want some blankets? . . . and something to eat?

Corrado makes an irritated gesture signifying no, then together with Sandro starts climbing up the rocky slope towards the stone hut. As they meet up with Claudia midway, the first drops of rain start to fall and it is clear that the storm is on the verge of breaking.

The three of them reach the door of the hut and Corrado tries to pull it open, but the lock resists. Then Sandro comes to his aid, and placing their shoulders up against the wooden door, they finally manage to force it open.

Inside the hut it is pitch black. Sandro strikes a match and finds a kerosene lamp on a nearby table. He lights it and the room is suddenly illuminated, revealing a miserable interior with a few broken chairs, several empty boxes, a shovel and a few other utensils. Over to one side is a small pile of straw suggesting a makeshift bed.

Claudia: As far as I'm concerned, I think she's alive . . .
Why, even this morning . . . that business about the shark . . . it wasn't at all true.
Sandro: And why do you tell us this only now?

Claudia: I . . . I don't know . . . I didn't think it was worthwhile . . . She was laughing over it . . .

Corrado: Really! Still, it remains to be seen why she invented a shark. What was her purpose in that?

Claudia (indicating Sandro): Maybe you'd better ask him.

Corrado (to Sandro): What were you and Anna arguing about? . . . Excuse me for being so indiscreet, but this is serious . . .

Sandro: Nothing but the usual argument . . . The only thing was—if I remember correctly—that she said she had a need to be alone.

Claudia: And how do you explain that?

Ignoring the question, Sandro begins pacing back and forth across the room. The silence is broken only by the sound of the rain outside which is now coming down harder and harder. Suddenly, footsteps are heard approaching the hut. Sandro, Claudia and Corrado quickly turn around and face the door, their faces clearly revealing the expectation that it might be Anna. Finally the door begins to open and an old man appears, carrying a sack in his hand.

Sandro: Are you the owner of this place?

Old Man: No. The owners are in Australia.

Sandro: But where did you come from?

Old Man: From Panarea. Why?

Corrado: Ah, then it was you . . . I heard a boat leaving here at two o'clock today . . .

Old Man (scratching his head): It must have been around four or five . . .

Corrado: In the afternoon?

Old Man: No . . . in the morning. Why? What's happened?

Sandro: Nothing . . . nothing at all!

Claudia: But why don't you tell him? *(Then turning to the old man)* A girl who was with us has disappeared.

Old Man: What do you mean . . . disappeared? Was she drowned?

Claudia: No, she didn't drown . . . She just disappeared, and nobody knows where.

Sandro: And I suppose it's my fault ... Why don't you tell him that too. That's what you believe, isn't it?

Claudia: Rather than being so occupied with my thoughts, you would have been better off trying to understand what Anna was thinking.

Old Man: Have you searched in back of the house to see if she might have fallen off that cliff? Last month that's what happened to one of my sheep ... I looked all over for it all day long and it wasn't until late at night that I heard it bleating ... It had been there the whole day ... and was almost dead.

Claudia suddenly jumps up and runs out of the hut and into the dark, calling out desperately.

Claudia: Anna! ... Anna! ...

But her cries are lost in the sound of the storm. Drenched by the rain, her shoes full of mud, her dress soaked, she stops, as Corrado, who had followed after her, grabs hold of her arm and leads her back to the hut.

Corrado: Come, Claudia ... come back inside.

It is early morning inside the hut, and the flame of the kerosene lamp has dwindled down to a tiny, flickering light. Claudia awakens with a bewildered look upon her face, wondering where she is and how she comes to be there. She notices Corrado dozing on an empty box in a corner of the room, then realizing that Sandro and the old man are no longer there, she gets up and goes out the door.

Outside, everything is covered by a thick haze, which is gradually beginning to lift. Sandro, who is standing a short distance away from the hut, hears Claudia approaching and turns around to greet her.

Sandro: Are you feeling better?

Claudia (nodding yes): I'm sorry about last night. Please forgive me.

Sandro: You're very fond of Anna, aren't you?

michelangelo antonioni

Claudia: Yes, very much so.

Sandro: Has she ever spoken to you about me?

Claudia: Occasionally, but always with affection.

Sandro: And yet, she seemed to feel that our love for her—mine, yours, even her father's, in a certain sense—weren't enough for her, or didn't mean much to her.

Claudia: I know. I keep asking myself what I could have done to prevent all this from happening.

There is a pause, then suddenly they both hear the sound of a motor growing louder and louder. They look out over the shore but the haze is so heavy that it is impossible for them to determine the source. Then, seeing the old man coming up the path, Sandro impulsively runs towards him and seizes him by the collar.

Sandro: Whose boat is that?

Old Man (astonished): What boat?

Sandro: Just a moment ago ... didn't you hear the sound of a motor?

Old Man: At this time of the year there are so many boats ...

Sandro: And how come you're up so early?

Old Man: Early? Is four in the morning early for you?

Sandro is visibly deflated by the old man's casual-
ness, and he decides to abandon his questioning. He
turns away from him and looks up to see Claudia
walking slowly towards the top of the cliffs, directly
behind the hut where the night before the old man
had said Anna might have fallen. She looks down over
the side and quickly withdraws, almost in fear of being
sucked down into the swirling waters below. She turns
away and starts walking towards the interior part of
the island. In the rocky hollows around her, she notices
small accumulations of yesterday's rain and, scooping
up some of the water from one of these rocks, she
rinses her face. As she gets up again, Sandro is there,
standing directly before her. Claudia is almost startled.
They continue to gaze at one another in silence. Then
Claudia abruptly turns away and heads towards a
higher point of land. A moment later, Sandro joins her
again and once more they find themselves staring into
each other's eyes, almost embarrassed by their own
behavior, yet unable to control it.

The wailing siren of a police boat resounds through
the air like a shrill lament. Only then do Sandro and
Claudia detach themselves from their trance-like state,
from the sudden compulsion of being drawn towards
each other. Through the haze, they notice a landing
taking place down at the shore. Realizing it is their

friends returning with the police, they both start descending the slope to greet them.

Stepping ashore are Patrizia, Giulia and Raimondo, followed by a Marshal of the *carabinieri* and two police agents. As Sandro and Claudia come rushing down over the rocks, Claudia suddenly stops and lags behind so as not to arrive on the beach simultaneously with Sandro.

Meanwhile, Corrado has already gone down to the shore and as he goes out to meet them, Patrizia, Giulia and Raimondo anxiously look to him as though expecting some good news. But Corrado remains silent, then throws out his arms in a gesture of despair.

Giulia: How did you spend the night? ... In that hut? ... And what did you have to eat?

Corrado: What do you think?

Giulia: We, too, you know. It was disastrous. First at Panarea, where there weren't any boats ... then at Lipari, where everybody was asleep ... And the phone call to Rome ...

Patrizia: We had to notify her father.

Corrado: Yes, that was a very good idea.

Patrizia: He'll be here sometime today. *(Then turning to Sandro who has just arrived on the scene)* I also phoned my house in Milan ... but Ettore had already left.

Marshal (to Sandro): Anything new develop?

Sandro: Unfortunately, no.

Marshal: Very well. First of all, I'll have them search the waters around the island. I brought two frogmen with me ... Meanwhile, we'll take a look up around here.

Sandro: Look, Marshal, with those deep crevasses, you'll need some rope and ladders ...

Marshal: Don't worry, we've got everything.

Sandro: Another thing; there's an old man who lives here on the island ...

Marshal (interrupting): I know, I know. One thing at a time.

The Marshal starts climbing up towards the interior of the island, with Sandro following behind. As Claudia sees them coming in her direction, she moves away to a lower section of the island to avoid coming in contact with Sandro. Peering over a precipice, she sees the frogmen below, and watches them slide into the clear water like two enormous fish.

Sandro and the Marshal have arrived on the edge of the same precipice, where two men are lowering a rope ladder into the depths. Moving up further to watch the operations, Sandro becomes aware of Claudia standing alone just a short distance away. He heads towards her but she tries to avoid looking at him. Sandro, however, is unable to take his eyes from her and continues walking in her direction. But seeing Patrizia and Raimondo approaching, he suddenly stops. A small stone, accidentally loosened from the ground, rolls along the path and comes to a halt directly in front of Claudia, almost like a message. She picks it up, looks at it, then throws it away. Sandro moves away and heads back to the edge of the precipice.

Patrizia and Raimondo join Claudia. Raimondo, who is carrying a box of crackers in his hand, offers them to both Claudia and Patrizia.

Patrizia: No, who wants crackers ... Why don't you go and have some coffee made instead?

Meanwhile, Sandro has arrived at the edge of the precipice where he finds Giulia and Corrado. They are looking down at one of the *carabinieri* who is dangling from a long rope over the side of the rock, exploring the crevasses where a body might have fallen from the precipice above. The Marshal leans over to see if anything has been discovered.

Carabiniere (calling up to the Marshal): Nothing here!

The Marshal turns around in disgust and looks at Corrado who is frankly sick and tired of the whole operation.

Corrado: Don't look at me like that, Marshal . . . I had nothing to do with it.
Patrizia (referring to the frogmen below): Let's hope they don't find her . . . If they do, they would find her dead.

All of a sudden, Claudia breaks out into tears. Patrizia doesn't say a word. She just lets Claudia cry, knowing it will do her good. Sandro comes over and as soon as Claudia sees him there, she stops crying, and avoids looking up at him.

Sandro: Listen, Patrizia . . . The Marshal says there's a current that passes by here and ends up at another island . . . I don't know which . . . He wants to send one of his men over to have a look . . . One never knows . . . Do you mind if I ask Raimondo to go with him?
Patrizia: I don't see why I should mind.
Claudia (to Sandro): I think that you might go and have a look yourself.
Sandro: Yes, maybe that is better.

He turns and starts heading down towards the beach.

Patrizia (to Claudia): What amazes me, is Sandro. He seems so calm.
Claudia (rising): Calm? . . . He doesn't seem so to me . . . He was awake all night.

One of the frogmen emerges with an ancient vase in his hand, evidently found in the depths below. Raimondo, who has just arrived with a thermos of hot coffee, puts it down and goes over to the frogman to fetch the vase.

Raimondo (to the frogman): What is it?
Frogman: An ancient vase. There's a buried city under here. It's full of this stuff.

Raimondo takes the vase and shows it to Patrizia and Claudia. It is an extremely beautiful amphora, in terra cotta, with a figured design around it. Patrizia and

Claudia momentarily drop their thoughts to examine it. Then Corrado, who had observed the scene, comes over, followed immediately by Giulia.

Patrizia (ironically): Come on, Corrado, tell us what century it belongs to.

Corrado smiles, then comes closer to examine it. Claudia also kneels down to look at it. A moment later she feels a presence at her side, and even without turning around she knows it is Sandro. Taking advantage of the discovery that was made, he purposely has returned to join the group in order to be near Claudia. They both now feel between them the warmth of that contact, and for a brief moment, succumb once again to that sudden sense of wonderment which they already had experienced at dawn.

Giulia: Corrado, why don't you ask them to give it to us as a gift?
Corrado: Really! So that you can stuff it with your geraniums.
Patrizia (to Sandro): But aren't you supposed to be on your way?

Claudia, stricken with dismay, immediately detaches herself from Sandro, who replies with a certain sense of embarrassment.

Sandro: Yes ... I'm going ... I'm going now.

A patrol boat is anchored off the cliff of a small island where the current running through the surrounding waters comes to an end. Sandro is leaning against the wall of a dilapidated building, which is constructed right on that part of the rock where the sea close by discharges all kinds of refuse. Four or five islanders are busy scouring through the accumulated rubbish. They are taciturn, poorly dressed people who every now and then come to blows over the possession of some article washed ashore by the waves. Sandro is watching them, feeling distraught and melancholy. One of the *carabinieri* who had accompanied him is walking up and down beside an elderly gentleman who is obviously one of the local gentry.

Sandro (to the carabiniere): It's already two hours ... What are we going to do?
Carabiniere: It takes about twenty to twenty-two hours for the current to reach here from Lisca Bianca.
Elderly Gentleman: And sometimes even twenty-four ... depending on the wind ...
Carabiniere: If the girl disappeared yesterday afternoon, we'll have to wait at least until three or four o'clock.

Sandro looks at them without commenting, then turns and walks away towards the center of the village. The houses and shops around the square are very plain and shabby. Sandro spots a barber shop and, fingering his day-old beard, enters for a shave.

Shortly thereafter, a clamor of voices is heard outside and Sandro comes dashing out of the shop. Seeing the islanders fighting and arguing about something drawn up from the sea, he runs over to find out what it is. As he arrives on the scene, two policemen step out of the confusion dragging a large crate, which they carry over to the door of a nearby shack, amid the protests of the islanders who are still arguing and shouting among themselves.

Voices: It belongs to me ... We found it ...
Gentleman: Back ... Stand back!

The two policemen set the crate down and lift the lid. It is full of cigarettes.

Carabiniere (to the islanders): You see? It contains cigarettes. We'll have to confiscate it.

The islanders react violently, shouting out all sorts of epithets. But the policemen manage to restrain them and soon the commotion is quieted down.

Carabiniere (to Sandro): These people are contemptible. They have no sense of dignity at all.

Sandro (referring to the crate): And you say that came from Lisca Bianca?

Carabiniere: It couldn't have come from anywhere else. At least, somewhere from that vicinity ... But I really can't understand it. Contraband cigarettes on that island! It's the first time that ever happened.

Sandro: Look ... I'd like to get back to Lisca Bianca.

Carabiniere: But how could we ... at a time like this when we just ... well, let's at least first have a look around the other islands. Could be that something might turn up there.

Sandro (impatiently): But even here we were supposed to find who knows what ... And all we bring back with us is a crate of cigarettes.

Carabiniere (shrugging his shoulders): As you wish.

At Lisca Bianca, a helicopter is hovering above the island and preparing to land. Waiting for it to descend are Claudia, the old man, the Marshal and Anna's father, just arrived from the mainland.

Marshal (to the old man): ... Is it also true that you saw no boat around here at Lisca between yesterday and this morning?

Old Man: How many times do I have to tell you, Marshal, that I was at Panarea.

Marshal: I believe you, I believe you ... But I'm also certain that you're hiding something from me. I can see it written all over your face ... And you know that I have never liked your face. And if you want to know something, that gentleman over there ... *(indicating Anna's father)* ... who's a very important person ... doesn't like it either. So, just keep that in mind. I'll talk to you later.

The Marshal moves away from the old man and goes over towards Anna's father who is watching the helicopter come down.

Anna's Father: I presume by this method that you'll be able to uncover some new clue, either a handkerchief or an article of clothing . . . In other words, something which your men have not been able to find as yet.

Marshal: Without any doubt, sir. If anything belonging to the girl who has run away is still here on this island . . .

Anna's Father (resentfully): Allow me to inform you that my daughter is not a fugitive.

Marshal: I'm sorry, sir. I didn't mean to put it that way. But, you must understand, sir, that I . . .

Anna's Father: I understand very well. Only I don't want any rash assumptions to be made.

One of the *carabinieri* appears with Anna's valise which he sets down on the ground.

Marshal: Here's her valise, sir.

The helicopter is now a few feet above the ground, and everyone steps aside to allow it room to land. The rush of wind from the propeller sends up a cloud of dust, and finally the helicopter touches down. The propeller stops, the door opens, and out comes two large bloodhounds accompanied by a police attendant. He immediately says something to the dogs in German which suddenly creates an atmosphere of resentment among the group assembled there.

Anna's father goes to his daughter's valise, bends down, but doesn't dare to touch it.

Claudia: Do you want me to open it?
Anna's Father: Yes, please.

Claudia opens the valise and starts pulling out several dresses, a few intimate garments, and several other items of clothing. As she continues rummaging, she suddenly comes upon two books, Fitzgerald's *Tender Is The Night* and a copy of the Bible, which she hands to Anna's father who, in turn, examines them with great care and deliberation.

Anna's Father: This looks to me like a good sign. Don't you think so? As far as I'm concerned, anyone who reads the Bible could not have committed an act of impropriety. Why . . . as a matter of fact, I remember when I was in China, many years ago, I happened to be involved in a similar situation, concerning an English woman, the wife of Ambassador Shafford, a good friend of mine. There, too, we found a Bible . . . And I said at the time that whatever had happened, that clue alone had definitely ruled out the possibility of . . . suicide. Why, it was logical, I said, that whoever reads the Bible believes in God and therefore . . . *(Then, turning to Claudia in an almost supplicating tone of voice)* No? You don't believe it? Well, as a matter of fact, I was right . . . The woman was found two days later. It was a case of amnesia.

Marshal: Sir, if you have no objections, may we start the search?

Anna's father turns around to look at the bloodhounds who are already sniffing the air for a scent and anxious to get on with the hunt. Then he throws a quick glance at his daughter's valise once more, and with an air of disgust and irritation, walks off in a huff, followed by Claudia.

Attendant (to the Marshal): Get everybody out of the way . . .

Marshal: Okay. I'll send them down to that part of the beach over there . . .

After they all have left the area, the attendant leads the two bloodhounds over to Anna's valise, instructs them to pick up the scent, then takes them up to the very top of the island, where he subsequently unties them from his leash and sets them off.

Claudia and Anna's father arrive on the beach where Patrizia, Giulia, Corrado, Raimondo and one of the sailors are seated on a pile of rocks.

As the dogs begin running in different directions over the island, trying to track down the scent from Anna's valise, the entire group remains silent, awaiting the outcome of the search. Suddenly, the bloodhounds come racing down the slope, heading directly towards the beach where they are gathered, apparently hot on the trail of some familiar scent. To everybody's amazement, the dogs stop in front of Claudia, jumping excitedly and barking at her as though they had found their prey. Claudia is nonplussed and almost petrified with fear. She turns around and sees the others all staring at her. But she cannot understand why they are looking at her that way nor why the dogs have stopped right in front of her. Then, as if struck by a sudden flash of memory, she touches her dress and cries out:

Claudia: It's because of this...The dress...It's because of this dress. Anna gave it to me yesterday, right after the swim.

Completely relieved, Claudia smiles and bends over to pet the dogs, as the attendant comes up to them and ties the leash back on to their necks. Then he leads them away and heads once again up the slope towards the top of the island. Anna's father seems almost disillusioned by the negative results of the search. Corrado also feels dissatisfied, and addressing himself to the Marshal, says:

Corrado: And what are we going to do now?
Marshal: We'll try again.
Patrizia: But is it really necessary? Those two beasts . . . How absurd!

Meanwhile, the patrol boat has returned and is pulling ashore. Giulia is the first one to notice its arrival and she calls out to the others that Sandro is back. Then she goes over to where Anna's father is standing.

Giulia: Sandro's here.
Anna's Father (coldly): I don't know him.
Giulia: It seems to me that at a moment like this . . .
Anna's Father: I don't want to know him.

By this time, Sandro has come ashore, followed by

the *carabiniere*, and immediately goes up to Claudia.

Sandro: Claudia, listen . . . Claudia.

But Claudia hardly looks at him, and seeing Corrado approaching, she moves away from Sandro.

Corrado (to Sandro): I didn't think you'd be back so early.

Carabiniere (interrupting): We didn't check the other islands, so . . .

Corrado: And why didn't you go there?

Carabiniere (referring to Sandro): He wanted to come back.

The sailors have unloaded the crate of cigarettes from the patrol boat and the Marshal is getting all the details from the *carabiniere.*

Marshal: Up until now those smugglers were operating only around the Palermo area. This will be a nice surprise for the Lieutenant in Milazzo . . . Call up headquarters. Bring them up to date and have them give you instructions on what to do with this crate.

Corrado: So . . . the boat we saw yesterday afternoon might have also been that of these smugglers. Could it be possible, then, that Anna . . .?

Marshal (evading Corrado's question and pursuing his own thoughts): I wonder where they could have unloaded the stuff . . . Maybe right here at Lisca.

Corrado: I was saying . . . it might even be possible that Anna had left with them.

Marshal: But for what reason would she have wanted to go away?

Corrado: Listen, Marshal . . . As for there being reasons for going away, anyone of us might have three thousand of them. So you can assume that she had them. What I want to know, is it possible that the smugglers might have taken her aboard?

Marshal: I think it's possible.

A Sailor (calling from the patrol boat): Marshal! . . . Headquarters is calling. They have an important message.

Marshal: What is it about?
Sailor: They've stopped a suspicious-looking boat a few miles from here ... yesterday afternoon. The crew has been taken to Milazzo for questioning.

The Marshal takes off for the patrol boat, and Corrado goes over to Anna's father.

Corrado: Did you hear that? What do you plan on doing?
Anna's Father (resignedly): We are in the hands of God.
Sandro: That's true ... But in the meantime, as far as I'm concerned, it's absolutely necessary to go to Milazzo. *(Directly to Anna's father)* I know that you have no desire to meet me, and I shall take pains not to impose myself upon you. But, besides you, I am the closest person to your daughter ...
Anna's Father: However that may be, at this moment my daughter has more need of her father than of you.
Sandro: Pardon me for being so frank, but there are certain things that a father—especially a father like you —cannot understand. So don't be stubborn. I'm coming with you.

As soon as he finishes saying this, Sandro turns around and looks at Claudia, as though he had just now realized that she was there listening to him. Claudia goes to the gangplank and boards the yacht, disappearing into the cabin. Having followed her with his gaze, Sandro then turns to Patrizia.

Sandro: Patrizia, what are you going to do?
Patrizia: What do you want us to do? I don't know myself ... But we'll do something.
Sandro: I'll go and get my valise.

Sandro goes aboard the yacht and enters the cabin. On the way to his room he meets Claudia who has just changed clothes and is about to return ashore. They stare at each other for a moment without saying anything. But the intensity in Claudia's look, mixed with fear and desire, is so overpowering that Sandro takes her in his arms and kisses her. Claudia immediately releases herself from his embrace, but for the moment it lasted, the kiss was full and passionate. Then she turns and goes out on deck. Sandro remains there, momentarily stunned, then picks up his valise and returns ashore.

As Claudia, followed by Sandro, steps back on the beach, she is met by Patrizia.

Patrizia: We've decided to go to Montaldo's place. In fact, Ettore should already be there.
Sandro (intervening): Good. Then I'll meet you there.

He says this primarily for Claudia's sake, hoping to catch her eye. But she keeps her head bowed low, and doesn't look up. After a moment of hesitation, Sandro turns away and heads towards the small motorboat in which Anna's father arrived from the mainland. And without saying another word, he climbs aboard.

Patrizia places her arm around Claudia's waist and together they start walking towards the yacht. But upon reaching the foot of the gangplank, Claudia stops.

Claudia: I'm going with the patrol boat to make a tour around the islands.
Patrizia: To do what?
Claudia: I just can't leave without first searching those islands, one by one.
Patrizia: But aren't you tired? I can just about manage to stand on my feet! *(Then turning around to look for Raimondo, she calls out)* Raimondo!
Raimondo: Here I am, Patrizia. I'm always here.
Patrizia: Claudia isn't coming with us. Will you please take care of her luggage. Thanks.

Raimondo goes aboard the yacht and returns with Claudia's valise. He consigns it to one of the *carabinieri* who, in turn, takes it aboard the patrol boat. Claudia follows him aboard. The Marshal comes out of the radio room, steps ashore, then joins Sandro and Anna's father on the motorboat, while Patrizia, Giulia, Corrado and Raimondo go aboard the yacht.

In the seaport town of Milazzo, on the Sicilian mainland, Sandro and Anna's father are seated in an office
at police headquarters. The sailors picked up on a
charge of carrying contraband are being questioned by
the police Lieutenant.

Sailor: No, sir, Lieutenant, we weren't even able to drop
anchor once . . . the sea was too rough.

The Lieutenant motions for the sailor to come up to
the desk, then points to a sheet of paper in front of him.

Lieutenant: Okay. Just sign here. (*Turning to a guard
standing at the door*) Have the next one come in. He's
the last, isn't he?

Another sailor enters and timidly approaches the
Lieutenant's desk. He is rather young, and his face is
completely bronzed by the sun.

Lieutenant: They tell me you have a lot of trouble at home. Is that right?

Young Sailor: Yes, sir. My sister is sick . . . and my father, too.

Lieutenant: So that's why you've turned to smuggling, eh? You need the money. Now, I can help you. I can see that you get some assistance from the government. But first there's a little formality we've got to take care of. Just a few questions and then we can all go to lunch . . . Your friend tells me you dropped anchor three times . . .

The sailor starts, as though taken by surprise, then quickly answers.

Young Sailor: Yes, sir. Three times.

Lieutenant (to Sandro and Anna's father): Now, we're getting somewhere! They're beginning to contradict each other. *(Then, facing the sailor again)* Now look here, your friend just swore to me that you weren't able to do any fishing at all because the sea was too rough . . . And what about the other boat?

Young Sailor: What other boat?

Lieutenant: Now look, my men saw it and they also saw you men throwing those crates overboard. What have you got to say about that?

Young Sailor (stuttering): I . . . I . . . wasn't feeling well . . . I . . . I was sleeping . . . I don't know anything . . . I . . . I'm all mixed up and . . .

Sandro is unable to control himself any longer. He gets up, walks over to the sailor and yells in his face.

Sandro: But what are you saying? . . . What are you saying?

The Lieutenant motions to Sandro to be quiet, then calmly rises from his desk and continues.

Lieutenant: Now look here, I'm ready to forget the whole thing: the cigarettes, the contraband—everything. If you would only tell me . . . you or your friends . . . whether the girl was aboard your boat and how far she went.

They all remain silent. The Lieutenant motions to the guard who then leads the sailors out of the office.

Lieutenant (to Anna's father): Just as I thought. Even if you caught them in the act, they'd deny it. They always deny everything. And then, in this case, if they were to admit having had the girl aboard, it would mean they'd be admitting to the charge of carrying contraband. Oh, it's easy to say: talk! But if they did talk, the following morning you'd find them cold dead in front of their doorstep.

Anna's Father: I think it would be worth my while to take a run over to Palermo. The Chief of Police there is a very good friend of mine and I'm sure he'll do whatever he can. I feel we're wasting our time here . . . Excuse me, Lieutenant. I hope we see each other again under better circumstances. And thanks for everything.

Bidding goodbye to the Lieutenant, Anna's father leaves, without looking at Sandro. A moment later, Sandro folds the newspaper he was reading, tucks it under his arm, and starts heading towards the door.

Lieutenant: At any rate, we'll continue investigating. I know that headquarters has sent out an alarm to all areas . . .

Sandro (showing the newspaper to the Lieutenant): Tell me, Lieutenant, do you happen to know this F.Z. who wrote this article here?

The Lieutenant takes a look at the paper which carries a two-column story headed: DISAPPEARANCE OF A ROMAN TOURIST AT LISCA BIANCA.

Lieutenant: That's Francesco Zuria. He's the news correspondent.

Sandro: Where can we locate him? Don't you think that by offering a reward to anyone who can give us some information . . .

Lieutenant: Zuria is in Massina. You might try him. Shall we phone him?

From the opposite end of the corridor through which Sandro and the Lieutenant are walking, appears the Sergeant who was in charge of the patrol boat on which Claudia toured the islands in search of Anna. After saluting his superior, the Sergeant says:

Sergeant: Have you any instructions for me, Lieutenant? May I return to Lipari?
Lieutenant: Yes. With whom did you leave the crate of cigarettes?
Sergeant: I left it at the warehouse.

The Sergeant again salutes his superior, then continues on his way along the corridor. Sandro abruptly turns around and follows after him.

Sandro: Pardon me, Sergeant, but when did you get back?
Sergeant: About two hours ago.
Sandro: And the young lady who was with you?
Sergeant: I don't know . . . She said she had to catch a train.

Sandro remains a while, absorbed in his thoughts, then hurriedly leaves the building, and heads towards the station.

On her way to the waiting room of the station, Claudia purchases a newspaper, then goes over to an empty bench and sits down. Turning to the local news section, she suddenly comes upon the article announcing Anna's disappearance.

A moment later, Sandro appears at the door. Claudia looks up at him but doesn't say a word. He walks over and sits down beside her.

Sandro: Where are you going? . . . To Montaldo's?
Claudia: Yes.
Sandro: Then I'll go with you.

There is a moment of silence, then Claudia shows him the newspaper article.

Claudia: Have you read it? . . . They're asking for any-one with information to get in touch with them.
Sandro: Yes. I had also thought of going there to talk with them . . .
Claudia: Yes, you should go!
Sandro: But then when will we see each other?

Claudia looks at him imploringly, intent on making him understand, without having to tell him outright, that it is not a question of their seeing each other. San-dro, of course, does realize and suddenly springs to his feet and nervously begins pacing back and forth across the waiting room. Claudia, in turn, also rises and goes over to him.

Claudia: I know it's difficult. But if you go on like this it will become even more difficult.

The bell announcing the train's arrival is sounded. Sandro turns around and faces Claudia, almost with a sense of helpless despair.

Claudia: Please, don't look so solemn . . . And don't wait for the train to come in.

But Sandro doesn't move. And again Claudia insists, imploring him not to stay, although she realizes full well that this may mean a final goodbye.

Claudia: Please, please leave. I don't want to look out of the window and wave to you with a handkerchief.

Sandro still doesn't move, and is about to say something, but Claudia looks at him so pleadingly and with such a determined expression, that he finally succumbs and starts walking towards the exit behind the train tracks.

The train has just pulled into the station. The platform is completely empty and Claudia is the only one to board the train. She climbs up the steps and the door is closed behind her. A second later, she appears at the window, looks out briefly, then disappears into her compartment. The station master raises the signal for the engine to start, a short whistle is heard, and soon the train gets under way.

Sandro dashes out across the tracks, swings open one of the doors, and boards the train as it picks up speed and pulls away from the station.

Claudia is seated in a corner near the window, looking out. She appears co.npletely relaxed and totally drained of energy, fatigued after so much tension. After a few seconds, she turns around and is abruptly startled to see Sandro standing nearby in the corridor. He comes over to her compartment and takes a seat directly opposite to hers. Claudia is absolutely furious.

Claudia: Go ahead, now say something! I want to know just what it is we have to say to each other.

Sandro remains silent, waiting for Claudia to settle down and calm herself. But she continues to reproach him.

Claudia: Sandro, I don't want you to come with me, I don't want to see you ... How can I make it clear to you? ... Why did you come?
Sandro: I don't know why. I just couldn't help it.

Claudia: But sooner or later we've got to end this relationship. And it's better to do it right now.

Sandro: I have no desire to sacrifice myself ... It's idiotic to sacrifice oneself ... Why? ... For whom? ... If Anna were here I might understand your scruples. But she's not ...

Claudia (deeply wounded): Oh, Sandro ...

Sandro: I'm sorry. I didn't want to sound cynical. But isn't it better to look things squarely in the eye?

Claudia: For me they are exactly as they were when we met three days ago ... just three days ago ... don't you realize? And you and Anna ... No, I guess they aren't like that any more. My God, is it possible to forget in such a short time, for things to change so quickly?

Sandro: It takes even less.

Claudia: But it's so sad. So terribly sad. I'm not used to it, I'm not ready for it ... You know ... I have never been so upset in my life. Sandro, why don't you help me?

Sandro: I think the only way to help ourselves, Claudia, is for us to be together.

Claudia: No, I'm sure it won't. Move over there. Let's make believe nothing happened. And when we get to the next station, get off.

Sandro: And what about you?

Claudia: Me ... I ... I ... Please leave me alone.

Suddenly, she stands up and goes into the corridor. The car is of an old type—one half is first class, the other second. Claudia stops in front of a second-class compartment from which the sound of two voices is heard. One is that of a woman—sweet, very delicate and very feminine; the other is that of a man with a Sicilian accent. Sandro joins Claudia. Standing there together they hear the conversation.

Woman's Voice: I work there but I'm really a stranger.

Man's Voice: I tell you this acquaintance of mine knows you and she has often spoken to me about you.

Woman's Voice: And who is she? Does she work in Catania?

Man's Voice: Yes, she takes care of the garden.
Woman's Voice: Then it's impossible for her to know me. In the villa where I'm at, we have a male gardener.
Man's Voice: So? That's logical. You see, both being gardeners, they spoke about you to one another.
Woman's Voice: And what did they say about me?
Man's Voice: They told me that you were a very nice girl, that you always mind your business ... In other words, things of that sort.

There is a moment of silence. Then, the sound of music is heard coming from the compartment. Claudia and Sandro look at one another with a smile on their faces. Then Claudia leans over to peek into the compartment. The woman is young; she has thick, wavy brown hair. He is one of those typical seducers from the provinces, with black hair. There is a tiny radio between them. Sandro also takes a peek into the compartment. Then they withdraw as the two resume their conversation.

Woman's Voice: We have a radio like this, too.
Man's Voice: No, not like this one.
Woman's Voice: And why wouldn't we have one like this?
Man's Voice: Because this is a Chinese radio.

michelangelo antonioni

Another pause. Sandro takes hold of Claudia's hand and presses it. She doesn't resist, but allows him to do it.

Woman's Voice: Certainly a radio this small is very practical. It's especially useful for ... I don't know ... for traveling.
Man's Voice: But for you, what comes first: music or love?

Claudia presses up close to Sandro, amused and, at the same time, obviously moved.

Woman's Voice: Music, of course. To get a sweetheart, one has to look around, but to get a radio, all you have to do is buy one.
Man's Voice: Ah, no ... For me, love comes first. I'm a man, and I know what's what: first love, and then music.

Claudia laughs but she is still very upset. All of a sudden, she starts and looks out the little window. The train is coming into a station and is beginning to slow down. Claudia grabs Sandro by the sleeve and pulls him through the corridor. Sandro tries to resist.

Sandro: Claudia, listen to me . . .
Claudia: No, Sandro, please . . . I ask you as a favor . . .

She continues to drag him through the corridor, until they finally reach the platform. Then she opens the door. They are both highly emotional. Claudia is almost hysterical.

Claudia: Promise that you won't try to look for me . . . you shouldn't try to look for me any more . . .
Sandro: But why, Claudia? . . . Why?

Sandro tries to grab her in his arms, but Claudia pushes him away, almost with a sense of violence, as though she were afraid she might change her mind once in his arms. In the meantime, the train has come to a stop in the station. Sandro pauses to look at Claudia once more.

Sandro: Even if you chase me away, I . . . Claudia, let's not wait any longer . . . After it will be too late . . . Come with me.

Claudia is visibly battling with herself. Then, in one last moment of decision, she pushes Sandro towards the door and goes back into the car.

Once on the ground, Sandro walks back and forth along the platform to see if he can find Claudia, hoping she might look out the window to wave goodbye. But she doesn't appear. The train starts to move, as Sandro desperately tries to catch a glimpse of Claudia. But she is not to be seen. Sandro starts running along the platform, but the train is now going too fast. He stops—angry, disappointed and upset.

At the entrance-way of a luxurious villa, Claudia, who has just arrived, is greeted by the Princess. She is an elderly woman, rather ordinary in appearance but very aristocratic in taste and manner.

Princess: Did you have a good trip? It is such a magnificent day! I am very happy that Sicily is able to give you so warm a welcome. And you do deserve it. You're such a lovely blonde. Come, my dear.

Claudia smiles, and follows the Princess into the garden.

Princess: And where are you from?
Claudia: From Rome.
Princess: Oh, how nice! So, you're from Rome ... And would you happen to know of some intelligent clergyman in Rome who might be willing to come here and stay with us? We have our own private little chapel ... It is a masterpiece, with seventeenth-century frescoes ... and the remains of all our dead ancestors, a wonderful collection ... He would find it very convenient there, and could say his own masses. Then he would have to spend a little time with my husband, who never sees anyone, to keep him occupied.
Claudia: An intelligent clergyman, Princess? But I think the intelligent clergymen of today have so many other things to do.
Princess: Well, perhaps one with a little physical handicap. One who is slightly lame, for example.

In the meantime, they have arrived at a shady alcove where, seated in various wicker lounge chairs, are Patrizia, Giulia and a young man dressed in simple, casual clothes. The first one to notice Claudia and to greet her with warm cordiality, is Giulia.

Giulia: Well, finally! We were beginning to get worried about you, too.

Claudia plunks herself down in one of the lounge chairs next to Patrizia. The young man rises and bows slightly.

Patrizia: But where did you finally end up?
Claudia: It was futile. We went all over.

There is a moment of silence; the thought of Anna returns to weigh on the group. Claudia pours herself an orange drink from a pitcher on the table beside her.

Claudia (referring to Anna): But why does she do these things? *(She takes a sip from her glass, then rises)* I can't stand it any more.

She takes a few steps, looks around at the villa, and at the other end of the alcove sees Corrado and Ettore saying goodbye to a pair of elderly gentlemen.

Giulia (to Corrado and Ettore): But how can you carry on a discussion in this heat?
Corrado: When one approaches fifty, my dear, he is affected only by the cold.
Ettore (noticing Claudia): And who is this?
Patrizia: This is Claudia, Anna's friend . . . *(To Claudia)* You've never met my husband, have you?

Ettore immediately recalls Claudia's name from a previous conversation that was apparently held before she arrived.

Ettore: By the way, have you phoned him?

Corrado: You mean Sandro? I told you already. He's not in. At least he's not at the hotel.

Ettore: Now look what has to go and happen ... At a time when I'll be needing him. How can we discuss things when we lack dates and figures? ...

Patrizia: But didn't he say he was coming here ...

Now, with all this talk about Sandro, the sense of relaxation Claudia had felt upon her arrival, has changed into a feeling of anxiety that becomes more and more noticeable.

Ettore: Well, what are you all waiting for? Send a car out to get him. He can't be more than a couple of hundred miles away ...

Giulia: To me, the fact that hasn't shown up is a good sign. Do you want to bet that he's found Anna?

Ettore: Maybe. But do you know that forty thousand persons a year disappear in Italy without leaving a single trace behind them. Forty thousand! Almost as much as the entire population of San Siro ... Raimondo, will you go and see if you can locate Sandro?

Raimondo: Okay.

A gong announcing lunch resounds throughout the garden.

Patrizia: First let the poor thing have something to eat.

Ettore: It wouldn't really do you any harm to skip a meal.

Princess: I've never met this Sandro. What kind of a person is he? ... He couldn't have done her in himself, by any chance?

Ettore (breaking out into a loud laugh): Sandro? ... Oh, sure ... I can see Sandro calling Anna over to him and saying: Listen, Anna, I intend to get rid of you, but since it's so painful and complicated ... and besides, I don't happen to have a gun on me ... why don't you do me a favor and get rid of yourself on your own ...

There is a moment of complete, dead silence, during which the same disturbing thought flashes across the

minds of all those who are present like a sudden reve-
lation.

Giulia: My God, how could we joke over something
like that! We should be ashamed of ourselves.
Princess (rising): Come on, let's go.

They all get up except Claudia. She is left so completely shaken by the conversation, by the thought, that
it seems she no longer has the strength to move. Giulia,
after giving Corrado a defiant look, turns and smiles
at the young man who had stopped to wait for her.

Giulia (to Claudia, referring to the young man): Goffredo
is the Princess' nephew. He's eighteen years old, the
lucky boy. And, what do you know—he paints.
Goffredo: Anybody can hold a brush in his hand. All
you need is to buy some oils and start painting. Even
Rembrandt did the same.

Giulia laughs with a strange sense of excitement, then
takes Goffredo by the arm and leaves. Claudia remains
alone. She watches the group heading towards the
house, Giulia holding tight to Goffredo, Ettore to
Patrizia. Their voices are heard, somewhat unclear.

Ettore: But . . . where is the Prince? . . . Is he well?
Princess: The last time I saw him, the day before yester-
day, it seemed he was well.
Ettore: Princess, why don't you sell this villa? I would
turn it into a lovely psychiatric clinic.
Princess: It's a little like that already.

Finally, even Claudia starts moving, slowly, behind
the others; but she is still very much upset.

A crowd of people that keeps growing and growing
from one moment to the next, is gathered in one of the
main streets of Messina, in front of a men's store with
its shutters half-shut. The local police are unable to
control the flow of traffic, which has been blocked as a

result of the crowd. The cars are packed close to one another, raising a great din with their horns. The throng is composed chiefly of young men pushing and climbing over each other to get near the shop to see inside. Sandro tries to make his way through the crowd in an attempt to get up close himself, but the confusion is so great that he finds the going very difficult. Remarks and comments are heard above the noise.

First Young Man: Who is it, Sophia Loren?
Second Young Man: Oh, no! It's some model from Turin with a low-cut dress.
Other Voices: It's Queen Saroya ... I saw her ... So, who could it be?
Third Young Man: They've torn her dress ... She's almost nude ... She ran into the shop to hide herself ...

A police siren is heard from afar, then before long it fills the air and dominates every other sound. An Alfa Romeo pulls up, followed by a police wagon full of policemen. Both vehicles maneuver their way through the crowd like snakes through a jungle, and stop right in front of the shop. Sandro takes advantage of the opening created by the two cars and thus finds himself a few steps away from the door. Bending over in order to see through the small space left open by the half-drawn shutters, he notices several newspapermen and photographers.

Sandro (to one of the newspapermen): Which one of you is Zuria?
Newspaperman: He's inside.

Meanwhile, the policemen have come out of the wagon and arrive at the door of the shop, with the Chief of Police leading the way. One of them raises the shutter, and the crowd, which has backed away slightly at the insistence of the police, begins pressing forward threateningly. Soon pandemonium breaks loose. In the confusion, Sandro manages to get inside the store along with the policemen and two photographers. The shutter is again lowered, just a few inches behind him.

Standing in the middle of the shop is a most charming and provocative young brunette with tight-fitting pants and a blouse that is open almost from the neck to the waist. She is wearing nothing under her blouse, so that with every movement of her body, one cannot help catching a glimpse of her naked breasts. As the policemen come forward, she receives them with a smile.

Sandro asks one of the journalists standing nearby if he can tell him which one of them is Zuria. The journalist points to a man who is only a few steps away—a man not very old but who has a ravaged face, and whose hair is almost completely white.

Sandro: Zuria?
Zuria: Yes. Until proven otherwise.
Sandro: I would like to ask you something.
Zuria: Wait a moment. Can't you see I'm busy?

Everybody is gathered around the Chief of Police and the girl. The store clerks are looking at her admiringly. The manager, most upset, is explaining the situation to the Chief of Police.

Manager: I phoned you, Chief, because, in view of the situation . . . I thought it best . . .

The girl interrupts him. She has a very self-satisfied look on her face.

Girl: I came down here to buy a foulard . . . Suddenly I realized that little by little, directly behind me, I was being followed by so many men, and more and more of them kept coming.

Chief of Police: Well, I should think so . . . Dressed like that.
Girl: But I have always gone around like this, everywhere in the world. Nothing like this has ever happened to me before.

Zuria turns to Sandro and clears his throat. Outside, the crowd becomes very noisy.

Zuria (to the girl): How old are you?

Girl: Nineteen. My name is Gloria Perkins. I'm married and a writer by profession. I write in a trance, almost always in contact with people who are dead. Tolstoi, for example, or Shakespeare. But the movies also interest me.

Zuria nods to Sandro as if to say: now watch this.

Zuria: How do you find the men of Messina? Are you shocked by their warm display of friendliness?

Girl: No, why should I be shocked? We're in Italy, not Finland.

Zuria: And how were you received in Palermo?

The girl turns around and looks down at Zuria with contempt, but she manages to remain calm.

Girl: In Palermo I was with my husband. Now I'm going to Capri to write an article for the Tourist Office.

Zuria clears his throat again and whispers to Sandro.

Zuria: She did exactly the same thing in Palermo.

Chief of Police (to the girl): If you want to go back to your hotel . . . we're ready to escort you.

Girl: Oh, yes, thank you . . .

Photographer snaps a flash photo. The girl immediately strikes a pose. Other flashes follow. The clerks ask for her autograph. One of the policemen raises the shutter; the girl comes forward smiling, and is greeted with a certain kind of roar from the crowd. The group leaves the shop. Sandro and Zuria also come out. The girl, ushered out by the policemen, climbs into the Alfa Romeo. The guard holds the crowd back. There are more camera flashes. More smiles from the pretty stranger. Finally the car pulls out, followed by the police wagon. Sandro and Zuria watch the car disappear through the crowd, which starts to disperse. The din, however, is still enormous, due to the unsnarling of the traffic jam.

Zuria: Do you like her?

Sandro shrugs his shoulders, somewhat surprised by the journalist's question.

Zuria: She costs a hundred thousand lire.
Sandro: You're kidding!
Zuria: No, I'm not. Why do you think she does all this? It's one of the many ways she can put herself on display. When you bait the trap, the mouse will snap. To tell you the truth, if it wasn't for the fact that one hundred thousand lire represents my whole month's salary, well ... But you had something you wanted to ask me?

Sandro is still looking at the journalist with a sense of incredulity, almost as if he felt Zuria's conversation was something out of this world. But he is brought back to reality by Zuria's last remark, which is made as the journalist starts walking at a very hurried pace.

Sandro: I read one of your articles regarding the disappearance of a girl. I'm that girl's fiancé.
Zuria: Oh ... I'm sorry I have to rush but I've got to write a story about this thing that just happened ... Tell me exactly how it all turned out.
Sandro (impatiently): Now listen, if I had any information, I wouldn't have come here to ask you. But I see that you, too, lack any information ...

The journalist casts a sidewards glance at Sandro. He is a bitter and sarcastic man, one who is completely absorbed with his own little problems and his own daily routine. But for this very reason he is quite capable of taking any kind of insult, either big or small.

Zuria: As a matter of fact, I've already had several phone calls on that article. One said they had seen the missing girl in an automobile somewhere in Rome. Another one said they saw her on the pier talking with some strange sailors ... Could be she secretly left the island by boat ...

Sandro: Is that possible?

Zuria: Who knows? ... Another one has it that she entered a store in Troina. This information comes from the storekeeper himself who stated that such and such a girl had bought I don't know what in his store ... at Troina.

Sandro: Is that far from here?

Zuria: About fifty miles or so. If you want, I'll give you the name of the storekeeper.

Sandro: Yes ... of course ... But you should also print that in your paper ... But right away, tomorrow morning ... It's the local Palermo paper, isn't it? ... I mean, it's widely read ...

Zuria: Yes, but why do you think our readers would be interested in such news now? Even if I sent it, the editors wouldn't print it.

Sandro: You really must do me this one favor.

Zuria: Pardon me, but why must I do you a favor?

Sandro: Then let's call it a business proposition. Something to round out your salary.

The journalist clears his throat without answering. Then he grabs Sandro by the arm and takes him back to the other side of the street where a few people, left over from the crowd, are still discussing the incident that just took place as they gradually drift away from the scene. The traffic is now back to normal.

At the Princess' villa, Claudia is in her room, applying some fresh make-up in front of a small dressing table. Although she appears thoroughly engrossed in all the minute details of her make-up, nevertheless, she seems considerably interested in any sound that comes through her window.

The rumble of a motor is heard. Claudia runs to the window and looks out into the garden. A dark car pulls up in front of the service entrance. A uniformed chauffeur gets out of the car and enters the house carrying a package under his arm. There is an obvious look of disappointment on Claudia's face. She is about to return to the dressing table when she notices, there in the garden, Giulia heading towards the house accompanied by the young Prince, Goffredo. Claudia is profoundly shocked by Giulia's behavior as she laughs, jokes, bends over to pick up some flowers, and skips along unashamedly.

In the meantime, Patrizia has entered the room with two wigs, one of which she is wearing and the other in her hand. She also has on a cocktail dress, but one that is more elaborate than Claudia's. Patrizia immediately goes up to the mirror of the dressing table and, while she finishes arranging the wig on her head, says to her friend:

Patrizia: Are you ready? I'm not. That's all we needed —a cocktail party . . . The vitality some people have irritates me! *(Then indicating the wig on her head)* How does it look?

Claudia, who has meanwhile tried on the other wig and is looking at herself in the mirror, turns around to Patrizia.

Claudia (ironically): It's divine!
Patrizia: You say that just to flatter me.
Claudia: Do you consider that a compliment?
Patrizia: No.

The two of them burst out laughing and together they leave the room. Then after a few steps through the corridor, they separate with a friendly gesture towards each other. Patrizia goes into her room while Claudia prepares to descend the wide stairway. Coming up the same stairway are Giulia and the young Prince, Goffredo. There is something of an embarrassing moment between them. Then Giulia, aware of Claudia's presence, detaches herself from Goffredo and, as they reach the top of the stairs, she comes over to Claudia and takes her by the wrist in order to confide with her more intimately.

Giulia: He wants to show me his paintings. He won't let go of me anymore. Poor thing, he must have a crush on me . . .

She laughs with an obvious sense of amusement, but she is also tickled by her own vanity. Claudia looks at her without knowing what to say to her.

Giulia (even more excited): Please, you come too . . .
Claudia: But for what reason should I come there?
Giulia: Please, do come . . . Don't leave me alone with him. He's capable of . . . I don't know . . . Have you noticed his eyes?

Claudia resigns herself to escorting Giulia to the floor up above. The very top of the stairway leads to an attic, where Goffredo is leaning over the railing, looking down.

Goffredo: Giulia . . .
Giulia: Here I am.

Seeing the two of them arriving together, the young Prince feels disappointed. But he knows he has to cover his intentions with a show of good manners. When the two women reach the top of the stairs, he bows to Claudia in a most respectful fashion. Then he leads them down a low and narrow corridor to a door they pass through.

The attic is bright and spacious, with slanted roof, and two huge windows. It is filled with paintings, easels, canvases, brushes and oils. As soon as Giulia enters the studio, she moves away from Claudia and attaches herself to the young Prince who is setting up one of his paintings on an easel beside one of the windows. Claudia looks around the room with a sense of indifference. Going over to the window, she looks out and sees a vast panorama of the countryside.

Giulia looks at the painting with a certain amount of surprise. It is a picture of a nude woman; a shapely figure, slightly plump, in the manner of Renoir.

Giulia: Claudia, come and see. It's a nude.

Claudia is looking through the paintings that lean up against the wall face backwards. She turns one around: a nude woman. A second: another nude woman. A third: the same.

Claudia: They're all nudes, if I'm not mistaken.
Giulia (to Goffredo): But why all nudes?
Goffredo: Because there is no landscape as beautiful as a woman.
Giulia: And where do you find the models?
Goffredo: Oh, there are as many as one wants.
Giulia (turning to Claudia): I thought the model was something obsolete nowadays. Didn't you, Claudia?

Claudia goes back to look out the window: a group of flying birds swoops down to land directly under the roof. The birds settle themselves in a little nest directly in front of the window. Claudia bends over to get a better look and is actually able to see the little nest, as she hears behind her the exchange of remarks between Giulia and the young Prince.

Goffredo: It's strange how anxious women are to display themselves. It's almost a natural inclination.
Giulia: But how could they pose like that? I couldn't.
Goffredo (with a grave, youthful sensuality): Why don't you try?
Giulia: Me ... Goffredo, you're mad! *(turning to Claudia)* He's mad.
Claudia: Not really.

Claudia moves away from the window, and continues to look at Giulia and Goffredo with a deep sense of amazement. Giulia is euphoric, kittenish and trembling with excitement. Goffredo is firm, resolute and serious.

Giulia: Don't you ever paint men?
Goffredo: Answer me, why don't you try posing? I'll paint you a beautiful portrait.
Giulia: But why me? ... Ask Claudia, she's much more beautiful than me.
Goffredo (insistent): But I want to paint you. You appeal to me more.
Giulia: (timidly): I appeal to you more?

Giulia glances over at Claudia, who is still preoccupied looking out of the window, then screws up her courage and boldly advances towards Goffredo, making her intentions clearly understood. Goffredo immediately responds to her invitation and draws himself close up against her. There is a moment of hesitation, then a kiss—awkward but passionately violent. Giulia, on her part, is completely shameless. Claudia turns around exactly at that moment when the two of them are caught up in a feverish embrace. She looks at them, completely dumbfounded, then takes a few steps forward as though she doesn't believe her own eyes.

Claudia (almost unconsciously): Giulia!

Giulia quickly turns around, her face is flushed with excitement but also with an expression that seems somewhat triumphant. Before anybody has a chance to say anything, she heads towards the door, swings it open and stands firmly on the threshold, obviously intent on telling Claudia to leave. In fact, Claudia doesn't wait to be told but immediately walks out into the hallway.

Giulia: And tell Corrado, too, that I'm here ... if he wants me. You can also tell him that my tiny little heart is beating like mad, and that at this moment, it's the only thing that interests me. Is that clear?
Claudia: It couldn't be any clearer.

Giulia takes a few steps backward into the room, and seeing Claudia still there looking at her strangely, exclaims:

Giulia: Now what do I have to do to be left in peace?
Claudia: I think all you have to do, Giulia, is to close the door.

And with a violent bang that leaves Claudia startled, Giulia slams the door shut. Claudia remains standing there for a moment, still very much amazed. But she is aroused from her stupor by the sound of a car pulling into the courtyard. Then she rapidly starts descending the stairs.

Claudia has reached the hallway leading out to the garden and is anxiously waiting there, looking at the car that has just arrived. But she is not able to distinguish exactly who it is, and her view is also blocked by Ettore and Corrado who have just come out of the house and are now standing in front of the car. So she walks out to the garden and joins the group. A certain look of disappointment spreads over her face as she sees only Raimondo come out of the car. Evidently, Sandro has not been located.

Raimondo: He's not at the hotel . . . and he probably wasn't even in Milazzo. The room clerk said he rented a car . . .

Claudia moves away from the group, as though she has heard enough. She goes over to lean against an enormous vase standing there on the side. Her hands are trembling. In back of her she hears the sounds of the others' voices but cannot distinguish what they are saying. Then Patrizia arrives and calls out Claudia's name. But she has to repeat it a second time before Claudia realizes she is being called.

Patrizia: Claudia . . . Let's go.

Claudia turns around but doesn't move. Another car pulls up, driven by the same chauffeur who had evidently picked her up the other day, and in which the Princess is already seated.

Claudia: I'm not coming.
Patrizia: But then why did you bother changing?

Patrizia remains puzzled for a moment as though searching for a motive behind Claudia's sudden decision, then discreetly turns away without insisting and goes over to the car. In the meantime, Giulia and Goffredo have come out through the hallway and head towards one of the two cars. Corrado looks at them with a cold and critical stare, then with a deliberate intent to prick Giulia's feelings, he says:

Corrado: Giulia is like Oscar Wilde; give her the super-fluous and she will do without the essential.

Ettore breaks out into a laugh as he helps Patrizia into the car.

Ettore: That's him; he'd die if he didn't have somebody to quote. He comes up with quotations like that even at a board of directors meeting . . .

Claudia watches them getting into the car. She is beside herself, completely wrapped up in her own thoughts.

In the rear of a general store, on the outskirts of a small Sicilian town, a woman is seated at the window. She is very young, thin and irascible. Up front, her husband is speaking with Sandro, and as she listens attentively to what he is saying, a sarcastic smile spreads over her face.

Husband: Be patient, I can't remember everything.
Sandro (indicating the newspaper article): But it even says what she bought: a bar of soap! So there's no point in making believe you can't remember.

After waiting a few seconds to give her husband a chance to explain himself, the wife jumps up from where she is sitting, comes over to Sandro and yanks the paper from his hands. Then she starts reading the article in a jerky manner typical of one who is not too literate.

Wife: "A young female stranger, whose description cor-responds with that of the missing girl, came into my store . . ."

She suddenly stops reading and turns toward Sandro.

Wife: She came and then she left. With him. But this one won't admit it. *(Then turning upon her husband furiously)* You think I wasn't aware of it . . .

The husband, a young man, tries to keep calm and carry on the conversation in a logical, persuasive manner.

Husband: But if I was carrying on with the girl, why would I want to give any of this information to the newspaper?
Wife: That's what I'd like to know myself.
Husband: Fine, that makes two of us who want to know. In fact, three, with him. *(Indicating Sandro. Then, seeing a fat, luscious female customer enter the store, he turns to her and continues)* Ah, Lady Amalia, would you be interested in knowing why I told the news-papers about a certain girl who came here the other day and then disappeared?

The woman, anxious to learn about any new bit of gossip, becomes immediately interested.

Lady Amalia: Disappeared? Who is she? . . . Where? When? . . .
Husband: And that makes four. Anybody else? . . .

Sandro, a little sick and tired of the whole matter, and wanting to put an end to what has by now become farcical, intervenes.

Sandro: You have to be precise. Did this girl enter your store or didn't she?
Wife (shouting): Yes!
Sandro (ignoring her): Was she blonde or brunette?
Husband (calmly): Brunette.
Wife (contradicting him): Blonde.
Sandro: How was she dressed?
Husband: I don't quite remember. Seems to me she wore a black dress.
Wife (intervening sarcastically): He doesn't look at dresses, he looks at what's under them.

The husband turns around and looks at his wife menacingly.

Sandro: Pardon me, but has anyone else been here asking about this girl?
Husband: No . . . I don't think so.
Sandro: Thanks.

Sandro leaves the store. He walks a few steps along the pavement, then sits down at a small outside table of a nearby café. He looks out over the square: a small Sicilian town, quiet and still in the hot afternoon sun. Every now and then, he glances up at the country road that winds around the town, as though he were waiting for someone.

A few moments later, in fact, a car comes into view and slows down as it reaches the square. The driver looks out for a place in which to park. Sandro rises to his feet. The car comes to a stop a few steps away from him. The driver rushes out of the car to open the door for the person inside: it is Claudia. Sandro immediately goes over to meet her, looking at her somewhat amazed. Not only does he see her more elegantly dressed than he has ever seen her before, wearing a smartly tailored polka-dot suit, but also as an entirely new person, as someone whose beauty he has discovered for the first time. For a moment they continue staring at each other, without even bothering to say hello.

Claudia: Any news?
Sandro: Yes . . . but it's all so conflicting . . . However, there is some slight indication . . .

Claudia drops her gaze, relieved by even that slight note of hope. Then she looks up at him again, as though inspired by another sudden thought: something which must have lingered in her mind from one of the Princess' humorous quips. Then, the owner of the general store appears on the scene. After having dealt his nagging wife a crushing verbal blow, he turns to

Sandro, but not without first glancing at Claudia, for whom it soon becomes evident he has really come out on the street.

Husband: Listen . . . In the paper they forgot to say that as soon as the girl left here she took the bus to Noto. The bus leaves from the square, over there. I saw her clearly . . . I came to the door to see her off . . . She was a beautiful girl. Lovely pair of legs!

While speaking, he continues to keep an eye on Claudia with the look of one who thinks his gaze is loaded with irresistible masculinity. All of a sudden, he pulls out a package of Nazionali cigarettes from his pocket and offers one to Claudia. She looks at him dumbfounded, then automatically declines with a shake of her head. In turn, he lights up a cigarette, inhaling the smoke voluptuously. Meanwhile, his wife has come upon the scene and looks at him suspiciously. Then, with a sad, wistful voice, she turns to Claudia.

Wife: You're from Rome, aren't you? I knew right away because I'm from Viterbo . . . He was a soldier there and so . . . (*indicating her husband, and then quickly continuing*) I don't like it very much, here.
Husband (interrupting): Then why don't you go back?

His wife turns and looks at him hatefully, exactly in the same manner he had looked at her.

Claudia: How long have you been married?
Wife: Three months.

Claudia and Sandro look at each other. There is a moment of embarrassment, then Sandro breaks the silence.

Sandro: Well . . . Thanks for the information.

They exchange goodbyes, then Claudia and Sandro move away from the store and head towards Claudia's car. Suddenly, Sandro takes Claudia by the hand.

Sandro: It's better if we present a happy picture, no?

Claudia is about to withdraw her hand but she is taken aback by Sandro's phrase, which also fills her with a warm and tender feeling after the squalid situation with the young storekeeper and his wife. Now Sandro opens the door of the car, looks at Claudia as if to ask her consent for what he is about to do, and since Claudia says nothing but just stands there trying to figure out which one of the feelings struggling within her will win, he removes Claudia's valise and closes the door.

Sandro (to the driver): Tell the Signora Patrizia that we are continuing the search . . . and that the Signorina Claudia will manage to survive somehow . . .

The driver bows slightly, then he climbs into the car and departs. Sandro and Claudia remain there, watching the car disappear out of view. Now Sandro turns to look at Claudia, and smiles at her. Claudia is visibly upset. She doesn't smile back but merely turns away and heads towards Sandro's car.

Claudia is intent on looking at Sandro who is doing the driving. The car is traveling on a country road but Claudia shows no interest in the landscape. She continues to stare at Sandro as if she wants to know his most secret thoughts. Suddenly, feeling himself being stared at, Sandro turns towards Claudia. She quickly drops her gaze. Then Sandro turns his eyes back to the road, and Claudia looks up at him again.

From a bend in the road up ahead, preceded by the loud and penetrating blast of a horn, the bus mentioned earlier by the storekeeper appears. Sandro barely manages to stop the car in time off to one side of the road. He gets out and places himself in the middle of the road where he starts signaling for the bus to stop. With a loud screech of its brakes, the bus comes to a stop almost directly in front of him. The bus driver opens the window and leans out.

Driver: Did your car break down?
Sandro: No. I only want some information.

Meanwhile, the driver's assistant gets down from the bus and the passengers lean out of the windows. Claudia has also gotten out of the car and appears on the scene.

Sandro: We're searching for a girl of about twenty-five ... Seems she boarded this bus two days ago, in the afternoon ... You should remember her because she was a stranger around here ...

The driver gets down from the bus and comes over to Sandro, scratching his head.

Driver: She was a little nervous ... dark-haired ... with a kerchief around her head?

He turns to his assistant for verification, who, in turn, searches his memory and then adds:

Assistant: Two days ago ... wasn't there that midwife on the bus, too? Sure, that's right, and she was talking to some young woman ...
Sandro: Can you tell me where she got off?
Assistant: All I can tell you is that the midwife is from X ...
Sandro: Okay, thanks.

Sandro turns and goes back to his car while the others climb back on the bus which begins to leave. Claudia and Sandro remain standing near the car, watching the bus disappear. Then Claudia turns and looks out over the fields. She sees a dry riverbed filled with stones that sparkle in the sun, beside it a high rocky bank. Sandro stands next to her and she becomes vividly aware of his presence. As she glances at him, he turns around, then she quickly starts up a conversation as though she were anxious not to have any romantic mood develop between them.

Claudia: My God ... Let's hope it was her.

Then, still feeling Sandro's eyes fixed upon her, she turns and starts heading towards the car. Sandro catches up with her and takes her hand. Before they climb into the car they look at each other intensely. A moment later, the car takes off at full speed.

In a courtyard of the midwife's house, Sandro and Claudia are questioning a middle-aged woman.

Midwife: I only exchanged a few casual words with her, as one would ordinarily do on a public bus...
Sandro: And do you remember where she got off?
Midwife: Well... probably at the last stop, which is Noto.
Claudia: After that you didn't see her anymore?

The woman pauses for a few seconds and looks at Claudia as though she had detected some hidden motive behind the question. And when she resumes speaking, what she has to say is in sharp contrast' to the way she says it. They are words of protest but spoken condescendingly, almost sweetly, yet leaving no doubt as to their meaning.

Midwife: What are you trying to insinuate, young lady? Why should I have seen her again? I don't do anything that's illegitimate.
Claudia: Oh, no... What are you saying? I'm not insinuating anything...
Midwife: And furthermore, my dear young lady... because you really *are* a dear, you know... if the story of that girl is merely a pretext, let us say, to get in touch with her, then I feel it is my duty to warn her. These things are very, very dangerous, especially in a neighborhood like this where people occupy themselves more with other people's affairs than their own.

Seeing Claudia being put into an uncomfortable position, Sandro, who had been following the midwife's discussion with a cagey attitude, intervenes.

Sandro: Then you should also be able to tell me where

a young girl might stay in Noto; are there any hotels or rooming houses?

Midwife: There's the Trinacria Hotel ... or the Regina, near the municipal building. As for rooming houses, I don't know ...

Sandro: Thank you.

Midwife: Don't mention it ... Pleased to be of service any time.

Claudia starts moving hurriedly out of the courtyard, followed by Sandro.

Sandro's car is speeding across a harsh, sun-baked landscape, bypassing long lines of peasants returning from the fields: the women seated on donkeys, the men on foot. The more fortunate among them have horse-drawn carts.

Claudia is looking at the surrounding countryside and spies an iron bridge that is all rusty and obviously no longer in use.

Claudia: Look at that bridge! Who knows why they even bothered to make it ...

The car continues onward, passing an abandoned factory, then a railroad station, also abandoned, its tracks covered by weeds, the ticket office haphazardly boarded up with old wooden planks.

Claudia: Look at that: a factory ... a station ... and look at those tracks, all full of weeds ... But why?

Sandro shrugs his shoulders and continues driving without saying a word. Up ahead a small town comes into view, with monotonous rows of newly constructed homes lined up along the side of the road. The car enters the town and stops. Sandro gets out and goes over to a fountain nearby, but the fountain is dry. Somewhat surprised, he begins to look around. And only then do Sandro and Claudia become aware that the silence around them is an unnatural one, that the doors and the windows of all the houses in the town are tightly shut. There is no sign of life anywhere, except for the weeds growing between the cracks in the walls, invading and suffocating everything in sight.

Claudia gets out of the car, joins Sandro, and together they start walking along the streets. The sun beats furiously down upon the crumbling houses, upon the church, upon the useless monument in the square on which a dedication is inscribed: "To The Agricultural Worker."

Sandro looks around in absolute silence. Claudia is also silent, somewhat dismayed. Instinctively, she presses up close to Sandro who leads her to a shady spot where the ground is overgrown with weeds.

Sandro and Claudia are lying next to each other on the grass. Sandro appears calm but is actually looking at Claudia as though he were about to embrace her with his eyes. Then he takes her hand. Claudia offers

no resistance; in fact, she entwines her fingers around his, almost with a sense of desperation. Sandro tries to kiss her. She makes a feeble attempt to resist, looks around, and sees the deserted town, the barren fields, the crumbling, sun-baked walls. She turns and looks at Sandro again, and now it is *she* who kisses *him*. When they break apart, they stretch themselves out upon the grass. Sandro kisses her violently, again and again and again . . .

The early twilight shadows are beginning to fall. The sky is still clear but the sun is fading. There is a deep silence and the air is absolutely still. In a certain sense, Sandro's car, standing there in the middle of the deserted street, is the only thing alive in that desolate town.

Huddled close to each other, Claudia and Sandro are asleep on the grass. Lazily, Claudia awakens, and then Sandro also opens his eyes. They are both somewhat disheveled.

Claudia (faintly audible): It's late . . . We should be going.

Little by little, she leaves behind the drowsiness of her deep and peaceful sleep, purring languorously in a typically feminine fashion. Sandro smiles and gently embraces her. A moment later, Claudia releases herself from Sandro's arms, sits up and realizes that the countryside and the town itself are as black and motionless as death. A cold shiver runs down her back and she quickly comes to her feet.

Claudia: Let's get out of here, fast . . . This is not a town, it's a cemetery.
Sandro: Who knows why they all left . . .

Claudia starts to move but her legs are still numb from her sound sleep and she hobbles along comically, laughing at the same time. Sandro also gets up and finds that his legs are cramped. Hobbling and laughing himself, he follows Claudia towards the car. But the car, baked by the sun, is like an oven. They both make boisterous and playful exclamations, then another embrace, another kiss. Finally, they climb into the car and drive off with a loud roar that echoes up and down the abandoned town.

Sandro and Claudia arrive in the town of Noto and pull up on the opposite side of the street from the Trinacria Hotel. As they climb out of the car, Claudia turns to Sandro:

Claudia: Sandro . . . maybe it's best that you go in alone.
Sandro: Are you joking?
Claudia: Don't think that I want to save myself from any embarrassment, from the awkwardness of meeting Anna . . . It's not that; it's that you can say certain things easier if you're alone. Please, Sandro, do try to understand me . . . It would look like I was trying to influence you, to force you, to control you . . . and that makes me feel uncomfortable . . .

Sandro agrees by a nod of his head and indicates that he understands very well. Nevertheless, he doesn't move. Several agonizing moments go by in which they both remain silent and still, looking at the hotel across the way. Then, tossing away his cigarette, Sandro finally walks off and goes into the hotel.

Left alone, Claudia strolls along for a few steps. She sees a letter box up against a building and deposits a postcard she had been carrying with her. She remains there for a moment, watching a parade of ants crawling along the wall, ending up who knows where. They come and go, scurrying up and down in vast numbers, incredibly busy. Then Claudia turns away and starts pacing back and forth, stopping from time to time behind townspeople who mill about in the streets; she pays them no heed. Several young men pass by and turn around to look at her. They are obviously the town's dandies. Circling around her, they exchange suggestive comments to one another. Even among the women Claudia arouses a certain curiosity. But she remains totally unaware of it; such is the intensity with which she concentrates her gaze upon the hotel entrance. Suddenly the sound of a shutter being lowered directly behind her causes her to start and turn around. It is a shop being closed. Other shops, further down the street, are also closing for the day. The people in the streets begin thinning out and it is not long before Claudia is left entirely by herself. In that total solitude, the doorway of the hotel emerges like the mouth of some dark and fearful cavern, so much so that Claudia is unable to keep her eyes fixed upon that spot. She turns her head away, but her attention is immediately drawn back again. From the darkness of the hotel's hallway, she spies Sandro coming out. Claudia doesn't wait to see if he is alone or not, for she has only one thought in mind: not to let herself be seen. But she doesn't know what to do since there is practically no one else in the streets and all the shops are closed. Then she notices a tobacco shop still open and she quickly dashes into it. She goes up to the counter as she opens her purse and starts looking for some change.

Claudia: Some cigarettes, please . . . Do you have any? . . . Nazionali with filters . . .

Her hands tremble as she searches for the money. Finally, she pays the storekeeper and immediately lights up a cigarette. Suddenly, she wheels about, having heard Sandro enter. He is alone. Throwing away his cigarette, he comes up to her, all nervous and excited, and they both step out into the street.

As soon as she is outside, Claudia leans up against the wall as if she has no strength left. She lets her cigarette fall to the ground and shuts her eyes.

Sandro: What is it, Claudia?
Claudia: Oh, Sandro . . . I'm so ashamed of myself, so ashamed . . . I tried to hide myself . . . I feel so small . . . I hate myself . . .
Sandro: Does it please you to say such things?
Claudia: Oh no . . . It doesn't please me at all . . .
Sandro: Then why do you say them?

Claudia: Because what I'm doing is so ugly . . . Because if you told me right now: "Claudia, I love you," I would believe you . . .

Sandro is about to say the phrase, somewhat jokingly in the hope that it might calm her, but also with a certain amount of seriousness. But as soon as he opens his mouth to say "Claudia," she places her hand over his lips.

Claudia: No . . . Because then I'd force you to swear it, I'd force you to tell me an infinite amount of things . . . and that wouldn't be right, it couldn't be right . . . It would be absurd.

Sandro tries to calm her with an embrace.

Sandro: Good. It's better if it were absurd. That would mean nothing much can be done about it.
Claudia: But just think—the very same things you had said to her who knows how many times . . . maybe even just before we left, while I was waiting outside your place . . .
Sandro: So, even if I did say them, I was sincere with her, as I am now with you.

Moved by Sandro's remark, Claudia lifts her head and looks deeply into his eyes. The statement reveals him as being someone quite different from the person she had imagined him to be, and at the same time, it opens up for her a new way of looking at things.

Shaking his head, and with much tenderness, he says:

Sandro: I have never seen a woman like you, who needs to see everything so clearly.

At the sound of a man's voice coming from behind him, Sandro turns and sees a gentleman with two large packages under his arms, pointing to a bell-cord dangling on the side of a door nearby.

Man: Excuse me, but would you mind pulling that cord for me?

Sandro pulls the bell-cord and the sound of a bell is heard inside.

Man: Thank you.

The door opens and the gentleman quickly steps inside. Sandro looks up at the building.

Sandro: At one time, all these houses were convents.

He takes Claudia by the arm and pulls her away towards the square, then looks attentively around the area. Bathed in the soft twilight, the buildings and the churches bordering the square reveal themselves in all their beauty. Sandro and Claudia climb up the steps of a church building and from there gaze at the scene. Gradually he allows himself to be overcome with enthusiasm.

Sandro: Look! What a fantastic scene! What movement, what disorder! They were very much concerned with scenographic effects ... an extraordinary sense of liberty ...

There is a moment of silence during which he continues to look at the scene before him. Then, giving voice to a sincere thought, he exclaims:

Sandro: Really, I've got to stop this business with Ettore ... I would like to go back and start working on my own projects again. You know, I had many ideas ...
Claudia: And why did you drop them?
Sandro: Once they gave me a job to draw up an estimate for the construction of a school. It took me only a day and a half to finish it, and I got paid six million lire. Ever since then I've been doing estimates for other people's designs.

Claudia looks at him as if she were about to render judgment, and Sandro becomes aware of it.

Sandro: Why are you looking at me like that?
Claudia: I'm sure you'd be able to design some very lovely things.
Sandro: I don't know about that. And then, who's interested in beautiful things nowadays?

The last words are spoken with a deep sense of sadness, Sandro avoiding Claudia's glance. He laughs to himself and for a while remains silent. He takes another look up at the dark outlines of the buildings, then turns to Claudia.

Sandro: Claudia, let's get married?
Claudia (astonished): What! Get married?
Sandro: Yes. We'll get married. You and I. What do you say?
Claudia: What do I say? What can I say? No. At least, not yet. I don't know ... I can't even think of it ... at a time like this ... Oh, but why did you have to ask me?
Sandro: You look at me as though I had said something foolish ...
Claudia: And are you sure you want to marry me? Are you really sure ... that you want to marry ... me?
Sandro: That's why I asked you ...
Claudia: So ... Oh, how I wish that everything were so much simpler ... that people could just come together by the color of their hair or the size of their shoes. What size shoe do you wear? Size 9. That's a very lovely size. But I'm sorry, I wear size 8.

Sandro smiles and playfully ruffles Claudia's hair. She also smiles, then slowly they both head towards the hotel.

It is morning inside the Hotel Trinacria. Claudia has just had breakfast in her room and is almost finished dressing. It is a rather large room, set out with old pieces of furniture. The place is in a state of disarray,

and the door leading into Sandro's room is wide open. Because of the general disorder, Claudia is unable to find her stockings. But instead of being angered by this, she appears quite jovial and laughs gaily. As she continues to look for her stockings, Sandro appears in the doorway.

Sandro: Are you ready?

Claudia comes up to Sandro and gazes upon him with a look of adoration.

Claudia (ironically): But why am I so infatuated with you?
Sandro (smiling): Hurry up now, or it'll begin to get hot outside . . .
Claudia: Yes, yes, yes, yes . . . Right away . . .

She starts looking hurriedly around the room again but is still unable to locate her stockings. Suddenly, up from the street comes the sound of music. It is a popular tune, wild and rhythmic, emanating from a publicity truck as part of some local advertising stunt. Claudia is overtaken by the music and cannot resist the temptation to do a little dance for Sandro. Little by little, she starts swaying back and forth to the music.

Then, kicking off her shoes, she begins to dance around the room in her bare feet. Sandro looks at her, amused but also somewhat impatient.

Sandro (leaving): Okay. I understand. See you later.

Claudia rushes up to the door, and feigning an exaggerated attitude of despair, says:

Claudia: And you leave me here all alone . . . in this hotel room . . .
Sandro: As soon as you're ready, you can come down and catch up with me. I'll be waiting for you right outside on the square.

Claudia is in a playful mood and she is anxious to demonstrate her exuberance.

Claudia (teasingly): Very well. But you must first tell me that when you go out without me it's like going out without one of your legs. Go ahead, have a look around the town all by yourself, but you'll have to hobble along on only one leg. And you must also tell me that you are filled with a great desire to embrace my shadow on the walls . . . Then you must tell me . . . *(Suddenly her tone of voice changes and she becomes quite serious)* You must tell me that you love me.

Sandro replies with the same good-natured tolerance with which he had been watching Claudia as she danced her coquettish dance.

Sandro: But you know it already. Why must I tell you?
Claudia: So, you wonder why?

Without waiting for him to answer, she goes back towards the center of the room and once again starts looking around for her stockings. Sandro begins to leave.

Sandro: Then I'll see you later.
Claudia: Okay. In a few minutes.

Sandro goes out the door. Claudia finally locates her stockings and proceeds to finish dressing.

Sandro comes out of the hotel and crosses over to the sunny square. He starts strolling down along a street which leads to a baroque church that opens up to a wide flight of stone steps. Beyond these steps is a small dead-end street that runs up against the façade of a large and magnificent old building. A few feet away from the façade, seated on a bench in the shade, is an old coachman whose horse is standing beside him with its head deep in a sack of hay.

Sandro goes down the flight of steps and approaches the door of the old building which is closed. He rings the bell but there is no answer. Then he notices a time schedule posted on the door indicating visiting hours. After glancing at it, he walks over to the seated coachman.

Sandro: It's closed. Isn't there any custodian or care-taker inside?

Coachman (apathetically): Nobody there.

Sandro: But it says it's open from 9:30 to 10:30 . . . and it's ten o'clock now . . . That's a fine way to greet tourists.

Coachman: Tourists? Last year a few Frenchmen came here and they all walked around in their bathing suits. So they were made to understand that it was better if they didn't come at all.

Sandro shakes his head and is about to say something but he sees the door opening and a man appears. Sandro goes over to him.

Sandro: Are you the custodian?

Custodian: Yes, come right in.

Sandro enters and finds himself inside a large court-yard of noteworthy architectural design, though some-what in a state of decay. The custodian goes on his way and Sandro walks further into the courtyard where two young men are studying the architecture. On hearing Sandro's footsteps, they turn around for a moment, then resume their observation. They are, in fact, young architectural students busily engaged in taking notes and copying certain architectural details. They do this with an extraordinary interest, almost with a sense of religious zeal. Sandro continues to stroll through the courtyard. His footsteps are the only sounds to be heard disturbing the otherwise absolute silence. The two young students exchange words be-tween each other but they speak in faint whispers, almost as though they were inside a church. Sandro gazes up at the arcades, the columns, the windows. He is obviously filled with a painful sense of regret, resent-ful and bitter. He turns to look at the two young stu-dents who are deep in their studies and ignore his presence. But he is unable to ignore them; they plainly annoy him. In a certain sense, they humiliate him. He turns away and heads towards the exit, walking on the tip of his toes so as not to make any noise. Then he goes out, quietly closing the door behind him.

In the hotel lobby, a maid is cleaning and dusting, and at the same time, singing little snatches from a popular romantic tune. The hotel manager, who is busy writing something in the register behind the desk, looks up and says:

Hotel Manager: Go ahead, keep right on singing ...

Disappointed, the maid immediately stops singing, and the manager resumes writing. But she quickly looks up again as she hears footsteps coming down the stairs. It is Claudia.

Hotel Manager (to Claudia): Excuse me for interfering, but I've heard about that girl ... Here in this place one gets to know about everything ... That girl you're looking for ... Why don't you try asking at the youth hostel in Pergusa? Almost all the young girls traveling through here end up there.

Claudia is immediately interested to hear this bit of news and is about to ask for additional information. But she is suddenly distracted by Sandro who enters the lobby at that very moment.

Claudia: I was just coming out to meet you. How come you're back so soon?

Sandro doesn't answer but merely shrugs his shoulders. Then he takes Claudia by the arm and gently leads her towards the stairway. He has a worried expression on his face and remains absolutely silent as he starts climbing the stairs. As they walk through the corridor, Claudia looks at him anxiously, wondering what is wrong.

Claudia: Sandro ... What's the matter?
Sandro: Nothing.

He opens the door to his room and ushers Claudia in. As soon as he enters, he takes off his jacket and throws it on a chair. Then he walks over to the window and closes the shutters. Then, without saying a word, he turns to Claudia, grabs her in his arms and squeezes her. Claudia smiles, and playfully yells "Ouch!" Then he goes to kiss her but Claudia tries to resist but doesn't succeed. This little struggle stimulates Sandro and is enough to make him forget all reserve. He drags Claudia on to the bed and forces her to lie down.

Claudia: No, Sandro . . . Please . . .
Sandro: Why?
Claudia: No reason why . . .

But Sandro hugs her and kisses her again. This time, Claudia lets herself be kissed.

Claudia: What's the matter with you?

Sandro only responds by kissing her again. Then Claudia yields. Sandro is angry and excited, as though he wanted to take his resentment out on Claudia.

Claudia: Sandro, wait a moment, just one moment . . . You seem like an entirely different person . . .

Sandro: And aren't you pleased? . . . That way you'll have a new kind of adventure.

Wounded, Claudia pushes him away with all her might, and exclaims:

Claudia: What are you saying?
Sandro: I was only joking, really . . . Can't I make a joke? And now you've got to tell me why you don't want to.
Claudia: Oh, Sandro . . . I want everything you do. But . . .

She stops short, then turns aside and reaches out to touch his jacket on the chair, looking into the pockets, not with curiosity but with a sense of love. Sandro grabs her by the shoulders and forces her to turn around.

Sandro: But what?

Claudia remains silent, then gets up from the bed, and in a subdued tone of voice, says:

Claudia: Did the hotel manager speak to you about that place nearby?
Sandro: Yes, she started to but I didn't feel like staying to listen to what she had to say. If we had to listen to everybody . . .
Claudia: No, Sandro . . . We should go. Besides, we haven't been in touch with anybody. Not even with Anna's father. We should have at least sent a wire or telephoned . . . Let's be fair, he must be feeling awfully lonely.
Sandro: I don't doubt it. But at a time like this we're the least suitable persons to be with him. And as far as telephoning him . . . Who knows where he is?

There is a moment of silence, then Claudia starts heading towards the door.

Claudia: Come, let's go. Pack your things, and I'll get mine ready too.

It is evening. Sandro's car is pulling into the town of Taormina on its way to the San Domenico. It comes to a small square and passes by a group of men and women seated on the steps of an ancient ruin. They are dressed in evening clothes and are laughing and giggling. The car turns into the street of the San Domenico and stops in front of the hotel. A porter immediately comes out and opens the door. Claudia and Sandro get out and head towards the small court-yard that leads into the foyer.
The lobby is full of activity and alive with people dressed in formal attire. Claudia is clearly intrigued by everything she sees: the surroundings, the people, etc. Sandro approaches the reception desk as Claudia walks slightly ahead, anxious to see what is going on. The sound of music is heard coming from one of the halls at the other end of the lobby. There is obviously a party underway: further on, through a glass partition,

michelangelo antonioni

couples are seen dancing. Suddenly, Claudia stops.
Directly up ahead, she notices Patrizia. As soon as she
see Claudia, Patrizia comes to greet her, smiling.

Patrizia: Well, I'm looking for somebody else and who
do I find but you.

Claudia smiles and they both kiss each other on the
cheek.

Claudia: How are you?

Instead of answering, Patrizia takes Claudia by the
hand and leads her over to a bench along the side of
the wall and sits down. Claudia remains standing, somewhat annoyed by the crowd of people around her.

Claudia: Shouldn't we try to find a quieter place?
Patrizia: Quieter? Oh, yes, of course.

Patrizia rises and leads Claudia out to a terrace that
overlooks the entire bay which is dotted with lights.
Claudia takes in the view but her attention is still
focused on Patrizia. She waits from one moment to the
next to have questions thrown at her, but Patrizia
remains silent. So Claudia turns around and looks at
her as though to say: Come on, say what you have to
say and let's get it over with. But Patrizia smiles at
her sweetly and only murmurs:

Patrizia: You look so wonderfully tanned.

Claudia feels relieved and presses Patrizia's hand,
almost with a sense of renewed friendship. Sandro
appears from behind the glass partition and comes out
on the terrace to greet Patrizia.

Patrizia: And here's Sandro. *(He kisses her hand)* Why
don't you two go upstairs and change?
Sandro: Yes, we will.

They leave the terrace and go through one of the

halls towards the corridor that leads to the rooms. Claudia walks ahead, with Patrizia and Sandro following slightly behind. The hall is still packed with people.

Patrizia: Did you manage to find good rooms?

Sandro: They didn't seem too good.
Patrizia: You should have told Ettore. He always manages to get what he wants.
Sandro: Ettore must be fed up with me by now.
Patrizia: Oh, no, not at all. And then you know very well that he'll forgive you anything; just as long as you admit to him that you're a worse driver than he is.

Claudia looks at Sandro, assured by Patrizia's reply. She remains thoughtful for a moment, then asks Patrizia:

Claudia: How do you manage to put up with all this confusion? You always said people bore you.
Patrizia: You shouldn't always take me seriously. Actually, I'm used to it by now. First my mother and now my husband; both of them are like dynamos.
Sandro: Your mother?
Patrizia: Yes, even I had a mother. She was part Austrian, but she was still my mother. My childhood was like a tennis match; they bounced me back and forth, here and there . . .
Claudia: My childhood, instead, was a very sensible one.
Patrizia: What do you mean by sensible?
Claudia: It means being without money.

Patrizia and Sandro burst out laughing, and Sandro reaches out and ruffles Claudia's hair. They have arrived in front of a room that is situated on the ground floor, and are greeted by a hotel clerk who is waiting for them with keys in hand. The door is already open and Claudia is about to enter.

Patrizia: See you soon, then.

Sandro nods yes and Claudia waves so long, as

Patrizia takes her leave. Claudia enters the room behind the clerk, and Sandro follows. Claudia stops in the middle of the room, as the clerk goes through his various duties with professional exactitude: he turns on the lights, draws the window curtains, checks to see if there are enough hangers in the wardrobe, then finally opens the door to the adjoining room, into which he disappears. All his movements seem completely automatic.

Sandro (commenting under his breath): You see? Just like a robot.

Then Sandro enters the adjoining room, where the clerk has in the meantime turned on all the lamps and performed all the other little duties. Sandro starts to undo his tie. Claudia remains standing in the middle of the room, listening to all of Sandro's movements in the other room. A knock is heard at the door of Sandro's room and Sandro is heard saying:

Sandro: Come in.

A few seconds later, the porter also enters Claudia's room with her baggage. She opens the valise and starts taking out her nightgown and other necessities. Her gestures are slow and imprecise because fatigue has overcome her. Several moments pass, and Sandro appears at the door in his pajamas.

Claudia: Sandro, listen . . . Try not to get yourself too involved tomorrow.
Sandro: Aren't you going to change?
Claudia: You said you wanted to quit working for Ettore.

Sandro shrugs his shoulders without, apparently, giving much thought to Claudia's statement. He goes into the bathroom saying:

Sandro: Sure, that's what I said . . .

The sound of the shower running is heard.

Sandro: Wow, it's ice cold . . .

Claudia goes up to the door adjoining the two rooms and stops at the doorway of the bathroom that is situated between the two rooms.

Claudia: Sandro, I'm not coming down.
Sandro: Why?
Claudia: I'm too sleepy.
Sandro: Sleep is something one must learn to overcome. I learned how to do it when I was a child. I never slept. And I had friends who even slept less than I did. The one who went to bed first, paid a penalty. And we really didn't do anything. After seeing a movie, we'd go to a café and discuss things for a while . . . then we'd sit down on a bench somewhere . . . listen to some drunkard . . . watch them putting up posters or manifestoes . . . or look at the sheep passing by . . . or go for a stroll around the market place . . . Or else we'd go and wake up some girl in the neighborhood by standing in front of her window and calling out her name . . .

Claudia has been listening to Sandro with her head leaning against the door jamb, her eyes closed. As soon as Sandro stops, she goes back to her bed and starts undressing. Sandro comes out of the bathroom, wearing a bathrobe, and going over to Claudia, says in an affectionate tone:

Sandro: You're that sleepy, eh? What time do you expect to get up tomorrow?
Claudia: Late, very late.

Claudia disappears into her bathroom, and Sandro returns to his room. After a while, his voice is heard.

Sandro: Did you know that when I was a boy I wanted to be a diplomat? Can you imagine that! Me, a diplomat? It's strange but I never thought I'd be rich. I saw myself living in a rooming house, full of geniuses . . .

Claudia has slipped into her nightgown and returned

to her room. Sandro is heard clearing his throat, and then continuing.

Sandro: Instead, I have two apartments, one in Rome and one in Milan. As far as genius goes, it's a habit I've never formed. What do you think of that?

Sandro reappears at the doorway, already half dressed. Claudia slides into bed and stretches herself out under the covers.

Claudia: I look at things differently ... But maybe it's best we talk about it some other time. Do you mind turning off that light over there?

Sandro turns out the lamp on the table while Claudia closes the main switch. The room is enveloped in darkness. Sandro approaches the bed and bends over Claudia to kiss her.

Sandro: Good night, my love.
Claudia: Good night. Tell me that you love me.
Sandro: I love you.
Claudia: Tell me once more.
Sandro: I don't love you.
Claudia (smiling): I deserve it.

Sandro goes towards the door, then turns and smiles.

Sandro: That's not true. I love you.

He returns to his room, closing the door behind him. He seems somewhat meditative, as though the little discourse he has just delivered has in some way touched him deeply. He also seems a little sad. Then he puts on his tie and jacket, lights up a cigarette, and goes to the door.

Sandro comes out of his room and walks along through the corridors, heading towards the reception halls down at the other end. Other persons are walking up and down the corridor in both directions.

Sandro's attention is attracted by the figure of a woman who is coming his way at a rather quick pace. She is wrapped in a tight-fitting evening dress that emphasizes the various harmonious parts of her body. Sandro looks at her. He seems to recognize her but isn't quite sure who it is. The girl passes alongside of him and apparently she too has the same impression, for she gives him a look that lasts much longer than it normally would between two complete strangers. She stops in front of a door but before entering, she casts another glance at Sandro, who suddenly recalls that she is the same woman who had almost provoked a riot in the streets of Messina and who was forced to take refuge in a men's shop. There is a moment of hesitation, then the girl opens the door and disappears into the room. Sandro continues on ahead until he reaches the bar, which is still very crowded.

Evening clothes of all kinds. Shiny silks. Jewels dangling from wrists, necks and ears that are either white or bronzed by the sun. Shoes of silver or lustrous black. Headdresses of many women—high, cropped or short and bobbed. Men with hair well groomed but also frequently mussed. A vast, tumultuous wave of people, all wealthy and respectable, talking, laughing and carrying on as though the whole wide world was right there and everybody in it was like them.

Snatches of witticisms. Faces of passing people. Hands reaching out for glasses. The expressions on the face of the barman, smiling and indifferent. The sad, sullen face of the cloakroom attendant. The dumbfounded look on the face of a thirteen-year-old elevator boy.

Sandro feels very much at home in this milieu. One thinks so little, forgets so easily. And things are so conveniently ignored, beginning with one's own self.

Sandro moves through the crowd, here and there. Standing next to the orchestra is a girl in black pants, singing strange songs in a soft, suggestive voice.

Sandro encounters Ettore. As soon as he sees Sandro, Ettore comes over and places an arm around his shoulder, almost in the form of an embrace.

Ettore: Well, finally . . . Come, I'll introduce you to my friends.

Sandro: I want to take a look around first . . . I'll join you later.

Ettore: Say, I hope it's understood that starting tomorrow morning, I'll need to have you around. If you don't give me some figures to work with, how can I proceed?

Sandro agrees with a nod of his head. But he is thoughtful and somewhat saddened. As Ettore returns to his friends with whom he had been speaking and laughing, Sandro looks at him almost with a sense of rage.

Then he goes back to the bar and orders something to drink. He is not aware that the girl from Messina is just a few yards away and is watching him. She is extremely tanned, extremely voluptuous, and extremely beautiful.

Sandro moves away from the bar with the glass in his hand. He passes in front of a semi-dark room and takes a peek inside: a television set is turned on but nobody is watching it. Sandro is restless. He comes to a terrace and stops to look down at the illuminated docks below. The headlights of cars passing by fan out across the road that runs along the shore of the

sea. With an angry gesture, Sandro finishes his drink, gulping the whiskey down in one fast swallow. He squeezes the empty glass in his hand as though he had wanted to crush it.

The early rays of dawn are faintly seen coming through a window at the far end of the corridor. Claudia comes rushing out of her room and runs over to Patrizia's door. She knocks, then without waiting for a response, she enters.

Claudia: Patrizia . . . Patrizia . . . Where's Ettore?
Patrizia: I imagine he must be inside sleeping.
Claudia: Would you please see if Sandro is with him? He's not in his room. I'm sorry to disturb you.

Patrizia gets up out of bed and goes into the adjoining room.

Patrizia: Ettore . . .
Ettore: What is it?
Patrizia: Nothing, nothing at all. I was just looking for Sandro.
Ettore: And you expect to find him in here? Go and ask Claudia.
Patrizia: Yes, yes, of course. *(She returns to her room.)*
Claudia: Patrizia, I'm afraid.
Patrizia: More or less, we are all afraid. Especially at night.
Claudia: I'm afraid that Anna has come back. I feel she's back, and that they're together.
Patrizia: But what's gotten into you? . . . We would have known. Sandro must be out in the garden somewhere, taking a breath of fresh air, or watching the break of dawn. It would be a lovely surprise indeed if he turned out to be the sentimental type.

Claudia sinks down into a chair, weak and exhausted.

Patrizia: Now, listen. For God's sake, try not to let

michelangelo antonioni

yourself become obsessed with that idea. Go to your
room and get back into bed.
Claudia: Just several days ago, the thought of Anna
being dead would have made me sick. And now, I don't
even cry, I'm afraid she might be alive. Everything is
becoming so damned simple and easy, even to deprive
one's self of pain and suffering.

Patrizia: You should never wish to get melodramatic
over anything.
Claudia: Yes, you're right. I'm sick and tired of being
like that.

Claudia gets up and leaves the room. She continues
walking down along the corridor, checking here and
there. But the hotel is deserted. There are still a few
lights on in the reception hall but not enough to
illuminate the place adequately. Finally, she reaches
the main hall and stops. The only signs of last night's
party is a certain disorder in the placement of the
armchairs and ashtrays filled with cigarette butts. Even
the main hall seems completely deserted. But all of a
sudden, Claudia becomes aware of something moving
on a sofa at the far end of the room. She takes a few
steps, walking silently over the thick carpet, so as to
get a better look. There seems to be a slight movement
among what appears to be a jumbled pile of male and
female clothes, partly hidden from view by the back
of the sofa. Claudia goes up still closer because she is
not able to see clearly what or who it is. Only that she
has the impression of having seen that suit before . . .
A man's suit. She is now able to distinguish what it is:
a couple embracing and kissing.
    Claudia approaches still closer. She is now just a few
steps away. Little by little, as she advances, her face
takes on such a painful look of astonishment that she
appears almost petrified. She hesitates and bumps up
against a little table that makes a small noise. The
couple on the sofa come out of their embrace and
look up. The man is Sandro; the woman is the girl
from Messina. Sandro looks at Claudia as though he
were filled with terror. The girl, instead, seems quite

amused. Claudia remains for a moment, staring at them
as if she can't believe her own eyes, and is incapable
of making any move. Then, she abruptly turns away
and starts running. She runs through the main hall, the
reception room, the courtyard, and out into the street.

There is not a soul to be seen. No sound. The day is
breaking clear and serene.

   Claudia comes over to a bench with its paint all
peeling off, but she doesn't sit down. Transfixed, and
with her eyes almost wide open, she stares out at the
sea, and at the waves which are also a mystery unto
themselves.

Footsteps are heard approaching from behind, but Claudia doesn't even bother to turn. It seems that nothing could distract her from that painful state of shock which is written all over her face. A young laborer in overalls, carrying a small bundle under his arm, passes by, glancing at her with a look of curiosity. He walks a few paces ahead, then turns around to look at her again as though she were some kind of strange creature.

The sound of footsteps dies down in the distance, and everything is silent once more. There is only the gentle lapping of the waves as they roll up against the shore. Claudia is completely oblivious to the scene. Several birds swoop down emitting their small cries. A sudden but almost imperceptible sea breeze ripples Claudia's hair.

Other footsteps are heard approaching: slow, heavy. Claudia is still not stirred from her thoughtful, trance-like state. The footsteps come to a halt directly behind her. It is Sandro. He appears thoroughly crestfallen. He doesn't even have enough courage to look at Claudia. His face is worn and disfigured, like that of a tired old man. And he lets himself fall limp onto the bench. They both remain completely motionless, without looking at each other. And detached: Claudia standing, Sandro seated. Behind them, the skeleton of cement. Further off, the sea.

Gradually, Claudia turns her head towards Sandro. Her eyes are filled with tears. She looks down upon him as though he were something that greatly pained her. She moves up closer to the bench. Sandro doesn't budge an inch. Claudia reaches out to him with her hand, then slowly, gently, and with an overwhelming sense of desperation, she caresses his hair.

la notte (the night) 1960

translated by roger j. moore

Credits

Director:	Michelangelo Antonioni
Cast:	Jeanne Moreau
	Marcello Mastroianni
	Monica Vitti
	Bernhard Wicki
	Rosy Mazzacurati
	Maria Pia Luzi
	Guido Ajmone Marsan
	Vittorio Bertolini
	Vincenzo Corbella
	Ugo Fortunati
	Gitt Magrini
	Giorno Negro
	Roberta Speroni
Original story and scenario:	Michelangelo Antonioni
	Ennio Flaiano
	Tonini Guerra
Director of Photography:	Gianni Di Venanzo
Assistants to the Director:	Franco Indovina and
	Umberto Pelosso
Scene Designer:	Piero Zuffi
Cameraman:	Pasquale De Santis
Sound Engineer:	Claudio Maielli
Script Girl:	Liana Ferri
Make-up:	Franco Freda and
	Micheline Chaperon
Hairdressers:	Amalia Paoletti and
	Simone Knapp Dougue
Director of Production:	Paolo Frasca
General Production Manager:	Roberto Cocco
Editing:	Eraldo da Roma
Music:	Giorgio Gaslini
Producer:	Emmanuel Cassuto

A Co-production Film by Nepi Film (Rome), Sofitedip (Paris) and Silver Film (Paris)

Milan, noontime. Window washers are working on the tall Pirelli Building, from which they see a wide panoramic view of the city, whose streets are jammed with traffic. Inside the building, people are leaving their offices to go to lunch. The sidewalks are crowded with people going to and fro; the police have their hands full directing traffic; streetcars are packed with sullen and tired people.

In a cheerfully furnished hospital room flooded with sunlight, Tommaso Garani, a man of about forty-five, is writhing in his bed in the grip of an excruciating pain. The pain squeezes stifled, almost animal-like moans out of him. A doctor and nurse are at his bedside, the nurse preparing a hypodermic needle.

Tommaso's face, disfigured with pain, starts twitching violently. The nurse hands the hypodermic needle to the doctor, who gets ready to give the injection while trying to calm the patient by murmuring a few words.

Doctor: Calm yourself. Now you'll feel better.

Tommaso continues to twist and turn, but less violently, for the injection is already having a psychological effect. He looks at the doctor with almost lucid desperation and murmurs:

Tommaso: What am I going to do? What am I going to do?

The nurse replaces the hypodermic needle in its tray. Meanwhile, the doctor leafs through one of the magazines on the night table, slowly and indifferently. Tommaso looks out the window at the topmost branches of a nearby tree.

The tree is in the garden of the ultramodern hospital, which is boldly styled with aluminum fixtures and enormous expanses of glass. Almost monstrous in its perfection, it evokes the picture of flawless and implacable science.

A standard model car pulls up the driveway and parks. Giovanni Pontano, thirty-seven years old, dressed with the sober and casual elegance of someone who is socially accepted, climbs out of the car, then goes around it to open the other door. As he is about to do so, the door opens and his wife Lidia, age about thirty, also elegantly dressed but in a simple and tasteful manner, gets out of the car. The two walk silently up to the hospital entrance.

Inside the lobby, which like the outside is in frigid architectural style, a receptionist is seated behind a desk by the switchboard. He turns to Giovanni and Lidia with an impersonal smile.

Giovanni: Garani. Tommaso Garani. Room 45.
Receptionist: Yes. Seventh floor. You're expected.

Giovanni gently takes Lidia's arm and leads her toward an elevator. As they enter, the elevator door closes behind them.

During the smooth elevator ride, Giovanni and Lidia avoid each other's gaze. These are the usual awkward moments of an elevator ride, but made even more uncomfortable by the impersonality of the decor. Lidia stares up at the ceiling, while Giovanni gazes at the button board. The humming finally stops and the door opens automatically.

Lidia and Giovanni step out of the elevator into a long, cold, highly polished corridor, where the sound of their steps is deadened by the polished rubberized floor.

About halfway down the hall, a door opens and from behind it appears a beautiful young woman with a fixed stare of great sweetness. She is smiling slightly in a mysterious, sensuous way. The striking thing about her is her eyes, which are soft, velvety, and extraordinarily steady. As Giovanni hesitates and then stops, her smile becomes a little larger and she says in a low voice:

Young Woman: Excuse me, but my telephone isn't working. I can't seem to get it to work. Do you mind?

Noticing Lidia, who had remained behind, she pays no attention and smiles even more broadly; but she changes her story, still speaking in low, furtive tones:

Young Woman: Can you notify the receptionist down-stairs?

Giovanni is about to answer her when, upon hearing the footsteps of a nurse, the young woman quietly closes the door. As she does so, she casts a languorous look at Giovanni and Lidia.

Giovanni and Lidia continue down the hall, crossing the path of a nurse, who comes from a side corridor and proceeds on her way, greeting them with a polite but impersonal nod.

A few steps more and they reach Room 45. Giovanni is about to knock when the door opens and out comes a nurse pushing a medicine cart. She, too, greets them with a slight nod. Right behind her comes the doctor, in his immaculately white uniform. His hair is short, his face handsome, and his expression deliberately expressionless. Closing the door behind him, the doctor looks at Giovanni, while seeming to ignore Lidia.

Doctor: He's still under the influence of morphine, but he's awake. You may go in.
Giovanni: There was some talk about an operation . . .
Doctor: We decided against it. Any operation now would be futile. Excuse me.

The doctor turns and walks away, casting a furtive glance at Lidia. Giovanni too looks at her, hesitates for a second, then knocks on the door and enters, followed by his wife.

Tommaso is resting quietly in bed, his face relaxed and his eyes clear and bright. He is sitting up and looking at a book. Giovanni forces a smile, trying to look cheerful.

Giovanni: Tommaso, are we disturbing you?

Tommaso gives him a weak smile, which he restrains somewhat upon seeing Lidia.

Tommaso: Of course not. Come in, come in.

He shakes Giovanni's hand, then Lidia's, who smiles.

Lidia: Hello, Tommaso.
Tommaso: I'm giving you a lot of trouble.

Now Tommaso is smiling also. He seems much younger when he smiles. He gives the impression of being an upright, very self-critical man, yet one who is basically modest and genuinely good-natured.

Giovanni: How do you feel?
Tommaso: The operation was successful and the patient died. Lidia, please sit down. Both of you.

Giovanni sits on the edge of the bed. Lidia remains standing, hesitating, but finally leans up against the foot of Tommaso's bed. Meanwhile, the latter continues, slowly but clearly.

Tommaso: Well, what's new? I read they're having a publication-date party today for your book. Are you pleased?
Giovanni: Oh, let's not talk about that.
Tommaso: But why not? These are things that have to be done. After all, the only thing that really matters is your book. Lidia, why don't you sit down? *(To both of them)* You can smoke if you want to.
Lidia: No thanks, Tommaso, I don't feel tired.

Giovanni hands Tommaso a magazine, which Tommaso places on the night table.

Giovanni: I brought you a copy of *Europe Letteraria* which has your article on Adorno.
Tommaso: I've already received a copy. How did you like it? Should I add it to my book?
Giovanni: It's very, very good, you know. I only skimmed through it, and I'll have to read it again, but it's very, very good. Certainly you should include it. It will be an excellent book.
Tommaso: Yes. *(Pause)* I'll have to give it some more thought. I haven't been able to do much thinking these

past few days, yet this is the first free time I've had in three years. What an ironical vacation! Lidia, how wonderful you look!

Lidia forces a smile.

Lidia: Marcella wanted to come too, but I thought . . .
Tommaso: You did the right thing. I'd rather not see anybody. You can't imagine how sick and tired I am with this pretending. With you, of course, it's different. I was hoping you'd come. You know, I see things in a clearer light now, and I regret that my presence ruined many of your evenings in that delightful apartment.
Giovanni: It's your home, you know.
Tommaso: Really? *(Pause)* I know. You get to realize so many things when you're all alone. And you realize all the things that remain to be done. You know, I'm beginning to wonder if I haven't stayed too much on the fringes of a job which really concerned me. I lacked the courage to get to the bottom of things. I often consoled myself with the thought that perhaps I never had the intelligence in the first place.
Giovanni (smiling): Oh, oh! If that's the case, then I may just as well stop writing and look for a good job. But you're just joking.
Tommaso (laughing): A little self-criticism once in a while is good for you. It helps put things in proper perspective; gives you courage.

Giovanni picks up the book that Tommaso had left on the bed, and looks at the title.

Giovanni: Don't tell me you bought a copy?
Tommaso: Not only did I buy it, I'm even reading it. I've only read about fifty pages; I just hope they let me finish it. I like certain things very much: That entire section on the bath, for instance. *(Seriously)* That's unquestionably the best thing you've ever done. *(Jokingly)* If the morphine hasn't affected my critical judgment! You know, with morphine everything takes on a different meaning.

Giovanni: Then it certainly must be the morphine. But seriously, do you really like it?

Tommaso: Yes I do, Giovanni. *(Jokingly)* You'll end up being a great success.

Giovanni: Yes, I'm really afraid I'll end up badly.

Tommaso (laughing): There! You see the advantage of premature death? You escape success.

Lidia, Giovanni, and Tommaso laugh. The door opens and an elderly woman enters. She is modestly dressed, with a black veil over her arm and a prayer book in her hands. It's Tommaso's mother. Her face betrays great weariness and internal suffering. Tommaso introduces her to Giovanni and Lidia.

Tommaso: Ah, my mother.

Mother: How are you, Tommaso?

Tommaso: Poor mother, seven hours on the train all alone! And now here you are, where you can't even sleep.

His mother shakes her head and walks over to an armchair, sitting down on the edge.

Tommaso: What day is this? Saturday, isn't it?

Lidia: That's right, Saturday.

Tommaso: Tell me about yourselves. Who are you seeing these days?

Giovanni: Oh, we hardly see anybody now. It seems so difficult to do anything lately. We just ride around in the car, that's about all. It's not very exciting, but aside from that, we don't get out much.

Tommaso: And what about your trip to Greece?

Lidia: We still haven't decided whether we'll go or not.

Giovanni: It was your idea, originally. So, when you get well . . .

Tommaso makes a gesture of slight irritation.

Tommaso: Treat me as a friend, not as a patient! I know very well how this is going to end. *(Smiling)* I'm sorry. By the way, as far as royalties are concerned,

I've given all the necessary instructions to my publisher. Besides, he's the one who's paying for all this. (*The pain recurs*) No, it's nothing. Please excuse me.

Giovanni and Lidia watch Tommaso, who is trying hard to maintain a calm face. Lidia approaches the bed and tries to comfort him.

Lidia (gently): Don't tire yourself. Do you want me to call the nurse? Or should we leave?
Tommaso: Oh no, no! Please stay! (*Pause. Then, almost cheerfully*) Nice place, isn't it? Everything I used to hate in the way of furnishings. I never thought I'd have such a luxurious end. I almost feel I'm cheating someone. Before you know it, hospital rooms will look just like night clubs. People want to have a good time right down to the end.

A beautiful nurse enters, carrying a tray with a bottle of champagne and glasses, which she places on a wheel cart, rolling it up close to the bed.

Tommaso: Ah, champagne! Didn't you know that in these cases, you get a desire for champagne? Just think: I don't like it, and yet I suddenly felt an urge for it. They didn't seem at all surprised.
Nurse: It gives you a lift; it's good for you. (*Turns to leave*)
Tommaso: Pardon me, Miss. I never dared to ask you before: What's your name?
Nurse: My name is Elena.
Tommaso: Elena. Thank you. Won't you have a drink with us?
Nurse: No, thanks. Don't tire yourself by talking too much.

The nurse leaves the room.

Tommaso: Did you see that lovely creature? They keep her here to cheer up the sick. She doesn't know how to do anything; she's just beautiful, that's all. Yet, under certain circumstances, beauty is really a discouraging thing. Giovanni, will you pour the drinks?

Giovanni gets up and pours a little champagne for Tommaso, then replaces the bottle.

Tommaso: Only for me? What about you, Lidia?
Lidia: No, thanks, Tommaso. I'd rather not.
Tommaso: Come on, Giovanni, don't make me drink alone. How about you, mother? A little champagne will do you good.
Mother: Just a little bit.

Meanwhile, Giovanni pours champagne into two other glasses and gives one to Tommaso's mother. They all drink without saying a word, except Lidia, who stares at Tommaso. Tommaso drinks avidly and then sinks back on the pillows. Giovanni barely moistens his lips. Tommaso's mother gives her glass back to Giovanni. Silence.

Tommaso: My throat is always dry. *(Pause)* How are things in Milan? The city must be lovely in this weather. If I were you, I'd go to the lakes tomorrow. *(Pause)* See, mother? These are my best friends. The only friends I have.
Giovanni: Don't believe him: Tommaso has plenty of friends. Everyone is very fond of him.
Mother: Yes, he's a fine boy.

She wipes away a tear, hiding her face. Lidia is just barely able to hide her feelings.

Lidia: I have to go, Tommaso. You stay, Giovanni. I have to go; I'll be back tomorrow.
Tommaso: Yes, thanks. Tomorrow.

Tommaso becomes serious and looks intently at Lidia.

Tommaso: Don't you want to go too, Giovanni?
Giovanni: No, I'll stay a little longer.

Giovanni looks at Lidia as if to say, "Wait for me downstairs." Lidia goes over to Tommaso's mother to shake her hand, then turns to Tommaso.

Tommaso (smiling calmly): So long, Lidia.

He holds out his arm. Lidia comes up closer and takes his hand. She is almost overcome by emotion but manages to control herself. Tommaso kisses her hand without ado, then smiles.

Lidia: Good-bye. See you soon ... tomorrow.

Tommaso resumes his conversation with his mother, calmly, trying to control himself, but his voice becomes more and more broken.

Tommaso: Those are the only friends I have in the world. The others are only acquaintances or colleagues. But Giovanni and Lidia are true friends, mother. He's a writer ... famous, too. If some day ... they ever go to see you ... you two must go there, some time ... make them a good dinner and give them the room overlooking the orchard ...
Giovanni: We'll go, if it'll make you happy. It's a promise.

There is a pause.

Tommaso: Thanks. *(Grimacing)* I bet that instead of morphine, they're giving me distilled water. *(With an effort)* How was that Backhaus concert, Giovanni?
Giovanni: I didn't go.

Long silence. Tommaso picks up his glass and drinks.

Lidia steps out of the doorway of the hospital and walks hurriedly to the car. She sits down, visibly shaken, on the front seat. She searches around in her purse for cigarettes, takes one out of the pack, and puts it into her mouth. But she flings it away and bursts into a fit of uncontrollable weeping.

Giovanni leaves Room 45 but hesitates outside for an instant, not certain whether he should leave his dying friend. He starts walking along the corridor, his face betraying his grief, lost in thought, when a voice distracts him.

Young Woman's Voice: I beg your pardon ...

Behind the partly opened door is the young woman who had spoken to him earlier. She looks nervous and excited.

Young Woman: Do you have a match, please?

Giovanni, somewhat confused, stops, then searches his pockets as though thinking of something else. Absent-mindedly he offers the woman his pack of cigarettes. She smiles, her lips trembling slightly.

Young Woman (whispering): No, matches.

Giovanni puts his cigarettes back in his pocket and pulls out matches. The young woman having disappeared, Giovanni is overcome by curiosity and looks into the room from the doorway. The room is similar to Garani's, except that the shutters are half closed.
Behind Giovanni, the girl closes the door and stares at Giovanni, her body trembling as though covered with chills. Suddenly, she approaches him. He starts to go but she seizes him and starts to kiss his collar, his clothing, panting. Giovanni, at first dumfounded, now suddenly pulls her to him and returns her kisses with violent excitement.
They remain glued to the door. The shadows are filled with the girl's sighs and occasional muffled cries. Nothing distracts her attention. All at once, there is knocking at the door and someone tries in vain to turn the handle. Giovanni jumps back.

A doctor and two nurses rush into the room from a second door. While the nurses take care of the girl, the doctor opens the door to the hall and vanishes. Giovanni, rearranging his hair and tie, looks at the now absurd spectacle of the young woman writhing on the bed, held down by the nurses. She lifts her head and, with her eyes closed, kisses the nurses' arms. The doctor returns and turns to Giovanni.

Doctor: You'd better go.

Giovanni leaves after glancing once more at the sick girl, whose body now lies on the bed motionless.

Giovanni goes out to the car and gets into the front seat next to Lidia, who, emotionally exhausted, is curled up on the seat. Giovanni, still bewildered, glances sideways at his wife. She dries her tears without either speaking or looking at him. Giovanni starts the motor, and the car moves away.

It's rush hour on a Saturday; everyone is in a hurry to get home and traffic is heavy. As the car nears the downtown district, it has to creep along. Giovanni is more and more nervous, and glances occasionally at Lidia. Neither speaks.

They turn into a narrow street. Traffic is at a complete standstill. Giovanni turns to Lidia.

Giovanni: The last thing I needed now was this nuisance about the book.

Lidia stirs and looks at him with a tired expression.

Giovanni: If you don't feel like going, I'll go by myself.
Lidia: Oh no, I'm fine.
Giovanni: Aren't you tired?
Lidia: Well, yes, maybe a little tired.

Giovanni cannot help telling Lidia what happened.

Giovanni: Lidia, I have to tell you something which isn't very pleasant.
Lidia: Must you?
Giovanni: Yes, I really must. Something happened to me at the hospital. Something rather unpleasant.

Lidia is curious despite herself. Giovanni fumbles for words.

Giovanni: I saw that girl again on the way out.
Lidia: What girl?
Giovanni: That girl in the corridor. She was at the door as I went by, and at first I didn't understand what she wanted.
Lidia: You went in her room!
Giovanni: She grabbed me ... like an animal, and with such violence that I was completely carried away.

Lidia looks at him emotionless, even without surprise. Giovanni is very nervous, while she is calm.

Lidia: Why do you call that an unpleasant incident?
Giovanni: Don't you think it's hideous? There I was, face to face with that desperate creature, and at first

I thought I was the cause. It was horrible. The nurses had to come . . .

Lidia: An experience like that is something you could turn into a nice story. Call it "The Living and the Dead."

Giovanni (brusquely): Is that all you have to say?

Lidia: And what do you expect me to say? That you did something vile? That you disgust me? No, I can understand: You were taken by surprise. But let's drop the subject, do you mind? I suppose this is the first time you betrayed me!

Giovanni (surprised): What do you mean?

Lidia: Don't worry, it wouldn't have made a bit of difference.

Giovanni stares at her, seeming not to understand. He finally parks the car. The two get out and walk to the entrance of a stately building. They walk up a few steps to the door of a publishing house.

They enter the publisher's reception room, where a number of guests are scattered around the room, engaged in animated conversations. There are some fifty people: ladies, noted authors, critics, as well as photographers, and two waiters serving soft drinks and cocktails.

They all turn around as Giovanni and Lidia make

their appearance. There is some applause; the publisher goes to greet them. Giovanni is embarrassed at first, but soon composes himself and, bowing his head and smiling at his well-wishers, walks to a large table covered with copies of his book, "The Season." An elderly gentleman speaks to him in a paternal tone.

Nobel Prize Winner: This is the anteroom to greatness.
Publisher (to Giovanni): I beg your pardon, would you mind dedicating a copy of your book to our Nobel Prize winner?
Giovanni: It's an honor.
Critic: I see you sign on the left.
Giovanni: That's right.
Critic: And when you're reading, do you skip the pages on the right?
Giovanni (smiling): Not always.
Critic: That's interesting. That has a bearing on your future.
Publisher: And now a copy for my collection.
Giovanni: For you, I'll just write, "With friendship."
Female Guest: What is your next book about, Pontano?
Giovanni: I have nothing in mind right now.

Lidia is still near the door, trying to avoid being noticed. She finds these formalities a bit ridiculous. An elegantly dressed woman goes by, saying:

Woman: Oh, how I'd love to write a book!

Lidia smiles weakly. A movie cameraman who is shooting scenes of the party walks over to Lidia holding a copy of Giovanni's book, and hands it to her.

Cameraman: Just like this, please.

Somewhat confused, she looks first at the camera, then at the book; then, realizing that the camera is grinding, she rouses and hurries to the door and down to the street. She starts walking slowly and aimlessly along the street, ignoring and ignored by the thick crowds.

Giovanni's car enters a street flanked with new apartment houses and pulls up in front of his entrance, right behind a car on which some young people are placing a boat. Two laughing girls in slacks come out of the building. The street is otherwise deserted. Giovanni climbs out of the car and goes up to his apartment.

Giovanni's and Lidia's apartment is furnished in a style that reflects the taste of a typical intellectual: walls lined with bookcases and covered with abstract paintings and prints. In a low voice, as though he really expects no response, Giovanni calls his wife:

Giovanni: Lidia.

He walks down the hallway and opens the door to the kitchen, which is empty.

Giovanni: Bianca, did my wife come home yet?
Bianca: No, sir.
Giovanni: She hasn't phoned, has she?
Bianca: No. Is there something I can do?
Giovanni: No, no, I'm expecting my wife. But you may go out if you wish.

He walks into the bedroom, turns on the light, and finds it empty and in order. Returning to his study, he automatically goes to his desk and looks briefly at the papers next to the typewriter. He takes a bottle of cognac and a glass from the liquor cabinet and drinks some. He sits down at the typewriter but then gets up again and lies down on the sofa, picks up a copy of his book, which he leafs through, then puts it on the floor as though he could not stand the sight of it.

On a deserted, sunlit street, Lidia strolls along looking at the modern apartment and office buildings. They appear cold and faceless. Lidia feels completely alienated from the surroundings. It is very hot.

She notices a sunlit building with very few windows, only one of which is open. A woman can be seen passing by the window, where the sunlight strikes her.

She is very scantily dressed and, upon seeing Lidia, she yanks the curtain closed.

Lidia walks on and reaches a spot where there is an open space between the tall, glass-covered buildings. The sun beats down on the narrow space. She looks at the patch of sky above the buildings as though longing to flee these oppressive walls. Suddenly, a low-flying jet thunders overhead, filling the streets and the open space with a sinister roar. Lidia hurries away as though terrified. Running to a tree-lined street, she looks behind her as though someone were following her. She feels calmer and wanders on slowly. She picks up a leaf and examines it.

It is late afternoon. Lidia takes a taxi to the outskirts of the city, where groups of buildings are separated by large uncultivated fields. The scenery is pleasant. Lidia leans toward the driver.

Lidia: Stop here, please.

She gets out and walks around a bit to look at the scenery. The taxi driver looks at her astonished and sits down on the curb. Lidia, embarrassed by the presence of the taxi driver, walks into the field. There is complete silence; the spot is deserted.

After a few moments, a group of people appear on the roadside and head for the field. They are six or seven youths in their early twenties, walking quickly without talking. They are strange to see, walking along so determinedly, so silently. Instead of crossing the field, they suddenly come to a halt near a wall. One of the boys removes his shirt and stands there with his torso bare; another one walks up and faces him. The others form a circle around them.

After a brief exchange of insults, the two of them break out into a furious fist fight. After some violent punching, one boy throws himself at the other and, clasped together, they fall to the ground. After rolling around, one of them manages to straddle his opponent and starts punching him in the face, harder and harder.

The others do not intervene; no one breathes a word. The only sound heard is the panting of the two combatants. The fight grows in violence.

Lidia watches them, fascinated. She has an urge to leave, to scream, to interfere. But she takes no action, remaining motionless and unable to lift her gaze from the two fighters. Blood starts trickling from the face of the boy lying on the ground. The one on top punches away right at the wound. With seemingly superhuman effort, the boy underneath throws his adversary over and is on top of him, pounding him with a series of violent blows, each accompanied by a long and rhythmic breath. The scene seems like a hallucination, and Lidia mumbles to herself, as though not wanting to be overheard.

Lidia: Enough now, stop! Stop!

One of the boys hears her and starts laughing. Now all of them turn around and look at her. Even the two on the ground stop fighting, as though by tacit agreement, and look at her. The boy with the bleeding face leaves the group and walks toward Lidia, while the rest slowly leave. He stops near the wall and gazes at her with a sensuous grin. Lidia gazes back, uncertain what to do, then turns around and starts walking away.

Boy: Wait.

Lidia looks for the taxi and sees that the driver is leaning against the car reading a newspaper, with his back to her. She runs toward the taxi. As she is about to reach it, the driver, calm as can be, goes to meet her.

Driver: Shall I wait? All right.

Her attention is distracted by a group of children playing with toy rockets. Two of them are around one of the rockets; they light it and throw themselves on the ground. The rocket shoots up into the darkening sky, leaving a white trail.

First Boy: There's a lot of wind up there, eh?
Second Boy: Yes. Do you think . . .
First Boy: Isn't that terrific? It's going up to ten thousand feet.
Second Boy: Would you go up to the moon?
First Boy: Not me!

Lidia is completely fascinated by the sight, which calms her immediately.

It is twilight. Giovanni is sprawled over the sofa in the dark study, asleep.

He wakes with a start and at first does not realize just where he is. He gets up, a bit worried, feeling as though everybody has abandoned him. No sound issues from the other rooms; the lights are all out. Giovanni walks into the kitchen and out onto the balcony. He hears a voice on the balcony next door.

Lucia: Hello, is that you?
Giovanni: Oh, hello, Lucia. By any chance, have you . . .
Lucia: I didn't know you were home.

Giovanni: Actually, I wanted . . .

Lucia: Oh, I'm so bored. Paolo has a cold, and we have to spend the week end in Milan.

Giovanni: I'm sorry. I wanted to ask you . . .

Lucia: Tell Lidia to come and visit with me.

Giovanni: I can't right now. She isn't home. I thought she was in your apartment.

Lucia: My apartment? I haven't seen her for two days.

Giovanni: Excuse me. Thanks. So long!

Lucia: Good-bye now.

Giovanni goes back to the study. He walks over to the telephone, starts dialing a number, but changes his mind. He goes to the window and looks out. The lights are out in the buildings all around him.

One of the windows lights up, and a man leans out, obviously without any specific purpose. He looks around and sees Giovanni. The two men look at each other for a moment. The other man is probably also alone at home and waiting for someone or something. Giovanni feels doubly annoyed and walks away from the window. The telephone rings. Giovanni runs to answer it. His face lights up a little, but he tries to adopt a reproachful tone of voice.

Giovanni: Oh, it's you! Where are you?

Lidia is at the other end of the line, in a store in the suburbs.

Lidia: I'm in front of the Breda plant. In the same old field, there are children playing. I'm sure you'll enjoy that. Imagine, they have rockets. They fly way up. It's beautiful. Don't worry, nothing's happened to me. No, no! I told you nothing happened! Come pick me up, will you?

An old, garishly made-up woman, who has been trying to listen in, approaches her and, in a raw, insidious voice, says to her:

Old Woman: If you have to meet someone, in secret . . .
I live right near here, you know.

Lidia turns to look at this decrepit, painted face, at
the dark and heavy circles around her eyes. Giovanni's
voice draws her attention back to the telephone.

Lidia: Come right over. I'll be waiting.

Lidia leaves the store and walks to the taxi.

Lidia: How much is it?
Driver: Twelve hundred lire.

Lidia returns to the field where the children are
playing.
The rockets are very well built. They shoot up
quickly into the sky to a considerable altitude, to the
children's cries of delight. But the two rockets with
which the boys are playing are apparently the last ones,
as it is starting to get dark. The children pick up their
equipment and leave. Lidia is alone, standing in the
field. The sunlight is nearly gone, and the scene again
turns squalid and desolate. Lidia walks back to the
pavement and waits.
After a few moments, Giovanni's car arrives at high
speed. He gets out of the car and goes to meet his wife.
He looks as though he wants to ask her something, yet
remains silent.

Lidia (somewhat sadly): They're gone.
Giovanni: Who?
Lidia: The children.

Giovanni shrugs his shoulders, looks at his wife a
few more moments, then says, in a tone of impatience:

Giovanni: What on earth made you come out here?
Lidia (obviously lying): Nothing. Nothing at all. I just
happened to be out this way.

Giovanni looks around and says:

michelangelo antonioni

Giovanni: It's funny. It hasn't changed at all.

Lidia points to skyscrapers beyond some crumbling walls.

Lidia: Oh, it'll change. Very soon.

Giovanni sits down on one of a group of stones heaped up in the field.

Giovanni: Come here.

Lidia comes closer and sits next to him. They stay close to each other for a few moments, tenderly. Lidia gets up and takes a few steps. Giovanni gets up and walks with her, keeping a certain distance. They walk toward the car, passing two children roller-skating. It gets darker; the street lights come on.

It is evening. Giovanni is in the bedroom getting dressed. He walks into the bathroom to put on his tie. Lidia is in the bathtub. He doesn't even glance at her.

Lidia: What do you think he wants?
Giovanni: I don't know. Maybe he wants to meet us. I've seen him only a couple of times. In any case, it's nice of him to invite us.
Lidia: Will there be a lot of people?
Giovanni: I imagine so.
Lidia: Nowadays, every millionaire needs his intellectual. You must be his choice. Would you pass me the sponge?

Giovanni picks up a large, balloon-shaped sponge and drops it into the water.

Giovanni: Hurry up.

Lidia looks at Giovanni, who walks to the door gazing at her with a husband's indifference. Lidia takes the sponge and passes it over herself with tired movements.
Later, Giovanni, in a dark suit, glass in hand, opens the refrigerator and, taking out a bottle of water, pours some into his glass which is already half full of whiskey. He closes the refrigerator, which reopens. He tries again, with the same result. He bangs it shut with his knee. Turning around, he sees Lidia, who is looking at him from the doorstep. She looks very attractive in her evening dress. He is pleasantly surprised.

Giovanni: Ah! you look fine.
Lidia: Would you please fasten me in the back?

Giovanni puts down the glass, and fastens her dress.

Lidia: You know what I just thought? Let's not go to the Gherardinis.
Giovanni: Why not?
Lidia: I'd rather we went out by ourselves. I want to be with you.

Giovanni gives Lidia a brief kiss on her neck, then moves away.

Giovanni (not too enthusiastic): Oh, well, all right.

He picks up the glass and drinks.

Lidia and Giovanni are seated at a night club table. There are very few customers. A girl is doing a strip tease. Instead of watching the show, Lidia looks at her husband. Giovanni tries not to notice this but finally stops looking at the stage and asks:

Giovanni: What's the matter?
Lidia: It's so amusing to look at you.
Giovanni: What do you mean, amusing?
Lidia: Oh, I don't know. Sometimes you seem to strike a pose when you're with me.
Giovanni: Strike a pose? Nonsense! Look! That girl isn't bad at all.

He again turns toward the strip tease. Lidia looks at her engagement ring. Giovanni notices it but feigns indifference. Lidia touches his cuff links, smiling as though to herself. The ring and cuff links are mounted in a similar setting and have the same kind of stone. Lidia looks at her husband in great detail: his face, his hair, his suit. Finally, Giovanni makes a gesture of exasperation, which he immediately restrains.

Giovanni: You're really trying to distract me from watching this act.
Lidia: Please, don't always try to belittle me. I'm also entitled to my own thoughts.
Giovanni: And what are you thinking at this moment?
Lidia: At this moment the thought hasn't come yet, but I'm expecting one. I can feel it coming. Here it is.

With a very feminine gesture, she puts her hand on her head, as though to rearrange her hairdo. Pause. He tries to go on watching the show but suddenly turns.

Giovanni: Well, did it come?
Lidia: Yes.
Giovanni: Is it a pretty thought?
Lidia: No.

Giovanni: Tell me what it is.
Lidia: No.
Giovanni: Why not?

Instead of replying, Lidia, while continuing to look at him, arranges his shirt collar with infinite tenderness.

Lidia: Where do the Gherardinis live?
Giovanni: Their house is in Brianza. Half an hour by car.

The stripper comes very close to taking off her brassière, and they both watch her. The act is over.

Giovanni: Life would be more tolerable if there weren't any pleasures.
Lidia (smiling): Did you write that?
Giovanni: No, I ran out of ideas. I have only memories. Don't you want to tell me what that thought was?
Lidia: Later. *(Pause)* Why don't we go to the Gherardinis?
Giovanni: How come you've changed your mind?
Lidia: Oh, I don't know. One has to do something.

Giovanni summons the waiter.

Giovanni and Lidia drive through a gate into a wide driveway on the large grounds of a luxurious house, and park next to a group of other cars. They get out and stand there for a few moments, silently contemplating the surroundings.

Giovanni: Is everybody dead in this place?
Lidia: Let's hope so.

Lidia and Giovanni walk to the stone steps, then stop, undecided. They see a lawn party, all the guests standing around a horse. Giovanni notices a large book on the ledge of the staircase and picks it up. The title is *The Sleepwalkers* by Broch. He puts it down.

Giovanni: Who on earth would read *The Sleepwalkers* here?

Lidia barely looks at him, then turns toward the lawn party. A woman comes toward them.

Mrs. Gherardini: Mr. Pontano, I presume?

She holds out her hand, which Giovanni kisses quickly. She also holds out her hand to Lidia and, in a slightly condescending but affectionate tone, says:

Mrs. Gherardini: I'm so glad you came. We're having a sort of family affair. *(Indicating the horse)* We're celebrating his first victory. He's good. He belongs to my daughter.
Lidia: What's his name?
Mrs. Gherardini: Volfango. Dear old Volfango, he's such a good horse!

Mrs. Gherardini turns her head toward Giovanni and, while they walk toward the festivities, says:

Mrs. Gherardini: But you're very young! I thought . . . You know, reading your books, one pictures an older man with many years of experience.
Giovanni: Did you really read them?
Mrs. Gherardini: Good Lord, do I look like such a frivolous person? *(laughs)* Come, let me introduce you.
Lidia: That might get a little too complicated. Why not introduce ourselves as we go along?
Mrs. Gherardini: Yes, you're right. Let's do that.

Luckily, at that moment a woman's voice rings out from the darkness.

Berenice's Voice: Lidia!

Detaching herself from a group of persons standing near the horse, a woman of about thirty-five walks forward. She has a heavily powdered face and a dissolute manner. The woman approaches Lidia, smiling.

Lidia: Hello, Berenice.

Berenice: How are you?

Mrs. Gherardini: Do you know each other?

Berenice (to Mrs. Gherardini): Yes, very well: We've hated each other since we were two. *(to Giovanni)* Well, Pontano, at last!

Giovanni shakes her hand with a polite smile, without saying a word.

Berenice: Well, we finally succeeded in getting you out of your house!

Mrs. Gherardini turns to the man holding the horse and says cheerfully:

Mrs. Gherardini: All right, Antonio, put him to bed.

Some of the guests protest. A young woman takes a step toward the horse and objects:

Resy: Oh, no, please, he's so sweet!

Mrs. Gherardini: My dear, if he doesn't get his sleep he'll get nervous.

Resy: Just this time! After all, it's his party, isn't it?

Laughter. Mrs. Gherardini rebuts immediately:

Mrs. Gherardini: Well, what do you expect of him? He's only two! No, no, Antonio, to bed. I wouldn't want him to pick up any bad habits. There are plenty of temptations here. Go on, Antonio.

More laughter. Antonio leads the horse away. Meanwhile, Lidia watches Berenice, who is lighting a cigarette. That pale, almost macabre face, disturbs her. Berenice takes a puff, in a vulgar manner.

Berenice: Don't stare at me so hard, for heaven's sake. The evidence of all those years is on my face, I know. *(Taking Lidia's face in her hands)* You've improved a lot, you know! How did you ever do it? You used to be

so plain. Am I offending you by saying that?
Lidia: I've heard it so many times already.

Two women walk by, arm in arm. One says to the other:

Woman: You act just like a whore!

The other one breaks into raucous laughter.
Lidia breaks away from her friend's grasp and, as though trying to guide the conversation, asks:

Lidia: Are you married?

Berenice shakes her head.

Berenice: I live all alone. I was born to be alone. You can see I'm too sensitive ... But that's what my dentist always used to tell me! *(Laughs briefly)* What kind of life are you leading now? Do you hang around with intellectuals? We're in Milan, both of us, and never see each other.
Lidia: Oh, we don't get out much. Imagine, this evening was something of an exception: We went out to a night club for the first time in years.

They notice the edge of the swimming pool; its bluish color stands out in the darkness.

Berenice: Look how beautiful that color looks over there! *(Turning back to Lidia)* You know who I see quite often? Grimaldi. Remember her?
Lidia (interrupting) Oh, no, please!

She pauses, looking at the desolate spectacle of her old friend.

Berenice: No, what?
Lidia: Don't bring up old memories, will you?

Instead of replying, Berenice continues to gaze at Lidia with increasing tenderness.

Berenice: You're very lovely now. You've heard that before too, haven't you?

Lidia, obviously embarrassed, doesn't reply.

In another part of the grounds, Mr. Gherardini, an elegantly but conservatively dressed man around sixty years old, is showing two of his guests a bed of roses, which he lights up with a candlestick.

Mr. Gherardini: There are three thousand roses all the way to that wall over there. Look at the deep rich tone they take on at night.
A Woman: In your opinion, Mr. Gherardini, do roses sleep?
Mr. Gherardini (smiling): Yes, I'd say so. All night long! *(Turning to a waiter next to him)* Antonio, the scissors. *(Cuts a beautiful rose and gives it to the woman)* Here you are! Isn't that a beauty? It just awoke.

Gherardini cuts another branch, handing it to his wife, who arrives with Giovanni.

Mr. Gherardini: Here, Giorgina. Give it to Filippo. He's the only one who knows how to arrange it so it won't look like a funeral.

Some of the guests laugh.

Mrs. Gherardini: Did you see who's here?

Gherardini looks at him, but seems not to recognize him at first. Giovanni holds out his hand.

Giovanni: Good evening.
Mr. Gherardini: Ah, it's you. Wonderful. I'm so glad you came. I believe I've seen you once or twice, if I'm not mistaken.
Giovanni: Yes, but I don't remember where.
Mr. Gherardini: I don't either.

In the meantime, Mrs. Gherardini starts walking away, accompanied by a few guests and the lady with the rose and her companion.

Mr. Gherardini: Giovanni, I have the impression that you two aren't having a good time.
Giovanni: Want me to jump in the pool?
Mr. Gherardini: Why not? Dressed, or nude?

Gherardini takes a long look at Giovanni, as though to evaluate him. He likes Giovanni's appearance and takes him by the arm.

Mr. Gherardini: I'm extremely glad you came.

Giovanni gives an embarrassed smile and looks around.

Giovanni: Who built this estate?
Mr. Gherardini: The architect was Vietti. What do you think of it? Cesarino, where are you, Cesarino?

An old, very deferent man steps forward.

Cesarino: Here I am, sir.
Mr. Gherardini: Show the gentleman around a bit.
Giovanni: Thank you.

Giovanni and Cesarino move on.

Cesarino: Too bad it's dark. You won't be able to see the park, which is magnificent.

Meanwhile, Lidia and Berenice have reached another section of the grounds and are looking at a group of people seated on the grass.

Berenice: I'm going to Göteborg. Do you know that city?
Lidia: No.
Berenice: It's way up north; it's rather cold up there. But I have a boat.
Lidia: A boat?
Berenice: Yes. A yacht.

An elderly man greets her.

Berenice: That fellow is extremely rich. His debts must run into the billions.

Lidia, annoyed by this indirect kind of introduction, hardly glances at the man. Her attention is suddenly drawn to a tall, distinguished-looking man of about thirty-five who has just stepped out of a luxurious car. Berenice notices this.

Berenice: Do you want me to introduce you?
Lidia: Oh, no! Are you joking?
Berenice: He's an extraordinary man. Wait, I'll go get him. Roberto!

Lidia starts walking away.

Berenice: Roberto! Don't send me any more postcards!
You make me so mad.
Roberto: How are things?
Berenice: Not bad.
Roberto: I got back a few days ago.
Berenice: Poor darling!
Roberto: It was a business trip.
Berenice: Go on! Go on!

Lidia enters the house, takes a few steps around the
hall, and stops to look at a dark-haired girl (Valentina),
who is sitting on the stairs reading. The two women
stare at each other at length.

In the garden, Giovanni and Cesarino meet a woman.

Cesarino: This is our great benefactress from Rome.
Mr. Pontano, let me introduce you to Mrs. Gentili, who
is a specialist in orphanages.

It just so happens that Giovanni has a pack of cigarettes in his hand. Naturally, he offers her one. She first
refuses, but then changes her mind.

Mrs. Gentili: Well, all right, I *will* have one. I'll have
one because I see that everybody smokes here in Milan.

At that moment, Resy, a girl with a lovely figure and
in a dress with plunging neckline, approaches. Giovanni
can't resist looking down her dress. They introduce
themselves to each other.

Giovanni: I'm Pontano.
Resy: Giovanni Pontano? You mean the author of ...
(Looking at him ecstatically) What a marvelous book!
One of the best books ever written.
Giovanni: Well ...

He shifts from one foot to the other in sign of protest.

Resy: Want to know something? I've read it three times.

I'm in love with it. I really think I'm one of your great-est admirers. Certainly the greatest in Italy.

Giovanni shows his embarrassment.

Resy: Oh yes I am! I beg of you, please allow me that privilege.

Giovanni cannot help being amused. They walk toward an exquisitely prepared buffet. The girl feels a bit bolder.

Resy: I'd like to read a novel in which there was, for example, the story of a woman who meets a man . . . but the man doesn't fall in love with her. No. But he does admire her intelligence and her temperament. They start living together . . . and then . . . how could a story like that end?
Giovanni (embarrassed smile): In so many ways.

The girl concentrates for a second.

Resy: She would have to be a very exceptional woman and sacrifice herself. There's your ending: She sacrifices herself for another woman's happiness.
Giovanni: Why does she sacrifice herself?
Resy: I don't know. It makes me want to cry.

Lidia, still alone, is outside again. The band is playing. She watches some guests near the pool. Giovanni comes over and joins her.

Giovanni: What are you doing there?

Lidia shrugs her shoulders, not knowing what to reply.

Giovanni: Come on with the others.
Lidia: Yes, in a moment. Just a little while.

She looks at her husband and in a slightly ironical tone, asks:

Lidia: How do you like it here? Find it interesting?
Giovanni: So-so. (Pause. He looks at her) How is it that you never seem to enjoy yourself?
Lidia (astonished): I'm enjoying myself like this. (Pause. Points toward the house) There's another girl in there having a good time all by herself. She's the one who is reading The Sleepwalkers. Pretty, too.

Turning, Giovanni notices that Mr. and Mrs. Gherardini are coming toward them. Lidia, trying to avoid any more conversation with the hosts, skilfully moves away and heads toward the pool.

Mr. Gherardini: Well, Pontano, is everything all right?
Giovanni: I realized I didn't know anyone here.

Lidia would like to move farther away but, just then, she sees Roberto approaching. She turns back toward Giovanni and the others, who are lounging on lawn chairs conversing.

Mr. Gherardini: It's absurd to talk about wealth these days. There are no wealthy people any more. If anyone should, nevertheless, think of becoming rich, I have only one piece of advice for him: Don't concentrate on money. He should devote his attention to his business. When an artist works, he doesn't think about the money his work will yield; he'll think only about his work. I always looked after my businesses like works of art. The money they produced was almost immaterial. The important thing is to create something. Something that will last.

Giovanni hides his displeasure. Mrs. Gherardini smiles. Lidia leans on Giovanni's chair.

Mrs. Gherardini: Yes, dear, but not everyone is able to create something lasting. You . . .
Mr. Gherardini (interrupting): The thing that sustains a

writer . . . let's take you, Pontano, for instance . . . is certainly not the thought of profit, but a feeling of necessity. You write because you know it's necessary for you and for others.

Mrs. Gherardini: But, still, one has to live!

Mr. Gherardini: I never gave it a thought. Life is what you make of it with your own inventiveness. You, Pontano, if you couldn't write, what would you do?

Lidia: I think he'd commit suicide.

Giovanni (looking at his wife with surprise): I don't consider myself that important; perhaps there are other ways out. *(Pause)* How often the writer of today wonders whether writing isn't an irrepressible yet antiquated instinct. The work is so lonely, the work of a craftsman putting down one word after another painstakingly, a job which you can't possibly find a way to mechanize.

Mr. Gherardini: Are you convinced of that?

Giovanni: No. But you industrialists have the advantage of building your stories with real people, real houses, real cities. The rhythm of life itself is in your hands. The future is in your hands.

Lidia (as if to justify her husband): Today happens to be a particularly bad day for my husband.

Giovanni (to Lidia): I think you're right.

Gherardini makes a motion as if to indicate that time takes care of everything, then resumes the conversation.

Mr. Gherardini: Are you one of those many people who worry about the future? As for me, I'm building my own future. Actually, I have enough to do with the present . . . there's so much work. The future will probably never come.

Mrs. Gherardini: The future will be something *horrible.* Don't you agree? What are your plans for tomorrow? Why not stay here tonight?

Mr. Gherardini (softly): Darling, you're forever interrupting me.

Mrs. Gherardini: I'm sorry, dear. *(To Lidia)* Well, why don't we leave these two alone. *(To her husband)* Go on with your conversation. You were saying that the future will never come.

The two women walk toward the center of the park.

Mr. Gherardini: Hum! Who knows what the future has in store for us? Our privileges will be swept away, but it will be a good thing. Yes, a good thing. When I was a young man, I imagined a world like this in my mind, and I set to work with a similar future as my goal.

Lidia and Mrs. Gherardini approach the buffet tablet.

Mrs. Gherardini: Would you like something to drink?
Lidia: Yes, cognac.

The two women continue along and turn the corner into a very quiet part of the grounds, between one building and the next. Remnants of antique statuary are on the ground, in the grass. One of them is the head and bust of a boy, lying as though asleep with his eyes open. Nearby is a cat staring at him strangely. Hearing Lidia approaching, the cat turns momentarily around but goes on staring at the marble statue.

Mrs. Gherardini: He's been looking at that statue all day. He's looking right at its eyes. Who knows what that animal is thinking? Maybe he's waiting for him to wake up. Try and figure cats out.

Resy and Guido, an elderly male guest, approach.

Guido (in a low voice): Resy, leave me alone just for a moment.
Resy: Why?
Guido: Go away!

Meanwhile, Mrs. Gherardini pushes Lidia toward the large buffet table.

Mrs. Gherardini: Excuse me a moment. *(Walks up to Guido)* Ah! I finally found you!
Guido: Hello, my dear!
Mrs. Gherardini: How are you, dear Guido? It was nice

of you to come. You seem to have lost some weight.

Guido: Think so?

Mrs. Gherardini: How did you do it?

Guido: I decided to take a little exercise.

Mrs. Gherardini: Who is that girl over there, Guido? Are you two-timing me?

Guido: What a thing to say!

  Lidia gazes at the extravagantly laden table. She pours herself a little whiskey, adds a little gin, then vodka, and tastes it. It's awful, of course, so she puts it right down. As she is about to leave the table, she notices Roberto staring at her. They look at each other for a second. Lidia wonders what he will do next; but he simply looks at her without even an indication of wanting to strike up a conversation. Lidia looks away and moves on into the park.

Inside the game room, Giovanni watches Valentina playing a game. She turns around and says:

Valentina: Can't you find somebody to play with me?

Giovanni: Won't I do?

Valentina: No. Too old.

Giovanni: Yes, but if I start playing with you I'll become younger.

Valentina: I don't want to become rejuvenated.

Giovanni (surprised): Why not?

He waits, but no reply is forthcoming.

Giovanni: Come on, tell me why not.

No reply. Valentina continues playing.

Valentina: See, I would have won. In order to win, you've got to make the compact stop on one of these squares . . . the ones at the end.

Giovanni: What are we playing?

Valentina: Each one should decide in his own mind what he wants to win. After the game, we tell each other our wish. I'm Valentina.

Giovanni: Valentina, do you often lose at this game?

Valentina: I invented it just now. *(Pause. Then, with a serious expression)* One time I lost everything.

Giovanni: What game was that?

Valentina (with a vague gesture): Let's say that to win, you have to make at least seven points.

Giovanni: I'll be frank, then. I came here to talk with you.

Valentina smiles and shoots.

Giovanni: Good shot. But no pity.

He shoots.

Valentina: Too much pity, this time.

Valentina shoots again and strikes the target.

Valentina (laughing with glee): One for me!

Giovanni: My turn now.

Valentina: Yes, yes.

Giovanni gets ready to shoot, but hesitates.

Giovanni: I'm afraid.
Valentina: Oh, come on, come on!

Giovanni regains confidence and shoots, but the compact goes out of bounds. Valentina goes to pick it up and notices that a jewel is missing.

Valentina: One of the stones fell off.

Giovanni goes to the spot where the compact fell.

Giovanni: Oh, I'm so sorry! Let's find it.

He kneels on the floor and starts looking. Valentina looks also.

Giovanni: It couldn't have gone very far, could it?
Valentina: It could have landed in the garden.
Giovanni: Oh, no!

Valentina quickly gets tired of looking and gets up.

Valentina: It doesn't matter. It was only a real ruby.

Giovanni also stands up and looks at her in a serious manner.

Giovanni: Do you enjoy playing the role of a cynic?

Valentina takes in the blow and replies, very sincerely:

Valentina: No.

Soon afterwards, the room is filled with guests watching Valentina playing with Giovanni and making bets.

Spectators: Ten thousand on Valentina.
Fifteen on Pontano.
Fifty on Valentina.

Giovanni is about to shoot but stops when he hears another voice saying:

Voice: Sixty thousand on him.
Giovanni: Come, now. You're joking!
Guest: Go on, shoot.
Giovanni: No.

He gets up. Valentina watches his reaction with great interest.

Valentina (ironically): You're one of those who is only worried about those who lose. A typical intellectual: egoistic but full of compassion.
Giovanni: Now, this isn't a racetrack. And don't take me for a horse.
Valentina: Is there a friskier horse in the room?
Voice: Right here!

Lidia is on an open gallery upstairs. She moves on when she notices that Roberto is staring at her from below. She notices a telephone in a nearby room and, as though on an impulse, she goes there, lifts the receiver and dials a number.

Lidia: May I have information on Mr. Garani, Room 45.

Her face suddenly fills with consternation and grief. In a feeble voice, she asks:

Lidia: When? *(Then, repeating as though to herself)* Ten minutes ago! *(Pause. Her throat is choked with tears)* Was his mother with him?

She hangs up, her face wet with tears. From below can be heard cries and laughs from the game room.

Downstairs, everyone is rushing toward the stairs. The
hosts want to retire, and the guests are on their way to
bid them good night. The last to leave are Valentina and
Giovanni. He stops her.

Giovanni: Valentina, I'm a little disappointed.
Valentina: About me. How can I make it up? Shall we
read a few pages together?

She picks up *The Sleepwalkers* from a table.

Giovanni: Well, that would be one way of getting closer
together.
Valentina: Are you badly in need of a little affection?
Giovanni: Aren't you?

Silence. They look at each other.

Giovanni: You owe me a debt, you know. I withdrew
from the game.
Valentina: Let me enjoy this debt a little while first.
Giovanni: All right, but don't forget.

Valentina, who had started walking, stops.

Valentina: Bah! It's getting so I seem to forget some-thing every day.

Instead of replying, Giovanni kisses her tenderly. Lidia watches them from the gallery. Now Valentina returns his kiss. The two walk toward the stairs.

They pause briefly on the steps leading to the garden. On the lawn, the guests are saying good-bye to the owner of the house. Mr. and Mrs. Gherardini come for-ward. Valentina walks down the steps toward them and kisses Mr. Gherardini.

Valentina: Good night, Daddy.

Only then does Giovanni realize that she is the indus-trialist's daughter. He looks at him and makes a gesture as if to say, "Well, what can one do?"

Valentina and her mother walk toward the center of the grounds, while Mr. Gherardini takes Giovanni's arm.

Mr. Gherardini: Pontano, I wanted to make you a prop-osition. I could use a man like you.
Giovanni: Where?
Mr. Gherardini: I run a cultural program for my em-ployees. I want to give my business a shot in the arm. I noticed there's not enough communication between the management and workers. And do you know why? Because they don't know the history of the company. They know nothing about me, who founded it. You see: I want to set up a press, publicity and public relations department, but especially an internal program. For instance, I'd like to publish a brochure on the history of my company . . .
Giovanni: And you want me to write it?
Mr. Gherardini: Yes, but not only that . . . I want you to become one of our executives.
Giovanni: What do you mean, a full-time job, in other words?
Mr. Gherardini: That's right. Wouldn't you like to be

with us, sharing in the life of our company? If you don't mind my asking, what are you making now? I believe your wife is from a rich family, isn't she?

Giovanni: Yes. But I also have some money of my own. And then, I write an awful lot of material for newspapers.

Mr. Gherardini: I see, but wouldn't you like to be independent?

Giovanni: Independent in what way?

Mr. Gherardini: Now, you think about it, Pontano, just think it over. And don't forget that my company follows a principle of high salaries.

Valentina and her mother are walking arm in arm in the park. They stop with some guests at the edge of the golf course.

Mrs. Gherardini: Look at what one of my cousins gave me recently. She just got back from America.

She lifts her skirt up to her thigh, revealing a little striped purse attached to her garter.

Guest: What is it?
Mrs. Gherardini: A wallet. There's even a dollar bill inside!

The men look at Mrs. Gherardini's well-shaped leg. One of them comments.

Guest: You see how far the dollar zone reaches!

Everyone laughs. The lady of the house looks around her with a self-satisfied look and notices Lidia all alone at the edge of the terrace.

Mrs. Gherardini: Mrs. Pontano, how come you're all alone?

Valentina looks at the woman, surprised and disappointed to learn that Giovanni is married. Lidia seats herself apart from the group. Giovanni appears behind her. The two exchange the briefest glance. Lidia is still overcome by emotion. Giovanni sits down next to her.

Giovanni: Isn't it beautiful here!

He immediately realizes he has said something trivial and glances quickly at his wife. She would like to tell him Tommaso is dead. Her eyes are wet. But Giovanni gets up and walks away; Lidia doesn't stop him.

Giovanni notices Valentina rushing back toward the house and starts after her. As he passes in front of Lidia, the sound of her meek voice stops him.

Lidia: Where are you going?
Giovanni (embarrassed): I'll be right back.

The band starts playing in the park. The dance floor soon becomes crowded. Guests are eating standing in front of a table. Giovanni approaches the stableboy taking care of Valentina's horse.

Giovanni: Have you seen Miss Gherardini?
First Stableboy: No, I haven't seen her.
Second Stableboy: Me neither.

Giovanni walks away.

Lidia walks along, immersed in thought. She comes near the band and stops. The rhythm begins to have an effect even on her. She starts to sway with the music. A young man approaches her.

Young Man: Shall we dance?

She nods, and the two of them step over to the dance floor and begin dancing. Lidia suddenly stops, with a look of amazement on her face.

Lidia: Why, you don't know how to dance!

Young Man: That's right.

She bursts into laughter and goes on dancing by herself. The young man walks after her.

All at once, a clap of thunder resounds in the sky. Rain starts pouring down. Everyone scurries toward the open pavilion, including Berenice, who grasps Lidia's hand. But the latter withdraws her hand and runs toward the swimming pool, where many guests are headed. Several guests jump in; some are fully clothed, while others, seized by a kind of frenzy, strip first. Lidia, tempted to follow their example, climbs on the diving-board and takes off her shoes, when a voice calls her.

Roberto: Now don't be foolish.

Lidia obeys him and comes down. They head for the

car under the driving rain. As she is about to enter, she stops. She is soaking wet.

Lidia: Where are you taking me, anyway?
Roberto: Get in!

They get in. The car drives off.

The hall of the house is full of people. Many of them are playing cards in the barroom. The lights go out, and the house and grounds are illuminated only by occasional flashes of lightning. Giovanni moves around in the crowd, looking for Valentina. He is nervous and impatient. Resy stops him again.

Resy: Pontano, where are you going?

Giovanni makes a vague gesture.

Resy: Wait a moment. Why don't the two of us ever talk? Why don't you tell me something?
Giovanni: Later on, I'll come back to tuck you in and tell you a nice fairy tale.
Resy: Make believe I'm already in bed and tell me the story.
Giovanni: No, later. I'll tell you about a hermit, an intellectual hermit, of course, who had fed on dew for years until one fine day he comes in the city. They make him taste wine, and he becomes an alcoholic. How's that?
Resy: Terrible. I meant a true story, something that happened to you.
Giovanni: Believe me, I have had worse experiences than that.
Resy (musing): My, I wish I could understand . . . The things that go through a writer's head.
Giovanni (smiling, almost moved by her simplicity): What's your name?
Resy: My name is Maria Teresa. My friends call me Resy.

Giovanni: Resy, are you only interested in understanding writers?

Resy: Oh no, other men, too.

Giovanni: I think you'll have plenty of work on your hands, then. See you soon.

Giovanni walks away, still in search of Valentina.

Roberto's sports car drives slowly along a lonely, tree-lined road. Inside the car, Lidia and Roberto are talking and laughing. The car stops at a railroad crossing, where the gates are down. Roberto and Lidia step out of the car, protected from the rain by a large tree. They look at each other. The train goes by and the gates go up.

After a long silence, Roberto stretches out his hand and caresses Lidia delicately, smiling at her. He tries to kiss her. At the last moment, she pulls back, saying:

Lidia: I can't. I'm sorry.

Valentina and Giovanni meet in the darkness of the game room. It is still raining hard.

Valentina: I'm not one to destroy a household. At least as far as that's concerned, I'm judicious.

Giovanni looks at her without saying anything. His face reflects a serious mood.

Valentina: Now go back to your wife and stay with her the rest of the evening.

Giovanni: But it's my wife who originally sent me to you.

Valentina: That makes no difference. Pay me your debt that way.

Giovanni (with irony): Valentina, it's too dark. How can I find her?

Valentina (sorrowfully): I was very sad tonight, but I cheered up when I played with you. Now I feel that sadness coming back. I don't know why. It's like the sadness of a dog.

She makes an effort to tone down the intimate nature of the conversation.

Valentina: Do you have a cigarette?
Giovanni: No, I only smoke cigars.
Valentina: Excuse me then. I'll go get mine.

She moves away toward the stairs. Giovanni remains alone to watch the falling rain.

Valentina enters her room and calls a servant:

Valentina: Angelo!
Angelo: Yes, Miss.
Valentina: Bring another candle.
Angelo: Right away, Miss.

The servant walks away. Valentina lights a cigarette and stands there, lost in thought. As she turns, she notices Giovanni at the door.

Giovanni: I think there are still some things we have to say to each other.

Valentina: Of course, but ... *(Pause. Takes a few steps around the room, then comes back)* I think love places certain limitations on a person. Something creates a vacuum around him.

Giovanni: But not inside him. Even in novels, sentiment is back in style now.

Valentina: I get it. I see you're writing a novel tonight.

Giovanni: Oh! The way I feel right now, I don't know how I'll ever be able to write again. It's not that I don't know what to write, but *how* to write it. That's what they call a "crisis." Many writers go through the same thing nowadays. But in my case it's something secret inside me, which is affecting my whole life.

Valentina: You're just a weak man. Like me. *(Pause)* Why do you say things like that to me? I might not understand them, you know. Actually, my hobbies are golf, tennis, automobiles, parties ...

Giovanni: Is that all there is in life? *(Pause)* Don't you like other things too?

Valentina: Oh, yes. Everything.

She gets up and fetches a miniature tape recorder, which she places on the floor. Giovanni watches her, astonished.

Valentina (with a strange, melancholic laugh): Promise you won't make fun of me?

She turns on the tape recorder. Giovanni bends down and listens attentively to a recording of Valentina's voice.

Valentina's Voice on Tape: From inside the living room today, I heard snatches of dialogue from a film shown on television: "Stop that car ... A little more whiskey? ... If I were you, Jim, I wouldn't do it." After that sentence, I heard the howling of a dog, slow, sure, rising in a perfect arc and coming to a stop with a great sadness. Then I thought I heard an airplane. But there was silence again, and I was glad. The park is full

of silence made of sounds. Put your ear against the trunk of a tree and if you wait long enough, you'll hear a sound. Maybe it comes from inside us, but I like to think it's the tree. Then that silence was broken by strange noises disturbing the sound waves around me. I didn't want to hear them, so I closed the window, but the noises persisted. I thought I'd go crazy. I don't want to hear useless sounds; I'd like to be able to pick them as the day goes along. The same goes for voices and words. There are so many words I'd rather not hear! But you can't avoid them. You have to resign yourself to them, as you'll resign yourself to the waves of the sea when you stretch out to die.

She turns off the tape recorder, ashamed.

Giovanni: May I hear that again?
Valentina: I erased it. It's so silly.
Giovanni: Why did you do a thing like that?
Valentina: Because I don't take what I write very seriously. Besides, mother says it's bad for my complexion to stay cooped up all day long writing.
Giovanni: It's a crime to waste such intelligence.
Valentina: I'm not intelligent: I'm alert. That's a different story. It's enough for me to observe things, without having to write them. Last year we went to the United States to see Julia . . .

Giovanni: Who's Julia?
Valentina: The hurricane.

Giovanni laughs. They look outside at the rain, which has diminished in intensity. Giovanni turns serious again.

Giovanni: Valentina, did you know that we'll probably be able to see each other often?

Valentina looks at him inquisitively.

Giovanni: Your father offered me a job with his company.

Valentina (seemingly lost in her own thoughts): Last year I thought I was in love with a boy, but ... Well, who knows? There must be something the matter with me. Eventually I'll change. It seems that each time I try to ... *(Groping for words)* communicate with someone, love disappears.

Giovanni: Was that the time you "lost everything?"

Valentina: Oh, no! (Pause) But why do you want to work for my father? You don't really need the money, do you?

Giovanni: Don't I?

Valentina: What you need is a girl to make you feel younger again.

Giovanni: Not a girl. I need you. *(Valentina backs away)* Don't be afraid.

Valentina: I'm not afraid.

They are about to kiss, when the lights come on. Valentina releases herself immediately from his arms.

Valentina: See how ridiculous this is?

Giovanni and Valentina leave the room, laughing. They head for the bar and see Lidia and Roberto coming into the barroom from outside, both of them drenched. Lidia heads straight for her husband and Valentina without the slightest embarrassment. Giovanni is likewise not embarrassed. Valentina hesitates, then approaches Lidia.

Valentina: Come; you can dry yourself in my room.

She politely shows Lidia to her bedroom. Giovanni first stares at the two women, then gazes at the young man who came in with his wife. Roberto mumbles an embarrassed, "Sorry," and Giovanni goes into the barroom.

Seeing Resy eating a sandwich, he walks behind her and makes her jump.

Giovanni: My, are you prosaic! How can you eat a sandwich at this time of night?

Resy strains to understand him.

Giovanni: Did you know that D'Annunzio's turtle died of indigestion from eating flowers?
Resy: Oh, come now! Cut it out!

Giovanni walks away, shaking his head.

Giovanni: Funny thing! Tell them lies, and they'll believe you. But tell them the truth, and they won't.

Lidia and Valentina step into Valentina's room. Valentina gets Lidia a towel, but Lidia does not use it.

Valentina: You ought to remove your dress. It's soaking wet.
Lidia: Listen, Valentina. I believe that's your name, isn't it? I'd rather you didn't make all this fuss over me. Just tell me frankly what's on your mind. Don't worry about my feelings. I don't think it's part of your nature, anyhow.

After some searching, Valentina finally locates a hair drier and brings it to Lidia.

Valentina: Actually, there's nothing on my mind at all. Do just as you wish. If you want to dry yourself, fine. If not, then don't. No one's going to bite you.

Lidia looks at her with a sense of curiosity, then breaks out laughing. Valentina starts laughing also. Lidia begins to dry her hair.

In another room of the house, Giovanni is in a group with the millionaire whom Berenice had referred to.

Millionaire (pointing to Giovanni): But isn't our author having anything to drink?

Giovanni: No, thanks.

Millionaire: One day, in Venice, I had that American author over for dinner ... What's his name? ... You know, the one who hunts elephants.

Giovanni: I suppose you mean Hemingway.

Millionaire: That's the one! Very good! Now there's a man for you! A real artist. When I said to him, "Dear Mr. Hemingway, I like you. I'll visit you some day on your estate in Cuba," do you know what he said to me? "If you ever come to visit me, I'll shoot you on sight."

General polite laughter.

Millionaire: Now there's a man who certainly knows his profession. Earns as much as he wants. Millions of dollars! Nobody can turn up his nose at that kind of money, not even an intellectual.

Giovanni: It's pretty difficult to say what an intellectual should have, or what he should turn up his nose at.

Millionaire: My boy, never throw money away.

Giovanni drinks without replying. The millionaire shrugs his shoulders. Roberto, who had been listening to one side, steps forward and addresses Giovanni.

Roberto: My dear sir, ours is a vile age, an anti-philosophical one. It lacks the courage to come right out and say what is of value and what isn't. As for democracy, to put it very briefly, it simply means: Let things happen as they will.

Giovanni: I'm familiar with that quotation; it's from an author I respect. But used in this particular context, I find it somewhat offensive.

The millionaire looks at him in utter astonishment.

Millionaire: And why, may I ask?

Giovanni: Because this gentleman here expressed it with a certain amount of satisfaction, whereas the author had written it with a sense of despair.

Millionaire: But what really counts is what the author says, not what he means.

Lidia and Valentina are sitting in Valentina's room. The latter pours whiskey in two glasses, adding ice.

Valentina: Shall I tell you what happened, or avoid it?
Lidia: Please skip it.
Valentina: That's fine with me. I'm not much good when it comes to confessions anyway. *(Pause)* I wonder what is my strong point. Love isn't. Neither are vices. Oh, I have plenty of vices, but really don't practice them. I don't even like whiskey.
Lidia: I'm just the opposite: I think I've found the vice that suits me perfectly. It's so warm and good. *(Drinks)* How old are you?
Valentina: Twenty-one. Plus many months more.

Giovanni appears at the door and listens in without being seen by the two women.

Lidia: You don't know what it's like to feel the weight of all those years on you ... to find them no longer worth while. *(Pause)* Tonight I only feel like dying. I really do. It would at least put an end to all this agony. At least something new would begin.
Valentina: Or maybe nothing.
Lidia: Yes, maybe nothing.

She turns around and sees Giovanni. As though completely unconcerned, she gets up and says:

Lidia: Let's go.

Valentina, who didn't see Giovanni, lifts her head.

Valentina: Go where? Don't you think it's better ...

She stops short upon seeing Giovanni. Lidia joins her husband, then turns toward Valentina again.

Lidia: In spite of what I said before, I don't feel jealous at all. Not in the least. That's the whole trouble.

Valentina looks at them, embarrassed.

Valentina (sadly and ironically): I suppose you'll invite me to your apartment?
Lidia: Yes, when you get back from vacation. We'll see you in September.
Valentina: Oh, this year I won't be back until much later. Much later.

Giovanni comes closer to Valentina and gives her a long, affectionate hug. Lidia also walks over to her and gives her a kiss on the cheek. Lidia and Giovanni then return to the door and turn around again.

Valentina is standing against the French window. Dawn is breaking.

Valentina: You completely exhausted me tonight, you two.

Giovanni and Lidia walk across the lawn. She stops to say to her husband:

Lidia: Do you mind going this way?

She points to the direction opposite to the path they should take to pick up the car. It leads them back across the park, to the dance floor, where the band is again playing. They sit down near a bench where two women are seated. One of them is Resy, who is crying softly. Berenice looks at her.

Resy (sighing): Don't pay any attention to me. I'm just crying out of silliness.

Lidia and Giovanni walk on.

Giovanni: Want to hear a good one? Valentina's father offered me a job. An important position with his company.
Lidia: Will you accept?
Giovanni: I think I'll turn it down.
Lidia: Why? It's a good opportunity. After all, your life would finally be your own. *(Long pause)* A while ago I telephoned the hospital. Tommaso is dead.

Giovanni (shocked): When was this? Why didn't you tell me?
Lidia: You were downstairs, playing. *(Pause)* Was he really a good friend of yours? He was a lot more than that to me. He always looked upon me as a person who had a certain kind of power and intelligence which I don't have. Yet he was so convinced of it that I ended up believing it myself. *(Pause)* He spent so many days just sitting with me, trying to get me to study, even though I myself wasn't at all interested. I was so absorbed with my own petty problems. Yet he kept insisting, he kept insisting so much that he nearly drove me insane. It got to a point where I began to hate him

for it. And never ... not once ... did he talk to me about himself. It was always me, me, me. And I was the one who never understood. I was the one who thought so little of myself. When we're young, we're so foolish ... so ridiculously fickle and restless that we can't imagine anything could come to an end.

She finds a dry spot under a tree.

Lidia: You, on the other hand, started to talk to me right away about yourself. And for me this was something new. I was so happy, so conscious of what you gave me, that nothing in the world could have seemed more beautiful. Maybe it was because I loved you. It was *you* I loved ... not him. That's why his affection for me became something that annoyed me, and at the same time flattered you. Isn't that so?
Giovanni: Yes, but not to any great extent. He was so vulnerable.

Dawn is slowly breaking. Rays of light filter through the trees. The sound of the band can still be heard in the distance.

Lidia: The reason I feel like dying tonight is because I don't love you any more. (Moving nervously) That's why I feel so miserable. I wish I were already old and that my entire life had already been dedicated to you. I wish I didn't exist any more, because I can no longer love you. There it is: That's the thought that came to me when we were sitting in that night club and you were so bored.
Giovanni: But if what you tell me is true, if you really feel like dying, then it means you still do love me.
Lidia: No, it's pity, that's all.

They sit down on the grass. After a long silence, Giovanni starts to speak, as though to himself.

Giovanni: I never really gave you anything. I was never aware of it, even. Here I have been, and still am, throwing my life away like a fool, taking without giving anything in return, or giving too little. Perhaps I don't have a great deal to give. If that's what you mean, then you're right.

Now Lidia speaks, following his same line of thought.

Lidia: I used to spend entire afternoons reading in bed. Tommaso would come and visit me and find me still in bed. He could just as well have taken me in his arms . . . I wouldn't have rejected him. But he would be satisfied just to sit there and watch me while I read to him. All those books which served no purpose. Two hundred pages a day. I read them so quickly.

Giovanni looks at her with great tenderness.

Giovanni: I've been selfish. Strange, but only today do I realize that what we give to others always comes back to us.
Lidia (pointing toward the band): What do those fel-

lows think? That their music will make this a better day? *Giovanni:* Please, Lidia, let's drop the subject. Let's try to be realistic. I love you. I'm sure I love you. What more can I say? Come on, let's go home.

Lidia opens her purse and reads from a sheet of paper.

Lidia: "When I awoke this morning, you were still asleep. I came out of my slumber very slowly. I heard your gentle breathing, and through the strands of hair that had fallen on your face, I saw your eyes ... and my emotions were aroused. I felt like crying out and waking you up, for you were sleeping so soundly you almost seemed lifeless. In the shadows, the flesh of your arms and your throat appeared so vibrant, so warm and moist, that I wanted to press my lips against it. But the thought of disturbing your sleep, of having you awake in my arms again, held me back. Instead, I preferred to have something that no one could take from me, something that would be mine and mine alone: an image of you that would be everlasting."

While reading, Lidia is carried away by her emotions. Giovanni stares fixedly at Lidia, as though trying to identify the person described in the letter.

Lidia: "Beyond your face, I saw a pure and beautiful vision in which you and I were reflected in another dimension that encompassed all the years of my life, all the years to come, and even those before I met you, when I was preparing to meet you. That was the most miraculous part of this vision: to feel, for the first time, that you had always belonged to me. That this night would never end, but would go on forever, with you beside me ... with the warmth of your body, your thoughts, your willingness united with mine. At that moment, I realized how much I loved you, and the sensation was so intense that my eyes began flowing with tears. For I felt that this must never end, that we should remain like this for the rest of our lives, not only to be near one another but also to feel we belonged to each other—a way of life that could never be destroyed by anyone or anything, except the torpor of habit which is our only threat. (*Pause. Lidia's throat is choked with tears*) And then you began to wake up and, still half asleep, you smiled and put your arms around me. And I felt there was nothing to fear, that we would always remain as we were that moment, bound together by something stronger than time, stronger than habit."

Giovanni gazes at his wife with a bewildered look.

Giovanni: Who wrote that letter?
Lidia (*staring back at him, after a moment's silence*): You did.

Giovanni looks at her in silence, crushed by the truth which she has so nakedly exposed—that love no longer exists between them. Lidia herself appears profoundly shaken. Brusquely, Giovanni takes hold of his wife and

tries desperately to embrace her. He manages to kiss her, while she struggles to free herself.

Lidia: No! No! I don't love you any more, I don't love you any more!
Giovanni: Shut up. Shut up.
Lidia: Say it . . . Say you don't love me! Why don't you say it?
Giovanni (softly): No, I won't say it.

Lidia closes her eyes and allows herself to be embraced. A kind of carnal lust devours her, in remembrance of that which was and which will never be again.

The musicians play a slow number, in harmony with the melancholy dawn of this new day.

l' eclisse (the eclipse)

1962

translated by louis brigante

Credits

Director:	Michelangelo Antonioni
Cast:	Alain Delon
	Monica Vitti
	Francisco Rabal
	Lilla Brignone
	Rossana Rory
	Mirella Ricciardi
	Louis Seignier
Original story	Michelangelo Antonioni
and scenario:	Tonnino Guerra
	and with the
	collaboration of
	Elio Bartolini and
	Ottiero Ottieri
Music:	Giovanni Fusco
Director of Photography:	Gianni Di Venanzo
Designer:	Piero Poletto
Editing:	Eraldo da Roma
Sound:	Claudio Maielli
Assistants to the Director:	Franco Indovina and
	Gianni Arduini
Make-up:	Franco Freda
Cameraman:	Pasquale De Santis
Script Girl:	Elvira D'Amico
Production Supervisor:	Giorgio Baldi
Production Secretary:	Sergio Strizzi
Assistant Editor:	Marcella Benvenuti
Production Manager:	Danilo Marciani
Producers:	Robert and
	Raymond Hakim

A co-production film by Interopa Film-Ciniriz (Rome) and Paris Film Production (Paris)

The lights are still on inside Riccardo's apartment although it is nearly dawn and the early morning light is already starting to come through the open window. It is the beginning of a cool summer's day in the sub-urban section of modern Rome. The room is in a general state of disorder, with bottles scattered all over the tables and ashtrays filled with cigarette butts. The doors of the living room are wide open and one can see into the other rooms.

Riccardo is seated in an armchair, in shirtsleeves and open collar, staring at Vittoria as she paces slowly back and forth across the room. She has a tired expression on her face and appears anxious, nervous and uncertain as to what her next move will be. Riccardo gazes upon her with a look of infinite love: at her face, her eyes, her mouth, her hips, her legs, her breasts. She senses his eyes upon her and feels ashamed, as if she were being undressed. She continues to wander around the room. Then she turns and looks at Riccardo who seems lost in some kind of abstract serenity.

Vittoria: Well, Riccardo?
Riccardo: What's on your mind?
Vittoria: Everything we talked about last night.
Riccardo: I see ... Well, then, let's make a decision.
Vittoria: The decision has already been made.

Vittoria speaks in a tired voice, as if she has reached the very limit of her resistance.

Vittoria: Riccardo, I'm going.
Riccardo: Do you have somewhere to go?

Vittoria makes a gesture indicating her annoyance with Riccardo's insinuating remark. She gathers the empty glasses, an ashtray, a napkin, then picks up the pieces of a broken vase from the floor and takes them into the kitchen. When she returns to the living room, she sees Riccardo still sitting motionless in the armchair. He is staring straight ahead at a fixed spot in front of him. He seems not to have heard Vittoria come back into the room. She looks at him, amazed at the absurd expression of tranquility on his face. She turns around to look at herself in the mirror and sees her own face which is tense and lined with fatigue. Then she moves across the room again and comes into line with Riccardo's point of vision. He is now staring directly at Vittoria—a stare so blank that it makes him appear somewhat like a madman. Vittoria is momentarily frightened. She quickly turns away and walks over towards the window. Daylight is gradually flooding into the room and overpowering the artificial lighting. Vittoria looks out through the window: a ray of sunlight has already fallen upon the rooftop of a house across the way. She is suddenly overcome by that deep sense of irritation which is felt when one comes close to something desired but unattainable.

All of a sudden, she starts. Riccardo is unexpectedly standing next to her, having walked across the rug without making a sound. He takes hold of her arm in an attempt to embrace her but Vittoria withdraws. To justify his action, Riccardo says softly:

Riccardo: It's the last time . . .
Vittoria: No, Riccardo, no. Please don't.
Riccardo (angrily): But what is it you want me to do? Come on, tell me what you want me to do and I'll do it. I promise you, I'll do exactly everything you say. Find something for me to do for you when you're gone.

There is a heavy silence. Then Riccardo continues, this time with a certain tone of humility.

Riccardo: I wanted to make you happy.
Vittoria: When we first met I was twenty years old. I was happy then.

Dispirited, Riccardo moves away from her and goes out of the room. Vittoria continues to look through the window. Down below a maid is washing the sidewalk with a sprinkler. Several people pass by. A laugh is heard, followed by the sound of voices. Vittoria reaches for the light switch on the wall and turns off the lights. The room remains in shadows. Only a shaft of sunlight

is seen across the dining room table. Vittoria rearranges the objects on the table and places them all within the beam of light. The various objects form an abstract pattern, making weird designs on the surface of the table. Vittoria appears completely absorbed with the fascination of these designs. Then, as if suddenly aware that she has let herself be distracted at a time when she shouldn't, she shakes herself out of her stupor and looks towards the room into which Riccardo has vanished. Concerned with his silence, she goes into the bedroom but no one is there. Bewildered, Vittoria looks around the room. Suddenly, she hears the sound of an electric razor coming from the bathroom. She turns and walks towards the bathroom, stopping in front of the doorway. Riccardo is shaving in front of the bathroom mirror. He hears Vittoria approaching but ignores her completely.

Vittoria: Listen.

Riccardo stops shaving. Then he quickly passes the comb through his hair and precedes her into the living room. They both remain standing. Vittoria is visibly nervous and speaks in a clipped and hurried fashion.

Vittoria: I meant to tell you last night that I had brought you the translation of that German article.

She points to a foreign magazine lying on the table which has a few typewritten sheets tucked inside.

Vittoria: I'm sorry but I won't be able to do this work for you anymore. However, I do know someone who can do it for you. I'll ask them if you wish. Besides, it wouldn't seem right for me to continue with it ... Although, if you really want me to, I can finish it for you.
Riccardo: Is that what you wanted to tell me?

Vittoria ignores his question, as though she hasn't heard him. Instead, she looks around for her purse and eventually finds it.

Vittoria (decisively): Riccardo, I'm leaving.

Upset by her determination to leave, he quickly reaches out and takes hold of her hand.

Riccardo: Wait a while ...
Vittoria: What is there to wait for?
Riccardo: Wait ... Please wait for a while ...
Vittoria: Now listen, up until now we've avoided saying certain things to each other. Why must you insist on drawing them out of me now?
Riccardo: No, there are certain things you just wouldn't say to me. You're not cruel.
Vittoria: But I am cruel with you.
Riccardo: Perhaps, but that doesn't matter. Be nice to me now and tell me one last thing. Is it that you don't love me anymore ... or is it that you don't want to marry me?
Vittoria: I don't know.
Riccardo: Tell me ... When did you stop loving me?
Vittoria: I don't know.
Riccardo: But, then, are you really sure?
Vittoria: Yes.
Riccardo: So there must be a reason ... There has got

to be some reason ... I understand these things very well.

Vittoria: Yes, I know you understand them ... But I don't know.

Riccardo is frustrated once again and at a loss for words. His tone of voice is one of despair.

Riccardo: I wanted ...

Vittoria (interrupting): I know ... to make me happy. You've told me that before. But in order for us to go on I too would have to feel happy.

Taking advantage of this apparent concession on the part of Vittoria, Riccardo regains his confidence somewhat and immediately tries to embrace her in an effort to suddenly and miraculously win back her affection.

Vittoria: Please ... let's not start that all over again.

Seeing that Vittoria is definitely set on leaving him, Riccardo becomes panicky. He runs his hands through his hair and loosens his collar, then breaks out into a rage. Grabbing a jar from the table, he throws it violently to the ground, smashing it to pieces.

Riccardo: Is there somebody else?

Vittoria: No; I told you a hundred times no.

Riccardo seems to feel a certain amount of assurance in her remark, a thread of hope that he may still have a chance. In a more conciliatory tone of voice, he says:

Riccardo: Then may I phone you ... within a few days?

Vittoria: No.

She gets ready to leave, but momentarily hesitates, not knowing herself why she does so. Riccardo leans up against the side of the wall and turns his eyes away from her. Slowly Vittoria walks to the door, then turns around to look at Riccardo once again; he remains motionless and doesn't look at her. She finally leaves, gently closing the door behind her.

michelangelo antonioni

Coming out of the doorway of the house, Vittoria walks hurriedly along the street. Then she suddenly stops and gazes out over the square: the early morning light illuminates the buildings with a pure, cool brightness. Several young boys, dressed in American-style clothes with tennis rackets in hand, pass by. Vittoria senses a feeling of relief from the heavy strain she had suffered through the night. She resumes her step, but no sooner does she walk a few paces than a car suddenly pulls up alongside of her. It is Riccardo.

Riccardo: I thought ... You must excuse me for not even having offered to accompany you home. Get in and I'll drive you there.
Vittoria (irritated): Please, Riccardo, leave me alone.
Riccardo: Walking?

Vittoria gives him a look as if to say, "Why don't you stop bothering me?" But Riccardo completely ignores her and insists.

Riccardo: Come on, I'm going with you.

He climbs out of the car, while Vittoria continues to stare at him.

Vittoria: Why do you want to come with me?
Riccardo: I've always come with you in the past, so why not today?

Vittoria is thoroughly exasperated, but Riccardo's attitude is so full of good cheer and he is so outwardly calm that she feels completely helpless. Without bothering to answer him, she turns away and continues walking ahead. Riccardo catches up to her and proceeds to walk alongside of her. Then he takes hold of her arm, squeezing it slightly. Several early morning risers walk past them. Riccardo leads her along, almost nonchalantly, as if suddenly struck by a wave of euphoria.

Riccardo: We've never gone out together so early in the morning before, have we, Vittoria?

Instead of answering him, Vittoria quickens her steps.

Vittoria: Riccardo, look, I'm in a hurry. I've got to get home.
Riccardo: Is somebody waiting for you?

Although Riccardo says this in a casual way, they are both well aware of the anguish hidden behind that seemingly innocent remark.

Vittoria: There's nobody waiting for me. I just want to get home quickly.

Shortly thereafter, they are walking along another road. As they pass a bar, Riccardo turns to her and says:

Riccardo: Would you like to have some breakfast?
Vittoria: No. I'm not hungry, Riccardo. I'm not hungry.

Her tone of voice is more one of self-pity and despair for herself as well as for him, than one of anger. As they approach Vittoria's house, a rather sumptuous

modern apartment building, she almost drags him forward towards the doorway as he continues to hold onto
her by the arm. At the entrance, she turns to face him,
staring silently at him for a moment, hoping that his
insistent attitude will change. Instead, however, Riccardo smiles at her. Vittoria would have wanted a less
foolish and more sorrowful departure, a more dramatic
farewell that would have therefore been more definitive.

Vittoria: Well, it's good-bye now ... It was a terrible
night for me, too.

She tries to say something else but all she manages
to add is:

Vittoria: I'm sorry ...

Riccardo shows no sign of asking her why she should
feel sorry. In fact, he pays no attention to her remark
at all, absorbed as he is with his own absurd and seemingly indifferent attitude. He extends a hand to her,
saying:

Riccardo: Good-bye ... But no, let's not say good-bye
... Let's keep in touch with one another by phone ...
No, better not phone. Let's just leave it at that.

He turns around and walks away, without once looking back. Vittoria remains standing at the doorstep for
a few moments, looking after him as he leaves and
hoping that this farewell gesture of his would give some
meaning to the years she has spent with him and which
have passed by so swiftly. With this thought in mind,
she looks out over the surrounding area: the morning
is now well advanced and people are seen coming out
of their houses on their way to work. Vittoria turns
quickly and enters the building, exhausted.

It is almost noon in the business section of Rome. A
taxi stops in front of the Roman Stock Exchange, and
Vittoria climbs out of it. As she is paying the fare to

the driver, another car from behind starts blowing its horn, anxious to gain the right of way. Vittoria makes a gesture at the driver of the car as if to say: "Take it easy; don't be so impatient." Then she enters the building through the doorway reserved for the general public.

As soon as she comes inside the Exchange, she stops in her tracks for a moment, overwhelmed by the pandemonium of voices yelling and shouting from the center of the Exchange floor.

It is already midday and the stock transactions are moving along at an increasingly rapid pace. The brokers, the clerks, the runners are all shouting and frenetically dashing back and forth from the floor to the long line-up of telephone booths against the walls. The visitors, holding admittance slips in their hands and sitting within an enclosure directly behind the floor, are also in a nervous state of excitement. Most of them have their eyes fixed on the quotation board on which there appears a list of the names of companies and their respective stock values for the morning. Some of them are looking through small binoculars while others are squinting anxiously in an attempt to read and follow the numbers that are furthest away on the board. Vittoria moves up towards the wooden railing next to a bench where two men are kneeling and bending over with their bodies and arms extended outward towards the nearby telephone booths as they try to attract the attention of one of the brokers on the floor who is dashing hurriedly back and forth without paying any attention to them.

Vittoria is anxiously looking around for her mother among the rows of people assembled within the visitors' section. Finally, she sees her: she is a woman of about fifty years and carries in her hand a white, floral embroidered purse. She is absorbed in watching the quotation board and every now and then she turns to the person standing next to her and exchanges a few comments. As she speaks, she pushes her glasses up over her eyes in order to draw closer to the ear of the woman alongside of her.

Vittoria is waving her hand, trying to attract her mother's attention but doesn't succeed. The mother has now risen to her feet and is conferring with a young broker whose telephone booth is just a few steps away from the visitors' section. The young man is called Piero and we discover this immediately for we hear his name being called out by a page boy who comes running up to him from the floor. Piero breaks away from Vittoria's mother and returns to the phone. He is a young man of twenty-seven, with an abrupt and businesslike manner, and with a smart, clever look on his face.

Piero (on the phone): Hello ... there's been no trading of Generali yet ... it seems to be falling ... yesterday it was still going down ...

Snatches of his conversation reach Vittoria's ears. She has now stopped signaling for her mother's attention and is busily and curiously watching Piero's actions in the booth. Piero, meanwhile, has picked up another phone.

Piero: How much for Finsider? Eighty?

Suddenly, apparently struck by the nature of the information he has just received, he hands the telephone to one of his assistants standing next to him and rushes over to the floor where the bidding is taking place.

Picro (shouting): Finsider ... Finsider ... Finsider. Buying Finsider at fifty-five ...
Speculator (responding to the bid): Sixty ...
Piero: I'll buy five thousand ...

Other speculators in the group raise their hands.

Another Speculator: Take a thousand more from me?

Piero makes a motion signifying his acceptance, then starts shouting again.

Piero: I'll pay sixty-five.
Another Speculator (signaling to Piero): Two thousand.

Suddenly they all disperse and run towards the floor where the quotation for the Finsider stock is now being established. Piero comes tearing across the floor like a race horse. He stops in front of his boss, the broker Ercoli, grabs him by the arm and whispers into his ear:

Piero: I just bought five thousand at sixty and two thousand at sixty-five. The broker writes the figures down on his note pad and then begins shouting into the middle of the floor.

Ercoli: Finsider . . . selling Finsider . . .

Someone on the edge of the trading-post offers seventy . . . eighty . . . Ercoli puts up two fingers, signifying two thousand shares, to the broker who offered to buy at eighty. Then he starts shouting out the name of Finsider again. They offer eighty-two, then ninety. With a motion of his hand, Ercoli sells three thousand shares of Finsider at eighty-two and three thousand at ninety. Then he leaves the trading-post, walks over to where Piero, worried and anxious, has sat himself down on a nearby bench, and with a great sense of self-satisfaction, confirms the transaction.

Ercoli: Done.

Piero heaves a long sigh of relief, then gets up and

runs to the telephone booth where he is being called. Meanwhile, Vittoria's mother finally becomes aware that her daughter is trying to attract her attention. Vittoria comes over to her and the mother looks up and says:

Mother: What are you doing here?

Vittoria is about to say something but before she has a chance to speak, her mother turns away and lowers her eyeglasses down from her forehead and back to the bridge of her nose to check a market quotation that has just been posted on the board which is quite a distance away. Then she turns around again to face her daughter, but suddenly Piero comes running up to her and leans over to whisper something into her ear:

Piero: I bought the Finsider at sixty. Look at what it's worth now! Seems like it's skyrocketing today.
Mother: I've got two thousand shares of it myself.
Piero: Hold on to it . . . it's going up . . .

Regretful of having so rudely neglected her daughter's presence, the mother then turns to Vittoria once again and tries to make up for it by telling her something that she feels would please her.

Mother: "Danaro" means that the stock is making money . . . and "Lettera" means that it's not doing so well . . .

Vittoria looks at her without showing any interest whatever, as though the words her mother had explained were completely from another world. Having watched her closely from the side until now, Piero finally comes up to Vittoria and introduces himself.

Piero: You don't know me but I do know you. How are you?

As he says this, his mind is obviously on something else so that it doesn't seem at all unnatural for Vittoria not to respond.

Suddenly, the bell rings out and all the brokers immediately stop shouting and fall silent. Within a few seconds, the entire Exchange floor is filled with an absolute silence. There is a curious look of surprise on everybody's face over the fact of this most unusual occurrence. A distinguished-looking gentleman steps up to the microphone in the center of the floor and begins to deliver what appears to be an important announcement. His is the only voice that is heard in the silence of the hall while the telephones throughout the Exchange continue to ring on incessantly with calls coming in from all the principal cities of Italy, apparently unaware of the falling stock market in Rome.

Distinguished Gentleman: It is my sad duty to inform you of some very unfortunate piece of news. Our colleague, Vitrotti Domenico, died this morning as the result of an automobile accident.

Piero, Vittoria and her mother are listening attentively. The uneasy awkwardness of the scene, with this

voice that speaks of death and the telephones that keep ringing on and on, is fully reflected in the look on Vittoria's face.

Voice of the Distinguished Gentleman: My feelings at this particular moment make it most difficult for me to find the words that would properly describe our esteemed colleague ... All I can suggest now is that we pay our respects with a few moments of silence and meditation ...

Now there is not a sound on the floor except the ringing of the telephones. Piero leans over towards Vittoria and whispers into her ear.

Piero: It's like a moment of silence at a football game...

Stunned by Piero's cynical remark, Vittoria looks up at him and says:

Vittoria: Did you know him?
Piero: Sure ... but in a minute's time do you know how many thousands of lire are at stake here?

All of a sudden, the noises and the shouts break loose once again, and even Piero's last words are drowned out by the general hubbub that follows as everybody makes a mad dash towards the telephones to answer the incoming calls.

Vittoria's mother appears very worried. She turns to her daughter and, as if she had just this moment found a solution, says to her:

Mother: Why don't you wait for me? It's only a short while before closing time ... just a matter of minutes ...

She walks away from Vittoria without waiting for an answer and stops to chat with an usher and then with an elderly man who is leaning against one of the columns.

Vittoria stands there for a moment, watching these people who belong to a world that to her is absurd and incomprehensible. She also notices Piero in the nearby telephone booth: he is on the line again, shouting and screaming, secretly conversing with a group of men in an intimate manner that is somewhat equivocal. She takes a few casual steps around the hallway of the visitors' section, then slowly heads towards the door.

Outside the Exchange building, she stops under one of the porticoes. She regrets having come to the Exchange to look for her mother. To her the few minutes spent inside seemed like hours. Meanwhile, a number of people start coming out and finally Vittoria's mother appears. She comes up to her daughter and, taking her by the arm, leads her into a sunny street.

Mother: Do you want to know how much I made today?

Vittoria makes a gesture of indifference. Then, after walking ahead for a few steps, she forcefully tries to insert her own personal problems into her mother's tightly-closed world.

Vittoria: Mother, I must tell you something . . .

Vittoria's mother stops and looks at her, waiting to hear what she has to say. But then she is distracted by a fruitstand directly beside her. As she picks out some peaches and places them in the peddler's scale, she says to Vittoria:

Mother: Tell me, dear . . . tell me what it is . . .

But Vittoria no longer wants to speak. Instead, she turns away and remains silent. The owner of the fruitstand takes the peaches from the scale and places them into a yellow paper bag.

Fruitstand Owner: One kilo and twenty grams; that makes two hundred twenty lire . . .
Mother: What, do I have to pay for the twenty grams too?

Irritated and embarrassed, Vittoria intervenes.

Vittoria: Come on, let's go . . . Don't start an argument over twenty lire.

Vittoria's mother takes the bag of peaches and they continue on their way.

Mother: But you must remember that millions are made with pennies ... not with thousand-lira notes.

Up ahead, Piero is standing with a group of employees from the Stock Exchange. They are busy discussing the list prices and quotations of the market. As Vittoria and her mother pass by the group, Piero greets them with a slight nod of his head. Vittoria's mother takes her daughter's arm again as she asks:

Mother: Listen ... Where are you eating today? With Riccardo?

Vittoria stares at her mother and deliberately lies to her.

Vittoria: Yes, with Riccardo.

The mother looks at her daughter with an expression of loving tenderness that is somewhat mawkish. Then she gives her a little hug, ruffles her hair, and finally offers her cheek for Vittoria to kiss, but not without first heaving a sigh with which parents are wont to demonstrate their eternal dissatisfaction with the affairs of their children.

Vittoria is horrified by these manifestations of motherly warmth and affection, especially when displayed in public, but she feels she cannot refuse, so she hurriedly kisses her mother good-bye and leaves.

Later that night, Vittoria enters the door of her apartment and turns on the light. She tosses onto the bedroom table a program of an open-air theatre from which she has obviously just come. She has a package in her hand and begins to open it with care. She appears unusually alert and wide-awake. All in all she has had quite an unusual day. The object in the package seems to interest her enormously. It is a piece of stone, about twenty by thirty centimeters in size, on which there seems to be painted a kind of twig. It is a twig with a long leaf and upon looking at it more closely one sees that it isn't painted on the stone but actually something which has the design of a twig and which seems to be imbedded into the stone itself, a fine, delicate thing that seems to have been made by the wind or water. It is a small fossil.

After having looked at it as one who gazes upon an article one has just purchased and has liked very much, she places it on the bureau, and goes into the kitchen to get a hammer and some nails. Then she tries to drive a nail into the wall but doesn't succeed because the wall is much too hard. She tries two or three times, then finally makes it. The fossil is framed in a wooden frame and made so that it can be hung like a painting. As she is hanging the fossil on the wall, the doorbell rings. Surprised, Vittoria goes to the door and opens it. Standing at the door is a young woman, somewhat stouter than she should be for her height, in her nightgown. The woman smiles apologetically for having called at such a late hour.

Anita: Excuse me; it's me.
Vittoria: Anita, what's happened?
Anita: Nothing. But that hammering on the wall . . . you have no idea how much noise it makes. Giorgio was awakened by it and he took it out on me, complaining that my friends keep such late hours!
Vittoria: Oh, I'm sorry.
Anita: And tomorrow he's leaving to deliver an airplane. For two days now he hasn't talked about anything but that airplane.

Anita sits herself down in an armchair, and in so doing the belt around her waist tightens itself, so she loosens it.

Anita: Wow, I'm getting fat . . . If I could only give up sweets . . . But look at you, you're getting thinner and thinner . . . I don't know how you do it.
Vittoria: Yes, I'm getting thin, but internally. *(Anita laughs)* The other night I didn't get any sleep at all, and yet I don't feel a bit sleepy.

Anita: Did you have a good time?

Vittoria: Ugh ... we spent the whole night talking and talking ... And for what? I tell you I'm so sick and tired and disgusted, so dissatisfied ...

Her tone of voice becomes ironic, and fearing what she might say, she stops talking.

Vittoria: What can I say to you? There are days when it seems that having a piece of cloth, or a needle and thread, or a book, or a man, is the same thing.

The telephone rings. Vittoria is about to answer it but she hesitates. Then she looks at Anita, who immediately understands.

Anita: Do you want me to answer it?

Vittoria: Say that I've left.

Anita picks up the receiver.

Anita: Hello.

There are a few moments of silence as Anita listens to the voice at the other end of the line. Then she breaks out into a laugh, takes a few steps over to the window and looks out. There is a light on at a window on the third floor of the same building and in front of the window a young woman is standing there telephoning. She looks down and signals to Anita. Vittoria comes to the window and she too looks out. Anita turns to Vittoria.

Anita: She wants to know if we'd like to go upstairs and keep her company.

Vittoria: But I hardly know her ...

Anita: So what? *(Into the receiver)* We're coming.

Anita puts the receiver back on the hook and goes out of the apartment, followed by Vittoria.

Vittoria and Anita enter Marta's apartment. Marta greets them with a smile. The place is furnished in an exotic style: the walls are decorated with many hunting trophies, guns, swords, Mexican rugs, travel posters and photos of Africa and Indonesian villages, etc.

Vittoria: Today I've done nothing but meet new people.

Marta invites them into another room of the apartment, and both Vittoria and Anita follow her into the bedroom.

Anita: How come you're awake at this hour of the night?
Marta: When my husband's away I can't sleep very well ... and then with all this heat ...
Anita: But you should be used to it. Isn't it supposed to be hot in Kenya?

Marta answers by simply making a gesture which indicates both yes and no. Anita sprawls herself out on the bed, caressing the flesh on her arms as if she were surprised to find it always so smooth.

Anita: As for me, I sleep better when my husband's away.

Before Vittoria lies down on the bed, she looks at it admiringly.

Vittoria: Oh, how lovely ... it's so low and so big.

All three women find a comfortable position for themselves on the bed. Vittoria happens to find herself directly in front of a large photograph of a lake.

Vittoria: What lake is that?
Marta: It's near Nairobi. It's called Naivasha. That's us in the back, see? The place is full of tropical birds and hippopotami.

Marta speaks with a slight foreign accent, frequently using French and English words.

Anita: But aren't the hippopotami dangerous?
Marta: Oh no. They come out at night and eat in the dark. One hippopotamus alone eats an acre of grass.

Every now and then we had to go out and kill one of them.

Vittoria points to a small table made out of an elephant's foot.

Vittoria: That elephant over there . . . did you kill it?
Marta: No, my father did. But I was there when he killed it.
Anita: And weren't you afraid?
Marta: I was born there. Tell me, are you afraid of automobiles?

Vittoria gets up from the bed to take a better look at the things that are scattered around the room: pictures, objects, statues. She picks up a shawl and tries it on. Then she tries on a mask. She stops in front of another photograph on the wall that shows a mountain with its snow-covered peaks.

Marta: That's Kilimanjaro.
Vittoria: Well, well, the snows of Kilimanjaro.

Marta: Kenya is one of the most beautiful countries in Africa. It's more beautiful than Tanganyika, than Uganda, than the Congo, than Rhodesia ... Kenya has everything: snow, the desert, the jungle, the grassy plains ... There, there it is, the great grassy plains of Kenya ...

She points to a photograph on the wall that shows the picture of a wide area of grassy plains. Vittoria runs her fingers over the photograph, as if she were actually touching the tall grass itself; then she runs her hand upward on the photograph and feels the sky that is covered with majestic clouds. She experiences a great sense of grandeur, of freedom, of nobility.

Then Anita also gets up from the bed and both she and Vittoria try on different exotic masks and costumes. Vittoria blackens her face and, putting on various pieces of African jewelry, she subsequently does a wild and exhibitionistic African dance to the accompaniment of an exotic drum beat from a phonograph record. At a certain point, Marta becomes fed up and annoyed with their merry-making and brusquely puts an end to it.

Later, the three women are back in the bedroom again, discussing Africa and Marta's life in Kenya.

Anita: And how is it that your father hasn't come back?
Marta: He has his own farm in Kenya, his own horses, and he cultivates flowers ... But there is a possibility

that he may return. I'm afraid that something will break out in Kenya very shortly. They are all equipped with guns again.

She gets up to pour some whiskey in a glass and then adds a piece of ice. She turns to Vittoria and Anita.

Marta: Would you like some?

Both Vittoria and Anita make a gesture indicating they don't want any whiskey, and Marta continues:

Marta: We're sixty thousand whites there, understand, and over six million blacks who want to throw us out. Luckily, the blacks are still in the trees, they have barely lost their tails; otherwise, they would have already thrown us out.
Anita: Well, so they're still trying to do it, even now!
Marta: All I can say to you is this: that there are about ten leaders who have studied at Oxford; the others are all like monkeys, six million monkeys.
Vittoria: But if you say you like it down there then they must be charming monkeys.
Marta: Oh, come now; look at the Congo! As soon as they finish elementary school, they think they're statesmen . . .
Vittoria: Then let's give them a chance to finish high school.
Anita: Pardon me, but tell me, why did you go back to Kenya to have your child?
Marta: Because Kenya is my home. Besides, it was an extremely modern and up-to-date clinic.

There is a slight pause and in the silence a light slamming of the front door is heard. Marta jumps to her feet and runs out of the room. Then her voice is heard from a distance.

Marta's Voice: The dog has run away!

Vittoria and Anita go into the hallway and find that the front door is open.

Anita: But how did that happen?
Marta: If the chain isn't on the lock, he opens the door by himself . . . he's a real . . .

She goes out into the outer hallway and looks down over the stairway.

Marta: Oh, my God . . . My husband will go mad if he doesn't find the dog when he comes home.

Vittoria and Marta come out of the doorway of the apartment building and start walking down the street to look for the dog. Being in her bathrobe, Anita remains behind in the lobby.

Marta: Giorgio and I are very attached to each other. But there's this one wall between us: this place. You know, if it wasn't that I had to go out shopping to buy something, I wouldn't ever go anywhere.
Vittoria: Are you anti-social?
Marta: No, I'm not anti-social; it's just that I'm not with my people.
Vittoria: You mean the monkeys.

Both of them break out into a laugh. Then they go out into the middle of the street, still searching for the dog. The bark of some other dog is heard. Marta cocks an ear but it is silent again.

Vittoria: Maybe they think less of happiness down there. They're satisfied if things just go their way a little. Am I wrong?
Marta: No.
Vittoria: Here instead it's all so complicated. Even love. *(She pauses)* Look, over there!

From the corner of the street up ahead, a group of eight or nine dogs have appeared. Among them is Marta's dog. They are headed towards another street, as though they were going to assemble at a special meeting place.

Marta (calling): Zeus! ... Zeus! ...

The dog shows a sign of having heard; he seems temporarily caught in a moment of indecision, but then turns away and continues along with the other dogs. The dogs, which were headed in one direction, change their minds and turn off into another street.

Marta (to Vittoria): You go that way and I'll go around this way ...

Vittoria goes off into another direction to get in front of the dogs while Marta blocks the street they are heading towards. For a while, the chase after the dog ensues. At first, the dogs scatter off into different directions, then they gather together again, stop to take a pee, sniff the air, wag their tails. They appear perfectly happy and content to be wandering around in the night like this, in absolute freedom. Marta comes running up close to the group of dogs, but they soon spread out in all directions again. Zeus runs off into another street. But Vittoria is there, hiding behind a tree and waiting for him. The dog comes closer to her; he stops and turns around to see if he is still being pursued. Another dog joins with him and they seem to be exchanging ideas as to what their next move should be. At that moment, Vittoria makes a leap for the dog and grabs him by the tail. The dog whines a little, but Vittoria doesn't let him go.

It is late at night and Vittoria is asleep in her apartment. Aside from a few nocturnal sounds of the city heard in the distance, there is absolute silence. Suddenly, right below the window comes the sound of footsteps. They come and go, come back once more, then fade away again. They seem to have vanished but then return and stop once again directly below the window. A voice is heard calling softly. It is Riccardo.

Riccardo: Vittoria! . . . Vittoria!

Vittoria awakens. A few seconds go by, then Riccardo calls again.

Riccardo: Vittoria!

Vittoria stealthily approaches the window and peers out from behind the shutters. She sees Riccardo as he moves a few steps away from the window. Then he sits himself down on the curb and rests his head between his hands. Vittoria quickly withdraws herself from the window.

Riccardo is crestfallen. A few seconds later, he gets up and goes to the window again. He calls out again, this time a little louder.

Riccardo: Vittoria!

Inside her room, Vittoria has slipped into a blouse and skirt. She is somewhat frightened and feels it would be best to ask for some help. She opens the door of her apartment, goes out into the hallway and goes up the stairs. She stops in front of the door to Anita's apartment and raps lightly two or three times. She places her ear against the door to listen to a muffled but apparently heated discussion going on inside. No doubt Anita and her husband are having an argument. Vittoria hesitates, wondering whether to knock again or not. Then she decides against it and descends the stairs again.

Quietly and cautiously, she re-enters her apartment. She feels that she is caught in a trap with emotional feelings closing in from all sides. She picks up the telephone, which has a long extension cord attached to it, takes it with her into the bathroom, and closes the door. She dials a number.

Vittoria: Sorry, Giorgio . . . It's Vittoria . . . Please don't kid around . . . it's a serious matter . . . I've left Riccardo and . . .

Giorgio interrupts with a joyous exclamation.

Giorgio's Voice: You've left Riccardo!
Vittoria: Please, I beg of you, it's a serious matter. Right now Riccardo is downstairs, just below my window and I don't know what he wants . . . No, it's not necessary for you to come; if by any chance I do need you, I'll

call you back ... but I just wanted to tell you that this is a very difficult moment for him ... please try to stay close to him ...

Giorgio's Voice: I'd rather stay close to you.

Giorgio keeps right on talking but Vittoria has disappointedly stopped listening. She removes the receiver from her ear and now the voice on the telephone seems to be nothing more than a mechanical grumble. Vittoria hangs up. When she returns to the bedroom, everything outside is silent again. She goes up towards the window once more and opens it. The street is deserted. Riccardo has gone away.

A small private plane is heading towards the airport near the city of Verona. It is a beautiful day with a clear blue sky and a few white clouds here and there. Riding inside the plane are Vittoria, Anita, her husband, Nando, a man of about thirty-seven years, and another, younger man, the pilot. The cabin is comfortable and almost luxurious.

Vittoria looks out of the window and down below she sees the city of Rome rapidly disappearing into the background—a tiny spot on the countryside that spreads out wider and wider under the wings of the plane. Vittoria turns her eyes away from the city, which is by now far away in the distance, and with a sigh of relief, she gazes at the interior of the cabin. She looks up front at the control board on which the pilot points to the lever that turns on the automatic pilot system.

Vittoria: Tell me, what is the hardest job a pilot has when flying a plane?
Pilot: To reach his destination.

Vittoria laughs, then looks out through the window again. The landscape below is extremely beautiful: a river, a group of small villages, open fields, the approaching mountains. Vittoria feels emotionally bankrupt and at the mercy of any new sensation. She is

quite pleased with the idea of flying through the air
and if it weren't for that slight touch of fear, she would
feel completely happy.

The plane passes through a cloud, then a moment
later emerges once again against a clear and placid sky.
Vittoria looks down once more and sees a city not too
far away.

Vittoria: Is that Verona?
Nando: Yes, that's Verona.

A river, with villages scattered along its banks, comes
into view. The plane begins to circle downward and
within a brief span of time, it approaches the runway
and makes a perfectly smooth landing. A squadron of
American planes are flying up above and a few others
are landing on different areas of the airport. It is evidently some kind of training school for military pilots.

Everything on the ground is quiet and peaceful.
People are sitting around, relaxed and calmly watching
the planes as they take off and come in for a landing.
The atmosphere is completely different from that of
Rome, and Vittoria finds it very comforting as she
stretches herself out on a chaise longue. Anita, who
had gone into a nearby bar which was filled with American soldiers and in which a juke-box is playing some
popular American tune, comes over towards Vittoria
and sits down alongside of her.

Vittoria: How wonderful it is around here!

Back in the city of Rome, the doors of the Stock Exchange have just opened and the business of the day
is about to begin. Piero and his employer, the broker
Ercoli, enter the building and walk hurriedly through
the corridor on their way to the Exchange floor.

Ercoli: Go light on the orders. The market is slightly
inflated ... buy only very little at the outset ... As for
me, I don't like the attitude of those Russians ...
Besides, it's hot and people tend to let themselves go
just before the holidays.

Piero slides his hand into his pocket as if he had just remembered something, and pulls out a tiny portable fan. Handing it to Ercoli, he says:

Piero: Feeling hot? Here, try this.

Ercoli holds the little gadget to his face, pressing the small button that sets the fan in motion.

Ercoli: It's pretty ... looks like an electric razor. But can you imagine what the others would say if they saw me with this!

He hands it back to Piero.

Ercoli: Here, give it to Dino; he's more the frivolous type.

Reaching the floor of the Exchange, they go their separate ways to prepare for the start of the morning's activities.

The section reserved for the general public is practically empty. It is occupied by only one person, a gentleman of about fifty years, who is seated on top of the long bench behind the wooden railing that encircles the floor. He is a light-skinned man with a quiet look about him—obviously a veteran speculator who has prepared himself well in advance for the opening of the market. Placed directly before him, on the top of the railing, is a metal box with cigarettes cut in half, a white cigarette holder, probably made of silver, a black notebook and the stub of a pencil.

Piero is already out on the floor, shouting amid a group of other junior brokers who have gathered in one area of the hall for the exchange of bond receipts. He leans up against one of the columns and calls out:

Piero: Rossi ... Rossi ...

He is immediately approached by another young broker who is carrying a stack of bond receipts in his hand. Piero removes the rubber band tied around his own stack of receipts and they both proceed to exchange their fixed shares.

Piero: A thousand Finsider at seventeen ... I'm selling five hundred Fiat at five-fifty.

Piero then immediately pushes his way into another group of buyers who are yelling and shouting out various names of stock.

Piero: Delfino ... Delfino ...

A sixteen- or seventeen-year-old messenger boy, aggressive and dynamic, comes up to him.

Messenger Boy: I'll take care of you right away.
Piero: I'm selling Generali at one seventy-two and five hundred.

As the messenger boy pulls out the check-slips from the stack of papers he has in his hand, Piero says to him teasingly:

Piero: Really, what you need to get you moving is a woman.

The messenger boy gives him the slips, then rushes off, sliding across the floor.
A balding remittance man comes forward, shouting in a distinctly feminine voice:

Remittance Man: Anybody want to help themselves to what I've got?

Piero comes up to him, and says:

Piero: God, but you're an awful louse! I'll take five hundred Liquigas at four-fifty and three hundred Anic at sixty-seven ...

The two of them exchange slips, then Piero walks away shouting:

Piero: Anybody see Foscolo?
Foscolo: Here I am. I'll buy Viscosa at two-fifteen ...

Piero checks his notes.

Piero: At forty-five, not at fifteen . . .

Foscolo checks his slips.

Foscolo: But I have them down at fifteen.

Piero pulls out his notebook to verify the price.

Piero (showing him the notebook): There you are, forty-five . . . I've got it down in black and white.
Foscolo: What should we do?
Piero: Not very much we can do; let's split the difference.

The two brokers adjust the amount and exchange slips. Meanwhile, the Exchange broker in charge of the stock listings comes out of the bar that is connected with the floor of the Stock Exchange and goes towards the center of the floor. Behind him, all the investment brokers start moving into their usual places around the railing. He seats himself at a table and then places a few sheets of paper in front of him. The usher is ready at his right, directly in front of the clerk who controls the postings on the big board. To his left is another clerk who is in charge of the daily quotations. The Exchange broker glances at his watch, then leans forward towards the microphone.

Exchange Broker: Mediobanca one thirty-four and five hundred.

As if rocked by a sudden explosion, the place becomes filled with brokers shouting out bids. Even more distinguishable than the words themselves, which are spewed out in a rapid, staccato fashion, are the brokers' gestures as they raise their arms and thrust their hands and fingers outward. In all, it only lasts for a few seconds. Then several of them hurriedly scribble something in their note pads. Meanwhile, the usher presses the button that reports the new stock quotation on the big board: Mediobanca 134, 700.

That number is already on the lips of all the brokers, and the messengers, the remittance men, the assistants are busy on the telephones, communicating it to all of Italy.

Piero is speaking long distance with a brokerage house in Florence.

Piero: Hello . . . Hello . . . Mediobanca has opened at seven hundred . . . Do you want me to do anything? Try to buy several hundred shares of it?

He places his hand over the receiver and makes a motion with his hand to somebody outside of the booth.

Piero (shouting): Dino . . . Dino . . . Hey . . . Hey . . .

Dino is at the trading-post, moving among the group of brokers assembled around the railing in order to get within earshot of Piero's voice. He is fanning himself with one of those tiny portable fans—a gift from Piero. After Piero relays a message to him with a gesture of his hand, three fingers down, he turns back to his party on the line and continues:

Piero (his eyes on the big board): Ninety . . . Finsider is opening up . . . ninety-two . . . ninety-four . . .

He repeats the quotation over the phone as he hears it coming over the loudspeaker. Then he covers his ear with his hand to block off the voice of the assistant who is standing next to him and is speaking over the other phone with somebody in Lucca.

Piero: Tell me. . . what's happening with Viscosa in Milan . . . Hello . . . hello . . . Vita opened at fifty thousand.

Motioning to the assistant to give him the phone call from Lucca, he places one hand over the Florence call and starts talking with Lucca. He moves further inside the booth to escape some of the noise coming from the floor.

Piero: Lucca? . . . Yes . . . there's a little leeway . . . seven hundred Mediobanca . . . ninety-four Finsider . . . fifty thousand Vita . . .

Then, leaving both phones dangling, he runs to that part of the floor where the small investors are busily transacting their business on the sidelines. He leans over towards the group of speculators and shouts out to them:

Piero: Vita, Vita, Vita . . .

With pad and pencil in hand, he stops in front of a group of investors but nobody is willing to take his offer. Other brokers come forward, shouting in a loud voice: "Finsider, Finsider . . . Mediobanca, Mediobanca, Mediobanca . . ."

Piero (beckoning to one broker trading Mediobanca): Let's have the Mediobanca. How much?
Broker: Seven hundred and two.

Piero makes an obscene gesture at the broker's price and shouts back:

Piero: And three.

Looking disinterested and slightly frustrated, he walks away from the area. Then, taking a long slide across the marbled floor, he returns to his telephone booth and places the receiver to his ear. Meanwhile, Vittoria's mother has entered the Exchange floor and walks over to the section reserved for the public. She stops at the usher's counter for a moment to sniff out the mood of the market, and, in a skeptical tone of voice, as if muttering to herself, she says:

Mother: Doesn't smell like anything much today.

Slowly, she ambles over to the large table in the center of the floor, fanning herself with a postcard, glances at an usher passing in front of her and says to him:

Mother: Why don't you sprinkle some perfume around this place? It could stand some fresh air.

The usher pauses for a moment and makes a gesture indicating that he doesn't quite understand what she is driving at.

Usher: What kind of air?
Mother (emphasizing her reply with an eloquent gesture): The kind that comes out of a spray.

In the meantime, a woman wearing a black hairnet comes up to greet her. The woman is shaking her hand to loosen the bracelet around her wrist.

Woman: Have any good tips for today, Nina?

Vittoria's mother barely gives her a glance, then moves away from her as she snaps back in a sharp tone of voice:

Mother: Yes, I do, but I keep them to myself.

Then she stops in front of a distinguished-looking gentleman standing nearby and says to him:

Mother: She certainly has some gall! Just like a rattle-snake . . . So, how are we doing?
Gentleman: For me, it's been pretty bad. All the stocks I sold yesterday are going up today.

Vittoria's mother gets closer to the railing of the floor and settles herself in a corner towards the right. She pulls out a small cellophane bag from her purse, opens it and sprinkles a white powder onto the floor, and starts to spread it around with her feet.

Mother (to the man next to her): Touch it; go ahead, you touch it, too. This salt should bring us some good luck.

The man accepts the offer and he too slides his feet over the salt on the floor. Meanwhile, Vittoria's mother searches around in her purse, takes out her eyeglasses, puts them on and starts checking the price quotations that have already been posted on the big board.

Mother (muttering to herself): That Catani stock moves like a snail's antenna—it keeps going up and down.

She pushes her eyeglasses up over her eyes and rests them on her forehead, then sidles up to a nervous old woman standing close to her and asks:

Mother: Sold anything yet?
Woman: Yes, a few shares of Marelli.
Mother: You did a smart thing; it's only a second-rate stock . . . You know, I didn't sleep a wink last night . . . I sat up all alone, by myself.

Then she goes back to her place behind the railing, which is only a few steps away from Piero's booth. Nearby, leaning up against the railing in the corner, is the solitary gentleman with the white cigarette holder whom we already have had occasion to notice before the market opened. He turns to one of the brokers, indicating with the appropriate gesture that he is not to breathe a word to anyone about the secret agreement they apparently had arranged between themselves earlier. Vittoria's mother kneels over on the bench in order to get closer to Piero who is shouting into the telephone.

Piero: Hello . . . what is it . . . four thousand and sixty for Sviluppo . . . Look, I'm on for two thousand Fiat . . . They should be worth about five hundred.

He feels someone tugging at his jacket sleeve. It is Vittoria's mother and he gives her a cursory nod but doesn't pay any attention to her. Meanwhile, Ercoli comes up to him. He appears quite calm.

Ercoli: Let me speak to the manager.
Piero (into the phone): Marco, will you please call the manager to the phone for a second.

Piero hands the phone over to Ercoli who enters the booth to carry on a private conversation with the person on the other end of the line.

Finally, Vittoria's mother succeeds in winning Piero's

attention. She whispers something into his ear and they start conferring for a while. Because of the loud clamor on the floor, we are only able to hear the first few sentences.

Mother: Did you see how well the Rumianca stock is going today?
Piero: It looks like they've developed a new kind of toilet soap.

Ercoli, meanwhile, is speaking on the phone in a low, subdued voice.

Ercoli: . . . Every once in a while they loosen up a bit. It's a rather weak market . . . a little unsteady . . . Did you manage to get any inside information from the Senator? . . .

Having completed the call, Ercoli leaves the telephone booth and heads towards the floor while an assistant distractedly untangles the telephone wire. In the meantime, another phone begins to ring. The assistant lifts the receiver and immediately turns it over to Piero.

Assistant: It's Milan calling.
Piero: Hello . . . Hello . . . Go ahead. What? Viscosa? It just opened . . . For how much? One hundred points under?

Piero dashes out of the phone booth and runs over to where a group of speculators are busily engaged in trading shares. Other brokers arrive there before him, coming from all the various phone booths. They are all shouting out the firm name of Viscosa . . . Viscosa . . . Viscosa . . . With his note-pad in hand, Piero keeps moving about.

Piero: I'm selling Viscosa at seventy-seven . . .
Another Broker (shouting): Selling at seventy . . .
Piero: Selling five zero.

Nobody seems to pay any attention to his offer, so

he turns and rushes over to the floor and calls out:

Piero: Dino . . . Dino . . .

He spots Dino, grabs him by the scruff of the neck and says to him:

Piero: Viscosa is falling in Milan . . . one hundred points under . . .

Dino hurries off towards the floor to inform Ercoli. In the meantime, the Exchange broker is announcing over the microphones the new price for Viscosa on the Roman stock market.

Exchange Broker: Viscosa eight-nine-nine-zero.

All the brokers on the floor gather around the railing of the floor and excitedly begin negotiating their bids. They are all selling. None of them are buying. The stock is falling lower and lower. Now even the small investors are trying to dump their Viscosa stock.

Voice From the Floor: Eighty . . . seventy . . . sixty . . . fifty-two . . . forty . . . thirty . . .
Mother (muttering to herself): They ought to murder him!

A crowd of people gather around the railing, and some of them start signaling for their brokers. A tall, thin man grabs hold of his broker by the lapel of his jacket and asks him:

Man: Should I hold on to the shares for a little while longer, or should I dump them right away?

The broker pulls himself away from his client, then in a loud voice so that everybody in the crowd can hear him, he says:

Broker: Be calm, now; don't get excited. There'll be trouble if we start dumping our stock all at once.

Then he turns and goes away. Worried and upset, the thin man finds himself in front of Vittoria's mother who looks at him and says:

Mother: You've always got to do exactly the opposite of what they say ... They're all against us. They'd shoot at us even behind our backs.

The Liquigas stock also starts falling rapidly, going down one hundred points. The new quotation that appears on the board is received on the floor of the Exchange with a cry of panic on the part of the investors. Ercoli is near the telephone booth, having it out with Piero.

Ercoli: I've been telling you ever since this morning to keep your buying light. Don't accept any more orders. Stop right now. If you're feeling dizzy, better go and get yourself an aspirin.

Piero steps inside the telephone booth and dials a number. He appears extremely nervous and upset.

Piero: Hello, operator? Now if you don't get me Florence right away ...

In the meantime, Ercoli is back at the trading-post where the bidding to sell has assumed dramatic proportions. The broker in charge of the board listings leans over to the microphone on the table and announces:

Broker: La Centrali 22,500.

Ercoli makes a motion with his hand.

Ercoli: Selling at 22,000.
Another Broker: I'll give it at 21,000.
Ercoli: I'll give it at 20,000.

At that point, the trading explodes into a wild turmoil of shouting and yelling.

Several hours later, all the departments of the Stock Exchange are overrun with people. There is an incredible wave of excitement. The general hubbub on the floor is augmented by the panic that spreads throughout the floor as all the small investors start shouting at the top of their lungs, pleading and begging with their brokers—calling to each other, looking around for advice, consulting with each other, exchanging gestures of anger and frustration. Troubled faces cry out to their brokers and buyers. Women scribble excitedly in their notebooks. Piero is clinging to the phone, speaking to Milan. He is nervous and exhausted.

Piero: Please, don't insist. They're not selling anything here . . . it's out of the question.

Someone grabs him by the sleeve. It is Vittoria's mother. She appears extremely worried and upset.

Mother: Tell me, what's happening? What should we do? Should we sell out?

Piero forcefully tears himself free from her grip. He is obviously very irritated, and he hands the phone over to an assistant.

Piero: Here, get me Zennaro 358269 . . . *(then turning to Vittoria's mother)* If you sell you'll only make the prices drop further . . . Now you tell me what to do . . .
Mother: No, no, I didn't mean that . . . I meant to try selling it in Milan or Genoa . . . In other words, some place else . . .
Piero: But it's like this all over Italy. What would I tell them?

The assistant hands the phone back to Piero.

Assistant: It's Zennaro.
Piero: Well, I finally got hold of you . . . You're one helluva wizard! After all that doing, you've managed to get the market really falling . . . At what price did you find out about Viscosa? At nine thousand? It could go

to twenty thousand ... Yes, yes, anything you wish, but from last night to this morning you've recovered everything, and with interest ... Very well, every two hundred points under, I'll cover you ... from five hundred.

Piero hangs up and comes tearing out of the telephone booth, running as fast he can to the section of the floor where a group of small investors are gathered.

Piero (shouting): I'm buying Viscosa ... Viscosa ... Viscosa ...

A number of the brokers turn around. Vittoria's mother pushes her way through the crowd around the trading-post and nervously inches along towards a small group of people who are animatedly conversing among themselves. She hears some snatches of dialogue here and there, but is unable to discover the reason for this unexpected break in the market. She looks up and sees a man waving his arms in a gesture of despair, addressing himself to his broker.

Man: Sell ... Sell out ... It doesn't matter anymore ...

Further up ahead, another group of people are arguing among themselves. She bypasses them and stops to look at an old pensioner who comes up to a group of small stockholders, huddled around a column.

Pensioner: The New York market is weak ...
Another man: Even Frankfort is selling ...

Vittoria's mother grimaces with disgust. She moves away from the group, muttering to herself:

Mother: Yes, Frankfort-on-Main.

She then approaches a man who is looking up at the board with a pair of binoculars.

Mother: Those people over there are talking about Frankfort, but it's always them, always the socialists who spoil everything.

She continues on and passes alongside an extremely worried-looking woman who is wiping the perspiration from her brow as she speaks excitedly to a young messenger boy hurrying by.

Woman: I've been signaling you for an hour! ...

Then, upon seeing Vittoria's mother, she turns to her and says.

Woman: And what do you have to say about all this, Nini?
Mother: What can I tell you, my dear. This place reacts to everything that happens ... Even the Pope can make a wrong move.

She turns around, sees an old man with white hair passing by, runs after him, takes him by the arm and starts speaking to him in a low and very excited voice.

In another area of the Exchange, a distinguished-looking gentleman beckons to an usher who comes running up to him. They exchange a few brief words which are not heard, and then the usher runs over to Piero's telephone booth, says a few words to Piero who hurries towards a quiet corner near the checkroom where the gentleman is waiting for him.

Piero: Do you have any instructions for me, Sir?

The gentleman has a cold and detached air about him.

Gentleman: Tell Ercoli that I don't intend to increase my losses. If necessary, try to strike some kind of average.
Piero (somewhat servile): Anything else?
Gentleman: Is there any talk about bonds being put up for loans?
Piero: There seems to be an offer of three hundred thousand in treasury bonds ... but it may only be a rumor ...

On the board the stock quotations for Chantillon,

Marelli, Stet, Bastoge are all going down. On the floor, the brokers continue shouting excitedly. The small investors crowd around the railing and try to get as close as possible to the remittance men and the messenger boys who are shuttling back and forth across the floor. The place is in a general turmoil. Many are no longer able to control their rage. One angry man throws an empty cigarette pack into the trading-post. Others follow suit and start flinging note-pads and pencils at the brokers assembled inside the enclosure. A woman tosses in a paper fan. The ushers try to restrain the more excited ones but right at that moment Vittoria's mother hurls two telephone directories into the middle of the group of brokers. Fortunately, they don't hit anyone. One infuriated usher immediately comes up to her.

Usher: Madame, did you throw a telephone directory . . .
Mother (irritably): No, I threw two of them!

Then she walks away into another crowd of people, cursing in a loud voice:

Mother: The pigs . . . They get rich on us . . . The whole thing is a plot . . . They're so disgusting . . .

In the section reserved for the public, the sense of desperation takes on a tragic tone. A woman is standing alone on the side, in tears. Another one sits there silently, staring out into space.

At that point, Vittoria enters the Exchange. Apparently, news about the market collapse has reached her ears and she has rushed down to see about her mother. As she comes onto the floor she stops near an excited woman who is frantically searching for something in her bag.

Vittoria: What's going on?
Woman: What is really happening here is that some of us have been taught a lesson by the loss we took today. From now on, we will pay attention to keeping our houses in order.

Vittoria turns around and glances at the visitors' section which is in a state of great confusion. She also notices that Piero's booth is empty, with only the telephone receiver left hanging on the handle of the door. Aware that one of the persons from the visitors' section, after having pushed an usher aside who had tried to keep him behind the railing, has entered the area reserved for those with special permits, Vittoria also pushes her way in and starts mingling with the people in the reserved enclosure.

Still looking around for her mother, she nears the railing that divides the public from the floor, at which point Piero comes upon the scene.

Vittoria: Have you seen my mother anywhere?

Piero stops for a moment but only to shrug his shoulders as if to say he has more important things to worry about at this time. Becoming more and more concerned, Vittoria starts walking around the area until she finally reaches the exit. There she stops to look at a group of people who are crowded around the columns. She then quickly switches her gaze to an usher who is fretfully rushing towards the central table, carrying a glass of water. He hands it to a young man who is seated at the table and who has a happy grin on his face. He drinks the water down in a single gulp, then says as he looks around him:

Young Man: This time I've really struck it rich ... I've finally made it ...

Vittoria stops a short, bald-headed man nearby and asks him:

Vittoria (pointing to the young man): What happened to him?
Bald-headed Man: That one! He's a vulture who speculates on lows.

Vittoria is bewildered by the answer. Everything seems so absurd and incomprehensible to her. At this point, she spots her mother in a corner of the check-room, seated apart from the others. She has an extremely worried expression on her face, her hair is down over her eyes, and she appears completely dazed. Vittoria watches her in silence for a moment, and although her mother is aware of her daughter's presence, she doesn't react.

They are about to cross the threshold, when the mother notices a group of people heading towards the steps that lead up to the main offices of the Stock Exchange. Vittoria's mother suddenly becomes reanimated, and approaching one of the old men in the group, she asks:

Mother: Where are you going?

Without further ado, Vittoria's mother joins up with the group. But before she does so, she turns around to her daughter and says to her:

Mother: I'll see you at home.

Vittoria watches the group of people disappear behind the glass doors of the Exchange. Then she turns around and looks back at the Exchange floor: it is a picture of desolation. Her gaze wanders across the area and comes to rest upon one of the telephone booths. Seated inside the booth, on a little stool, is Piero. He too is spent and seems to have lost his usual verve. He notices Vittoria standing there and he smiles. Then he gets up and comes over to her. Vittoria looks at him somewhat surprised and chagrined, but her sense of indignation is really very slight and filled with a deep curiosity.

Vittoria: Is what's happening today very serious?
Piero: With money everything can be repaired ... but for many it is a complete disaster.
Vittoria: And what about my mother?
Piero: It shouldn't have been too much of a blow for your mother. She probably lost around ten million lire ... When you stop to consider that in Italy close to

eighty billion have been snatched out of the people's hands. *(pointing to the fifty-year-old gentleman with the white cigarette holder whom we have seen earlier in the day)* For example, see that man over there . . . Well, he's lost two to three hundred million.

Vittoria looks at the man with amazement. He is standing there, dumfounded, and with a completely empty expression on his face, staring out into space. He glances at Piero as he walks by, greets him, then moves away as though he were no longer able to stand the sight of that place and those people so alien to him and his ways.

Almost hypnotically, Vittoria walks away from Piero and starts to follow the man as he leaves the building. His walk seems almost strangely assured, his appearance normal. Vittoria sees him crossing the street and entering the drug store at the corner of the square. Curious, she keeps following him and she too goes into the drug store. She stops at the counter as if she had intended to buy some medicine, but instead she is actually studying attentively this man who has just lost two to three hundred million lire and who is now whispering something to the clerk. The clerk searches for an item inside the counter, then comes up with a small packet and hands it to the man. He pays for it, then leaves. Vittoria follows him. Outside now, he seats himself at one of the sidewalk tables in front of a café. He orders something from the waiter, as Vittoria comes up closer, stops and remains off to one side. The man takes out his handkerchief and blows his nose. Then he removes his beret, puts it back on again, and finally opens the little packet he has just bought a moment ago — two little white pills which he places on the table in front of him. Then he asks the waiter who is serving him his coffee to bring him a glass of water.

Vittoria manages to get up closer so that she can observe him better. But instead of drinking either the coffee or the water, the man is busy writing something on a small slip of paper. He seems to be concentrating on it with great intensity. Suddenly, he stops and puts his pencil away. Then he swallows the pills, gets up and, putting down the amount of money to cover the bill, he leaves without even having touched his coffee. For a moment, Vittoria watches him as he leaves, then she sidles over to the table he has just left and picks up the slip of paper to see what he has been writing. With the slip in her hand, she enters the café. Piero and Ercoli are at the counter finishing an aperitif.

Ercoli: Well, was I right or wrong when I told you to trade light with your clients?
Piero: However, I always saw to it that they gave me some kind of guarantee.
Ercoli: But be very careful. They'll either have to give us some other kind of protection or we'll have to refuse them.

Ercoli places his empty glass on the counter and leaves the café. Piero remains behind, absorbed in his thoughts. Then, as he turns around, he sees Vittoria coming into the café and smiles at her.

Piero: Can I offer you something to drink?

Without waiting for her to reply, he goes over to the public telephone which is occupied by a small and meek little woman who is quietly speaking into the receiver. Without excusing himself, Piero leans over the woman's shoulders and inserts a coin into the phone. The woman looks up at his arm extended over her head, then glances at him and says into the receiver:

Woman: I'll say good-bye now ... somebody else wants to use the phone ... yes ... good-bye ...

She places the receiver back on the hook, then turns around but Piero is no longer there. He is back at the counter with Vittoria.

Piero (to the barman): An iced coffee.

Vittoria shows him the slip of paper she has in her hand.

Vittoria: Look, he drew a picture of some flowers.
Piero: Who?
Vittoria: The man who lost all that money.

Piero looks at the slip of paper briefly and then shakes his head as if to say: what foolishness! Then he goes over to the phone again and dials a number. Vittoria looks at him furtively and then turns to the barman who has just placed an aperitif down in front of her. She picks up the glass, looks at it, then puts it down again without drinking any of it. The barman looks up at her. Beaten down as he himself is, he feels a solidarity with Vittoria's black mood.

Barman: It was pretty bad this morning, wasn't it?

Vittoria raises her eyes, pretending to understand him. Meanwhile, Piero returns and the barman pours him his iced coffee. But Piero is busy eating a sweet roll and ignores his coffee.

Vittoria: Don't you ever stand still?

Piero looks at her in amazement.

Piero: And why should I stand still?

He goes over to the cashier to pay the bill, and when he comes back to Vittoria, she says to him:

Vittoria: But all those millions that are lost in the market ... where do they go to?
Piero: Nowhere.
Vittoria: But if someone wins, he gets the money.
Piero: That's right.
Vittoria: He gets someone else's money, doesn't he?
Piero: No.
Vittoria: But if he loses, then where does the money go?
Piero: It doesn't go anywhere.

Two people enter the café, engaged in an animated conversation.

Man: What I don't understand is that the only stock which didn't go down is XY ... it's a small stock that nobody ever buys.

Vittoria loses her patience, and suddenly makes a motion to leave.

Vittoria: Well, I've had enough!

As she begins to go out of the café, Piero follows her.

Piero: I'll come with you ... Where are you going?
Vittoria: To my mother's place. Where do you want me to go? You know she's not the type that draws pictures of flowers ...

As they walk away from the café, she tears up the slip of paper and throws it into the wastebasket. They cross the street, weaving in and out of the traffic. The commotion in front of the Exchange building has died down considerably. Vittoria stops in front of a young vendor who is selling chamois cloth for polishing cars. She picks one up and gives it to Piero.

Vittoria: Here, I feel like giving you a present.

Piero smiles as he holds the chamois cloth in his hand.

Piero: But I already have one.
Vittoria: Now you have two.

She is about to walk away but is stopped by the young vendor who says to her:

Vendor: This way I'm the one who's giving the present.

Realizing she has not paid, Vittoria smiles and starts to give him the money.

Vittoria: Oh, excuse me. How much?

She pays and walks away, followed by Piero.

Piero and Vittoria are in her mother's bedroom, standing in front of a bureau on which a number of mounted photographs are lined up as though on an altar. One of them shows a man with Vittoria's mother, another has the same man by himself. Still another photo shows them together on a trip. Then there are wedding pictures. In these photographs is the story of a love—a love between poor people. The background in one of the pictures reveals a sordid neighborhood, and standing in front of the door of a shack is Vittoria's mother when she was young.

Vittoria turns to Piero who is there beside her, looking intently at the photographs.

Vittoria: I've never been able to understand this kind of mania. *(Piero looks at her as if he does understand)* I'm sure my father doesn't mean a thing to her anymore. And even so, she still keeps asking herself if his death wasn't too much for her. They say he was so strong.

Piero laughs gently. There is a moment of silence.

Vittoria: I don't remember him. I was much too young.

She picks up the photo that has the sordid neighborhood in the background and shows it to Piero.

Vittoria: This is what my mother is afraid of: poverty. That's the thing.
Piero: Everybody is afraid of poverty.
Vittoria: No, not me. I don't think about it ... just like I don't think about getting rich.

She moves towards a door that leads into another room. It is a bedroom and there are small pictures hung along the walls. A spare room, dusty and seldom used. Piero looks in from behind her.

Piero: Is this your room?

Vittoria looks over the room with both horror and tenderness.

Vittoria: How I've changed!

She throws herself down on the bed, which is so small that her feet stick out at the end.

Vittoria: Look at this, I don't know how I was ever able to sleep here.
Piero: Maybe you were much smaller then.
Vittoria: Not really. My mother says that I was much taller as a child.

They laugh. Piero comes up closer and sits down on the edge of the bed. He tries to kiss her but Vittoria is quick to dodge him and she immediately jumps to her feet. At that point, her mother comes in through the door. She looks tired and worried, and her hair is disheveled. She shows no surprise in seeing them together.

Vittoria: Oh, you're here.

Vittoria immediately returns to the living room, as Piero and her mother follow behind her. Meanwhile, the mother is saying to Piero:

Mother: I'll give you some of my jewelry as collateral. Have you eaten?
Piero: Yes, thank you, I have.
Mother: Then I'll go and prepare myself something to eat.

It is late afternoon inside Ercoli's brokerage office. Ercoli is seated at his desk with his elderly secretary beside him. They are checking over the files of their clients.

Ercoli: Let's take a look at how our clients stand ... beginning with those who have the most investments.

The secretary takes out a folio from the files and settles herself in front of the telephone. Ercoli gets up from his desk and goes into the waiting room where

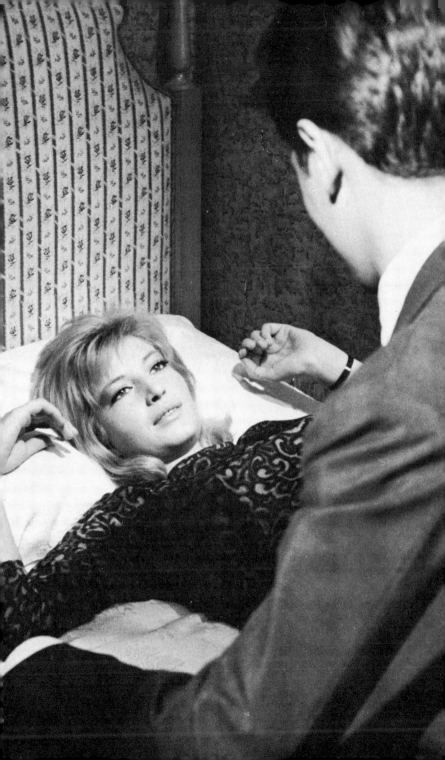

he finds a group of about ten clients. Some of them are standing around while others are seated in chairs. They are all expectantly waiting for some bit of good news that might give them a glimmer of hope. They all appear so tired and worn-out that they don't even have the strength to protest any more. As Ercoli appears, they all gather around him.

Ercoli: Now don't forget that the stock market reflects an industrial situation that remains essentially sound. The economic situation is good too. And the rate of capital is still very high. It seems that the foreign markets are going to step in and give us a helping hand. Switzerland is buying...

A client who is seated with his head between his hands looks up and comments:

Seated Client: That country always buys.
Another Client: I'll bet somebody's behind it—the Ital-

ian financiers and perhaps even someone in the government.

Ercoli: Well, anyway, somebody's buying . . . and then the Bank of Italy is extending a little extra time to those who are in shaky positions. And, of course, there always remains the hope that the Ministry will decide to do something.

He opens a door near him and enters the office where the various company employees are at their desks. Beyond the open door is Piero, busily computing some figures on an adding machine. He tears off the strip of paper with the total amount, looks it over, then hands it over to Ercoli.

Ercoli: Hm . . . we're a little heavy. *(Pause)* Say, what are you doing about Tonini?
Piero: I sent him a telegram.
Ercoli: Where did you have it sent?
Piero: To Riccione—they'll find him . . .

Ercoli is irritated.

Ercoli: What! But how can you, at a time like this, let clients leave town without getting their forwarding addresses?
Piero: I'm not the one to let them leave . . . they go on their own.
Ercoli: And I have to put out four million lire. I just don't know . . . You're so intelligent, so smart and so shrewd . . . and yet every now and then you do something like this.

Saying this, Ercoli turns and walks away, the long strip of paper from the adding machine trailing on the floor beneath his feet. This carelessness in a man ordinarily so calm and collected is an indication of his enormous concern.

Piero (calling out): Franco, bring me those records.

A girl appears with a folder in her hand which she

places on Piero's desk in the middle of a bunch of tele-grams, pencils and memoranda. Piero looks up at her, after having reached out to pick up the phone.

Piero: How come Franco isn't here?
Girl: He went out to buy some stamps.

The girl is about to leave but Piero stops her.

Piero: Can you tell me what's going on over there? You're all angry just because you have to work late. But what can I do about it?
Girl: Who's saying anything?

Piero picks up the phone and dials a number. He speaks into the receiver, balancing it in between his shoulderblades while using both hands to sharpen his pencil.

Piero: What are you doing tonight? Am I going to see you? *(Pause)* I don't know. Wait for me at the usual place. Don't keep telling me to be on time. If I'm late, just cool off and have an ice cream. What else can I say? Good-bye. Bye.

He puts back the receiver, leaving his hand to rest on the telephone for a while. Then he looks up and sees that a client has entered the office. She is a woman of about sixty, with heavy make-up and dyed blonde hair. It is the same lady we saw in the Stock Exchange wearing so many bracelets around her wrists. Piero jumps up from his desk, angrily.

Piero: Now, look here . . . I don't even want to speak to you . . . How can I make you understand . . . Now that you've lost, its my fault. But what about the other times? You never came around before. You just took the money and good-bye. You may have your troubles, but I also have mine . . . You'll just have to make the best of it . . .

Saying this, Piero disappears into the office next door to speak with the other employees.

Many hours have passed by. It is now late in the evening. Piero is in his shirtsleeves, with his tie loosened around his collar. His face shows signs of much fatigue. He is accompanying a pretentiously distinguished client to the door. The man is in tears, and he stops in front of the door which Piero has hastily opened.

Client: But give me some assurance ... Don't force me to sell ... don't make me just throw it all away ...

Piero: Now listen, you can't speculate on my hide and with my money ... It's all very simple: if the market goes down I pay ... if it goes up, you're the one who gets the difference. Do you think that's fair?

Client: I know it's not fair but tell me, what am I supposed to do about it?

Piero (pointing to his wristwatch): It's taken until ten o'clock for me to explain to you. Besides, when you first came to me you only had two hundred thousand lire ... You remember that, don't you?

Client: Sure ... sure, I remember ... What's right is right ...

Piero: In the past two years I've made you earn seven or eight million. Then I told you to stop, but you wouldn't listen. You got a little too hungry. And now where have those millions gone to? Did you buy anything with them?

Client: No, nothing. I didn't buy anything. I hardly had a chance to look at the money before it was gone.

Angered, Piero opens the door and pushes the client out.

Piero: Then it's your own fault. You've got to raise it somehow by yourself. Cough it up!

Piero manages to get the door shut, then remains standing at the door for a while, almost as though he were trying to catch his breath back again. Finally, he goes through the waiting room and re-enters the large office where the other employees are seated and collapses into his armchair.

Inside the office, a waiter who was apparently called a short time ago is pouring some refreshments into a

334

michelangelo antonioni

number of glasses on a tray that is resting on the top
of a desk. A few street noises creep up through the
open window and break the silence of the office. The
elderly secretary and Maria, another young employee,
are getting ready to leave. The messenger boy and Dino
are sitting quietly in the corner of the room.

Dino (To the two women who are leaving): Aren't you
going to have something to drink?
Secretary: Well, just a drop.
Dino: How about you, Maria?
Maria: At this late hour I've even lost my appetite.
Piero: I know why he's so angry ... And it isn't over
yet ... It'll be the same tomorrow night ...

Meanwhile, Ercoli appears in the office. He seems
deep in thought. He stops in the middle of the floor and
says:

Ercoli: A little weeding out once in a while does a lot
of good. Only the better clients remain ... those who,
God willing, don't have so many anxieties.

He goes over to the tray, selects a glass of beer among
the various refreshments and walks over to the window.

Ercoli (after the first sip): Bardini just phoned ... He's
lost a hundred million and he didn't even bat an eye-
lash ... What a guy!

Piero is still slumped in his armchair. He looks up
and signals for the messenger boy to bring him an
orangeade.

Piero: Please ... I don't have the strength left to lift
a finger.

The messenger boy brings him the orangeade and
Piero drinks it down slowly and with his eyes half-
closed, as though he were thinking of something far
away. Then he rouses himself from his sluggishness,
jumps up, goes to the window, looks down and then

rushes out towards the door. Dino looks up and asks him:

Dino: Where are you going?
Piero: I have a sweet little chick waiting for me down-stairs.

Out on the street, in front of the office, a beautiful young girl, elegant though somewhat slightly over-dressed, is leaning against the wall and looking into a store window. She appears quite annoyed and dis-couraged for having waited so long. Piero runs to her.

Piero: Am I late?
Girl: Do you want me to say yes or no?
Piero: Whatever you like.

As if seeing her for the first time, Piero looks at the girl from top to bottom: at her purse, her hair, her dress. Somewhat startled, the girl puts up with his curious stare for a brief while, then makes a gesture as if to leave. Piero stops her.

Piero: What did you do? Did you dye your hair?

The girl breathes a sigh of relief.

Girl: Just a little lighter; don't you like it?
Piero: When I first met you, you were a brunette ... then little by little you became discolored.

He resumes staring at her. Piero's reply has dis-couraged the girl once more.

Girl: Oh, we've started well!

She makes a gesture indicating she is about to leave. Many people are passing by and the men turn around to look at the girl and her beautiful figure. Piero con-tinues staring at her as if he were absorbed in thinking of something or someone else. The girl turns to him and, seeing that he is still scrutinizing her, she becomes quite annoyed.

Girl: Will you stop it!
Piero: Sure ... sure ...

Then he waves his hand as if to say good-bye and offers to shake her hand. The girl doesn't budge.

Girl: Shall we go?
Piero: Where do you want to go?
Girl: And what are we going to do here?
Piero: You're right. You go and I'll stay here.

Insulted, the girl abruptly leaves. Piero remains there for a while, absorbed in his thoughts. Then he goes towards his car which is parked nearby and climbs in. He starts the car, swings it first to the right and then suddenly changes his mind and turns to the left.

Piero's car proceeds along at a slackened pace through an empty, dim-lit street. The row of houses along the roadway are landscaped with tiny but well-kept garden plots. The lamp posts are partially hidden among the foliage of the trees.

The car pulls up to the curb and comes to a stop. Without removing the key from the dashboard, Piero climbs out of the car and walks along in an effort to locate Vittoria's house. The faint tap-tap of a typewriter is heard in the silence of the night. Piero turns a corner and discovers that the sound of the typewriter is coming from a half-opened window in a small but fashionable apartment house. The room inside appears to be lit by a small table lamp. From where he stands, Piero can only see a wall with a shelf on which some books are scattered pell-mell. There is no sign of any-one or anything outside of the continuous tap-tapping of the typewriter.

Piero is almost about to leave, but his attention is suddenly attracted by the appearance of an elegant young blonde who is coming out of the gateway of the building. The tap-tapping of the typewriter stops. The young blonde closes the gate and climbs into a car that is parked in front, without once glancing up at Piero who is standing nearby. But neither does Piero give her more than a fleeting glance. Then he moves up closer to the lighted window of the apartment from which the sound of the typewriter had apparently been coming. Still no typing, the silence is profound.

Someone approaches in the dark, a young man who has obviously had too much to drink. His face is slightly swollen, his eyes glassy, and he is unable to walk a straight line. As he passes, he looks up and smiles at Vittoria in the window, and in a gruff, alcoholic but serious voice, he says:

Young Man: Hello, dear.
Vittoria: Hello. And who are you?

The young man waves good-bye and goes his way. Then Piero approaches the window.

Piero: Good evening.
Vittoria: 'Evening.
Piero: What are you writing?
Vittoria: I'm translating some material from the Spanish.
Piero: How do you say in Spanish that I want to come up to your apartment?
Vittoria: You say that you can't come up. Spanish is an ugly language, isn't it?
Piero: I can't understand why one should waste his time on this.
Vittoria: Neither can I.

Vittoria and Piero laugh, but soon their laughter is drowned out by the roar of a starting motor.

Piero: I'll bet that's my car.

Before he has a chance to say anything else, he spots his car as it comes speeding down the street. He makes a futile attempt to stop it but is forced to jump back as the car whizzes by, driven by the same drunken young man who had just spoken to Vittoria.

Piero: It's that drunk we just saw go by. Did you see him in the car? He had to take *my* car!
Vittoria: Sorry.
Piero: Where's the police station?
Vittoria: I don't know.
Piero: Are there any taxis?
Vittoria: I'll phone for one.

Vittoria disappears into the room.

A small crowd of people are gathered around the edge of the embankment on a stretch of road that runs along the side of a lake in the EUR section of Rome. They are being held back, without offering much resistance, by two patrolmen. Two men from a towing service are operating a large crane that is pulling Piero's car up out of the lake. The car is a few yards underwater and a diver is hovering over the area, guiding the crane operator. The surface of the water is illuminated from below by the headlights that were on when the car ran off the embankment and into the lake. The car in the water is like some sort of magnet that draws the total interest of the crowd assembled there. Off to one side of the road is an ambulance.

Piero is there, talking to one of the servicemen. Everybody is pushing and shoving to get a better view. Even Piero is trying to get up closer, though he is also watching the road for Vittoria who now comes walking into view. Piero comes up to her and greets her solicitously.

Piero: Hello.
Vittoria: Hello. Where is it? Let me see. You were right in insisting that I come.

She too is as curious as the other spectators and she is about to head towards the edge of the embankment when Piero stops her.

Piero: Yes, but I didn't know that there was a corpse in the car.

Vittoria: A corpse? You mean the man we saw last night?
Piero: It must be him.

Vittoria is stunned with horror. But, as is often the case, this very sense of horror drives her to further curiosity. She gets up closer as the crane starts lifting the car out of the water. Everyone is silent as the automobile emerges from the water.

Hanging over the driver's seat is a limp hand. The rest of the body has apparently fallen to the floor of the car.

Vittoria shudders. She covers her eyes and turns away. Piero is about to follow her but is distracted by a loud thump and a brief outcry which is soon drowned out by a sudden burst of laughter. One of the curiosity seekers who had gotten too close to the embankment during the general confusion has fallen into the lake. As he is being helped out of the water by one of the divers, a group of people in the crowd are laughing at the comical incident. They continue laughing even as the car is lifted completely out of the water with its tragic cargo: the tense atmosphere has been broken.

Piero and Vittoria walk away from the scene. They go ahead for a few paces in silence; then Piero turns to Vittoria and says:

Piero: It must have sunk to the bottom very slowly. There's not even a scratch on it.
Vittoria: Is that what you are worried about—dents?
Piero: No, I'm also worried about its motor. Between one thing and another, it'll take at least a week to have it fixed.

They continue walking, again in silence. Then Piero casually asks:

Piero: How are you?
Vittoria: Fine. And you? How was the market this morning?
Piero: A little better than yesterday. Only that this business has made me waste a lot of time. Somebody came to me this morning and asked if I was the owner of the

car, how come it was stolen, the number of the license plate, etc. . . .

Vittoria: I'm wasting your time too. Isn't that so?

Piero: You! No. I had to come here anyway.

Vittoria laughs. Piero realizes that he has committed a *faux pas* and he tries to make up for it, but before he has a chance to do so, Vittoria says:

Vittoria: Instead I, like a fool, was the one who came to see you.

Piero now smiles, beguiled, his vanity satisfied. But Vittoria suddenly becomes serious. In the meantime, they have come in front of a café at the entrance to the subway. Many people are seated around the little out-door tables along the terrace. They are drinking their refreshments and listening to a record played on a juke box. It is a jazz piece for piano. Vittoria stops and listens attentively. Piero also seems absorbed.

Piero: He's a good pianist. Who is he?

Vittoria: I don't know. He must be an old-timer.

Piero and Vittoria leave the café and, walking on for a distance, they arrive at Marta's house. A guard of the EUR area passes by. Vittoria hides behind a tree trunk and gives out with a short whistle. The guard turns around, looks up and down, then continues on his way.

An empty baby carriage is standing in front of the doorway of the building. Attached to the carriage is an inflated balloon. Vittoria looks around furtively, then unties the balloon and takes it with her. She looks up and calls out:

Vittoria: Marta! Marta! *(then to Piero)* She's a friend of mine who was born in Kenya. She's killed elephants and hippopotami . . . You should see what her place is like . . .

In the meantime, Marta has come out on the balcony of her apartment and looks down at Vittoria who shows her the balloon. Marta understands her immediately and goes back inside, coming out in a few moments with a rifle in her hand.

Vittoria, meanwhile, has let go of the balloon and it begins to rise higher and higher into the air. It passes in front of Marta's balcony, then continues to float further away. When it reaches a certain point, Marta takes aim with her rifle and fires. She hits it on the first shot. The balloon bursts. Then Marta returns inside to her apartment.

It is almost twilight and Vittoria and Piero are still walking about the streets in the EUR section of Rome. They come running into a small open square, nearly out of breath. Vittoria is gay and happy and she is laughing. Piero is likewise, but less obviously so. He catches up to Vittoria on the run, and says to·her:

Piero: Do you see that stop sign over there? When we reach that point, I'm going to kiss you.

Piero continues ahead but Vittoria lags behind and when Piero reaches the designated spot, he turns and waits for her to join him. Slowly, Vittoria closes the space between them, almost as if to get herself into the right frame of mind, to take a rest, and to prepare herself inwardly.

She finally reaches Piero and looks up at him with tenderness. Piero draws her close to him. First, Vittoria neither resists nor responds. Her arms remain stretched out along the side of her body. Then she raises her arms and is about to throw them around his neck, but instead she rubs them against his arms and along his face, as a substitute for the actuality of the embrace. Then she quickly checks herself.

Vittoria: I'm going.

Piero hardly has time to reply. She is already on her way, going across the square and towards her house. Passing by a hedge, she breaks off a twig, which she

then tosses into a barrel of rainwater inside the enclosure of a building under construction. Then she continues walking ahead, deciding that she will not turn around. But instead, even before she turns off on another street, she looks around. The little square is entirely deserted. Piero has left.

It is late at night inside Piero's apartment. He is in bed while talking on the telephone. He hangs up, then takes several newspapers and starts glancing through them. The phone rings and, with a slight gesture of annoyance, he lifts the receiver.

Piero: Hello . . . Hello . . .

He waits for a few seconds, then repeats.

Piero: Hello . . . Who is it? . . . Hello . . .

At the other end of the line, Vittoria remains silent as she listens to Piero shouting "hello." She is nearly tempted to answer him but manages to restrain herself. Then she quietly, slowly, places the receiver down and hangs up, leaving her hand to rest on the phone. She is lying in bed with her back against the wall, and she appears tired and exhausted.

The bright light of the hot afternoon sun makes the small square in the EUR section of Rome appear shabby and forlorn: an even, precise square, with bags of cement on each side; in the center a little fountain, also made of cement, and the bus stop with its guide posts.

There is nobody in the square except Vittoria. She doesn't seem at all like someone waiting for another person.

A young girl hurriedly passes by, knowing exactly where she is going. She is wearing white sandals and carries a white handbag—apparently a housemaid, let off for the day.

A few moments later, Piero appears on the square.

Piero: How are you?
Vittoria (somewhat listless): Fine.
Piero: You know, I just ordered a new car . . . a B.M.W.

Piero keeps looking at Vittoria, trying to figure out her mood. He hesitates slightly before he finally says:

Piero: Shall we go somewhere?
Vittoria: Yes, let's go some place.
Piero: To my house?
Vittoria (disinterested): To your house.

Vittoria starts to move but no sooner does she take a few steps than her attention is attracted by a tall, strong and handsome young man, with a tough, virile face, who passes by and gives her a furtive glance. Vittoria looks at him with unusual interest. Then she turns to Piero and, without the slightest malicious intent, she says:

Vittoria: Isn't he handsome?

Piero and Vittoria enter Piero's apartment, which is typically Roman middle-class. The entrance is dark, spacious and cool. Overcome by the sudden contrast between the glaring brightness of the sunlight outside and the gloomy atmosphere of the interior, with its high-ceilinged walls, its rooms leading into other rooms, its dark and ponderous furniture, Vittoria pauses, then sits on a hallway bench near a stand containing two umbrellas. Piero stands in front of her and says in a somewhat puzzled tone of voice:

Piero: Is this where you want to sit?

He reaches out and caresses Vittoria's hair. She looks up at him. There is a blank, resigned expression on her face. Piero withdraws. Suddenly, Vittoria rises to her feet and starts walking through the long hallway which has several doors on each side. Piero follows her. Vittoria's attention is attracted by a large old-fashioned painting on the wall. It is hardly visible in the dimness of the hall, so Piero turns on the light. Vittoria moves back a step to get a better view of the painting. It is a landscape with some allegorical figures in the background.

Vittoria: What is it?
Piero: Who knows?

Piero laughs. He is pleased with her change of attitude. They enter the living room. Vittoria looks around; the style is like that in the other rooms—heavy and cluttered.

Vittoria: You actually live here?
Piero: Not always, but I was born here. Would you like to have something to drink?
Vittoria: No . . . No . . . And when you're not living here, then where do you stay?

Piero is somewhat embarrased by the question.

Piero: Well, I have another place, a smaller apartment.

Vittoria: You mean a *pied-à-terre?* Why didn't you take me there?

Piero ignores her question. Instead, he picks up a box of candy.

Piero: Would you like some?

He offers her the box of chocolates, opens it, turns it upside down, letting all the empty papers fall out. They both laugh.

Vittoria: Let that be a lesson to you. Now maybe you'll learn to treat me as a guest should be treated. From the sofa on which she is seated, she beckons to Piero:

Vittoria: Come . . . come here, and tell me just what you did last night.
Piero: I had dinner with seven or eight billion lira.
Vittoria: Or was it with a call girl?
Piero: Who has time to go out with call girls! I'm the one who plays the role of the call girl.

Vittoria laughs. Her mood has changed completely. She gets up and walks over towards the window. The shutters are closed.

Vittoria: Do your parents always stay in the dark?

Piero draws up close to her.

Piero: And you, what did you do last night?
Vittoria: I managed to amuse myself. I was with some very charming people.
Piero: Do I know them?
Vittoria: No, I don't think you would. They don't play the stock market.
Piero: You don't like the market, do you?
Vittoria: I still don't know what it is—an office, a marketplace, a boxing ring.
Piero: You have to come often in order to really understand it. And once you get used to it, you can't stay away from it. It becomes an obsession.

Vittoria jumps to her feet as though she had suddenly remembered something of great importance, and says in a high, sullen tone of voice:

Vittoria: But . . . an obsession with what, Piero?

Once up, Vittoria takes a few steps around the room, casting a furtive glance at Piero who is somewhat non-plussed and remains seated on the sofa alone. Both of them are drawn together by a strong attraction, but it is quite evident that Vittoria is trying to ignore it and not admit it to herself.

A moment later, Piero gets up and comes close to her. Now they are both facing each other, serious. Piero pulls her towards him, and before she has a chance to resist him, he kisses her violently. At first, Vittoria is about to surrender but then she rebels. Piero persists, and in the brief struggle that ensues, he accidentally rips the shoulder strap from her dress. Then, embarrassed and slightly mortified, he releases his hold on her. Somewhat shaken, Vittoria continues to look at him; then, in an effort to ease the embarrassment, she says:

Vittoria: If dresses tear so easily, it's their own fault.

She then decides to draw away from him and walks through the open door of the living room into the hall. She continues along the hall until she comes to the door of another room which is Piero's. She opens the door and steps inside. The window is wide open and through it, directly across the way, can be seen the wall of a neighboring building which is so close that it casts a dismal shadow over the room, filling it with an atmosphere of infinite melancholy. Vittoria pauses by the window for a moment, then turns and goes back into the hall. She comes to another door, opens it, and sees a large double bed and a window that looks out over the street. She enters, closing the door behind her. She begins to unbutton her clothes, apparently intending to undress. But gradually she changes her mind, inhibited by the overbearing solemnity of the room. The

enlarged photographs of Piero's parents hanging on the
wall over the bed seem to look down upon her with a
kind of hypnotic stare. And then there are those dark
shadows and that open window which resembles an
abandoned pit. Vittoria goes to the window and looks
out. There is little sunlight outside and the city is bathed
in a soft, ambiguous light. In front of the house, the
street widens out towards an enormous church. Buildings are bunched together on all sides, one on top of
the other, with countless vacant windows. The entire
world is here laid out in front of her, tired and still, as
though waiting to die: the grotesquerie of the church
building, the group of people coming out of the afternoon mass, the soldier leaning up against the side of
the wall, eating ice cream. Vittoria lifts her eyes and
catches sight of a priest on a terrace, pacing back and
forth, reading his breviary. From behind her, Vittoria
hears Piero's voice.

Piero: Vittoria . . . May I come in?

Vittoria draws away from the window, closing it slowly and with meticulous care, going through that same routine in an effort to forestall the inevitable. Piero, meanwhile, persists.

Piero: Vittoria . . .
Vittoria: You can't come in.

And she leans with her body up against the door, sensing him on the other side, wanting him, yet incapable of doing anything to communicate her desire. Meanwhile, Piero has opened the other door at the opposite side of the room, and having tiptoed across the rug without being heard, he draws up close behind her.

Vittoria is only aware of some shadowy figure

approaching. She turns but has barely time to let out a small, startled cry. She almost swoons from fright at the sudden apparition. Piero catches hold of her in his arms and presses her tightly to him, then quickly follows up with a kiss. She succumbs instantaneously. In the passionate embrace that ensues, the two of them fall on the bed, kissing each other ecstatically.

It is daytime in a small park within the EUR section of Rome. In the background is a race track and all around the area there are flowers and the glare of aluminum: ultra-modern houses and the long curved tubing of the lamp posts. Piero and Vittoria are lying on the grass. Piero raises his head and looks around him.

Piero: I feel that I'm in a foreign country.
Vittoria: How strange! That's exactly how you make me feel.

Piero looks at her in surprise.

Piero: Then you won't marry me?

Vittoria sits up.

Vittoria: I don't miss marriage.

Piero: How can you not miss it? You've never been married.

Vittoria: No, that's not what I meant.

Piero: This is where I just don't understand you. *(Pause)* I wonder if you had the same kind of understanding with your ex-fiancé.

Vittoria: As long as we loved each other, of course we understood. There was nothing to misunderstand.

Piero stares at Vittoria, studying her.

Piero: But tell me something, do you think that we can get along together?

Vittoria: I don't know, Piero.

Piero: There you go again . . . That's all you know how to say: "I don't know, I don't know, I don't know." Then why do you go with me?

Vittoria hesitates for a second; then, as she is about to answer him, Piero interrupts her.

Piero: And don't tell me you don't know.

There is a moment of silence.

Vittoria: I wish I didn't love you . . . Or that I loved you much more.

Piero stares at her, not able to understand.

Later, inside the Ercoli brokerage office, Piero and Vittoria are lying on the couch. Otherwise, the office is completely empty. Vittoria is turning and twisting around in search of a more comfortable position on the couch, which is much too small for two people. After a few vain attempts, she says ironically:

Vittoria: There's always one arm too many.

She sets herself into a sleeping position but doesn't

seem to find enough room on the couch where she can comfortably lay her arm.

Piero: Leave it here.
Vittoria: Yes, but now there's yours.

Piero is about to remove his arm from under Vittoria's head.

Vittoria: No, don't. It hurts but I like it.

Piero embraces her.

Piero: Do you remember that couple we saw the other day?

He helps her get up and places his arm on her shoulder. She stands erect in front of him and stares straight into his eyes. He does likewise to her. They both feign a comic seriousness for a moment, then Vittoria breaks the mood and says, happily:

Vittoria: Those other two on the bench were much more interesting. Do you remember? She had her finger in her mouth ... like this ...

She puts her pinky in her mouth and he begins to tickle her. Vittoria laughs, but she is unable to stand his tickling, so she draws away from him.

Piero: And I remember another couple.
Vittoria: Which?

At this point, the playful scene takes on a decidedly ironic tone. Piero and Vittoria re-enact themselves as they had behaved during the earlier love scene that took place in Piero's house, but exaggerating the comical aspects of their gestures and attitudes.

Suddenly, the doorbell rings. Vittoria immediately becomes serious. Piero motions to her to be quiet. The doorbell rings again, and again and again. Piero doesn't make the slightest move to open the door, although Vit-

toria is embarrassed by the awkward situation and prepares to leave.

Vittoria: It's late; that is, for you, not for me.

Piero slips into his jacket and straightens out his tie.
Vittoria gets ready to leave and Piero sees her to the
door. But before he opens it, he pulls her to him and
puts his arms around her. They remain together like this
in a long embrace, without saying a word. When they
finally come out of the embrace, they both appear emotionally excited, as though they had just indulged in a
violent kiss. She touches his mouth with her finger. In
turn, he kisses her eyelids and her hair.

Piero: See you tomorrow?

Vittoria nods yes.

Piero: See you tomorrow and the day after tomorrow?
Vittoria: And the day after and the day after that ...

Piero: And even the day after that...
Vittoria: And tonight.
Piero: At eight o'clock. Same place.

They continue to look at each other, as though in a daze; then all of sudden she presses him close to her, almost as if in a frenzy, but also with a certain amount of desperation. Piero's face now takes on a serious expression; hers is one of fear. She is practically trembling. He senses her state of mind and forcefully responds to her embrace. When they come out of the embrace, he opens the door and looks out to see if anyone is around. No one is there. So Vittoria slips out through the door and, with a youthful gracefulness, she quickly runs down the steps and disappears.

Piero closes the door and goes back inside the office. As he passes by the various telephones he replaces the receivers which he had previously taken off the hook. He seems to be in a fog. He sits down on the chair be-

hind his desk and leans back—his eyes closed and a faint smile upon his lips. A moment later, a phone rings in the other room. Piero doesn't budge an inch. Another moment passes by, then another phone starts ringing, and then another. Piero still doesn't move. He seems rooted to his chair, his eyes still closed, in a kind of ecstatic mood, only this time a serious one. The telephones continue to ring, creating a light echo that resounds throughout the empty office.

There follows a rapid succession of visual images, at times realistic, at other times abstract:

An overall view of an intersection somewhere in the EUR district of Rome—Piero's and Vittoria's meeting place. An automatic sprinkling system is watering the grass of a public lawn. A nurse pushing a baby carriage.

A pile of bricks heaped high inside the enclosure of a new house under construction. Many of the bricks are either broken or chipped.

A wooden fence encircling the house and a rain barrel filled with water.

Close-up of the barrel. A panoramic shot that comes to a stop on a tree that is planted on the corner of the street.

A view of a house under construction with its straw matting that serves to shade the interior from the sun. The scaffolding rods that protrude from the matting.

Detail of the scaffolding rods and the surrounding trees.

The scaffolding rods against the sky.

A panoramic shot that follows a race horse and its sulky passing by at a lively trot. The exact spot at the intersection where Piero and Vittoria have frequently met before and which is now deserted. In the background is the nurse pushing the baby carriage.

The shadow of a tree against a white wall.

Two shadows on the asphalt pavement, cast by the rays of a sun that is not very bright.

A panoramic shot of the stadium behind which Piero and Vittoria had often strolled together and which is now vacant. The street is completely empty.

The white traffic stripes painted on the asphalt for the benefit of the pedestrians. Footsteps are heard. They are those of a passing stranger.

The wooden fence along the house under construction. The stranger disappears into the background.

The leaves of a tree trembling in the wind.

Close-up of the bark with ants running across the trunk of the tree.

Long shot of one of the streets that form the intersection where Piero and Vittoria meet. The corner is now deserted.

A bus is seen pulling out. The roar of its motor fades away into the distance.

Full view of the house under construction. The sun has vanished behind a cloud.

The barrel of water with the small stick and empty matchbox that Vittoria and Piero had thrown away during their first encounter. There is a hole in the barrel through which a jet of water is pouring out.

Side view of the water-jet as it gushes from the barrel. The camera follows the stream of water as it trickles down to a public sewer near the curbstone.

A building situated at another corner of the intersection: an ugly, modern house.

The janitor of the house is standing in front of the entrance.

A lady waiting at a bus stop under the trees.

Close-up of a girl waiting for someone.

The same girl in full view.

An overall shot of the street where the girl is waiting. A bus arrives, pulling up to the curb.

The wheel of the bus as it screeches and comes to a halt.

The bus stops. A man and woman descend. The man is reading the weekly newspaper, *L'Espresso*. The front page headline reads: THE ATOMIC AGE.

The inside section of the newspaper which the man is reading has another headline with large black letters: PEACE IS WEAK. The man walks away in a panoramic shot that picks up several children playing in the background.

Two or three of these same children come up to the automatic sprinkler that is watering the grass.

Close-up of the sprinkler. In the background, a park attendant turns off the water. The spray stops.

Some drops of water fall on the branches of a plant.

A white house with jutting balconies.

Detail of three balconies.

Detail of two balconies.

Detail of a roof terrace.

A racetrack post against the sky where a thin trail of smoke from a sky-writing plane can be seen.

View of the terrace seen previously; now two people

are standing on it. One of them is pointing towards something in the distance.

Footsteps are heard in the street which is now dark with the evening shadows. The blonde head of a woman comes into view. She resembles Vittoria from the rear. The girl turns and we discover that it is not Vittoria.

Detail of the barrel with the wooden stick and empty matchbox floating around inside.

Detail of the curbstone with the sewer into which the stream of water continues to trickle.

Close-up of the curbstone with the frame composed in the manner of an abstract painting. The downward flow of the water carries small scraps of refuse along with it.

Close-up of an uncertain image which later turns out to be the jaw of an old man.

Close-up of an eye behind a pair of glasses belonging to the same old man.

Close-up of the man's head.

Full view of the old man leaving. A vertical panoramic shot of the corner with the house under construction.

The rivulet of water coming from the barrel, running gently between the loose gravel. Close-up of a crack in the asphalt pavement.

The baby carriage being pushed by the nurse, disappearing into the background. The shot is framed with the white curbstone running down the middle from top to bottom, separating the asphalt pavement from the grass.

The racetrack posts against the sky which is barely lit up by the rays of a sunset that has already disappeared below the horizon.

The face of a woman peering out from behind an iron grating.

A street light is turned on.

View of the intersection with its street lights all illuminated.

View from another part of the intersection which also has its street lights illuminated. To the right, the house under construction with the scaffolding rods jutting out against the sky.

Still another view of the intersection. A bus arrives and turns around in front of the house under construction.

The bus stops. Several passengers descend. Neither Vittoria nor Piero are among them. The people who got off the bus disappear into the background.

The house under construction, with the street corner illuminated by the light from the lamp posts against what is now the heavy darkness of night. A panoramic shot that swings towards the racetrack in the distance. The street lights appear like white dots against a black background.

A sudden close-up of an illuminated street light with a glaringly bright halo encircling the lamp.